MINITAB
User's Guide 1:
Data, Graphics, and Macros

Release 13

for Windows®

Windows 95®, Windows 98® and Windows NT™

February 2000

ISBN 0-925636-43-6

Printed in the USA

1st Printing, 11/99

♲ Text and cover printed on recycled paper.

Table of Contents

3 Opening, Saving, and Printing Files 3-1

4 Using ODBC and Special Text Files 4-1

5 Generating Patterned Data 5-1

part II: Manipulating and Calculating Data

part V: Using Session Commands and Macros

Welcome

How to Use this Guide

This guide is not designed to be read from cover to cover. It is designed to provide you with quick access to the information you need to complete tasks. If it fails to meet that objective, please let us know in any way you find convenient, including using the Info form at the back of this book, or sending e-mail to doc_comments@minitab.com.

This guide is half of a two-book set and provides reference information on the following topics:

– managing data
– manipulating and calculating data
– managing the Session window and generating reports
– graphing data
– using session commands and macros

We provide task-oriented documentation based on using the menus and dialog boxes. We hope you can easily learn how to complete the specific task you need to accomplish. We welcome your comments.

See *Documentation for MINITAB for Windows, Release 13* on page xvii for information about the entire documentation set for this product.

Assumptions

This guide assumes that you know the basics of using your operating system (such as Windows 95, Windows 98, or Windows NT). This includes using menus, dialog boxes, a mouse, and moving and resizing windows. If you are not familiar with these operations, see your operating system documentation.

Register as a MINITAB User

Please send us your MINITAB registration card. If you have lost or misplaced your registration card, contact your distributor, Minitab Ltd., Minitab SARL, or Minitab Inc. Please refer to the back cover of this guide or the *International Partners Card* included in your software product box for contact information. You can also register via the world wide web at http://www.minitab.com.

Registered MINITAB users are eligible to receive free technical support (subject to the terms and conditions of their License Agreement), new product announcements, maintenance updates, and MINITAB newsletters containing useful articles, tips, and macro information.

Global Support

Minitab Inc. and its international subsidiaries and partners provide sales and support services to Minitab customers throughout the world. Please refer to the *International Partners Card* included in your software product box. You can also access the most up-to-date international partner information via our web site at http://www.minitab.com.

Customer Support

For technical help, contact your central computing support group if one exists. You may also be eligible to receive customer support from your distributor, or from Minitab Inc., Minitab Ltd., or Minitab SARL directly, subject to the terms and conditions of your License Agreement. Eligible users may contact their distributor, Minitab Ltd., Minitab SARL, or Minitab Inc. (phone 814-231-2MTB (2682), fax 814-238-4383, or send e-mail through our web site at http://www.minitab.com/contacts). Technical support at Minitab Inc. is available Monday through Friday, between the hours of 9:00 a.m. and 5:00 p.m. Eastern time. When you are calling for technical support, it is helpful if you can be at your computer when you call. Please have your serial and software version numbers handy (from the **Help ➤ About MINITAB** screen), along with a detailed description of the problem.

Troubleshooting information is provided in a file called ReadMe.txt, installed in the main MINITAB directory, and in Help under the topics *Troubleshooting* and *How Do I*.... You can also visit the Support section of our web site at http://www.minitab.com/support.

MINITAB on the Internet

Visit our web site at http://www.minitab.com. You can download demos, macros, and maintenance updates, get the latest information about our company and its products, get help from our technical support specialists, and more.

About the Documentation

Printed MINITAB documentation provides menu and dialog box documentation only. You'll find step-by-step "how-to's" throughout the books. (You'll find complete session command documentation available via online Help.)

MINITAB's new StatGuide provides you with statistical guideance for many analyses, so you get the most from your data analysis. Chapter overviews, particularly in *User's Guide 2*, provide additional statistical guidance to help determine suitability of a particular method. Many examples in both printed documentation and online Help include *Interpreting your output*.

The software itself provides online Help, a convenient, comprehensive, and useful source of information. To help you use MINITAB most effectively, Minitab Inc. and other publishers offer a variety of helpful texts and documents.

To order from Minitab Inc. from within the U.S. or Canada call: 800-448-3555. Additional contact information for Minitab Inc., Minitab Ltd., and Minitab SARL is given on the back cover of this book.

Documentation for MINITAB for Windows, Release 13

MINITAB Help, ©2000, Minitab Inc. This comprehensive, convenient source of information is available at the touch of a key or the click of the mouse. In addition to complete menu and dialog box documentation, you can find overviews, examples, guidance for setting up your data, information on calculations and methods, and a glossary. A separate online Help file is available for session commands.

MINITAB StatGuide, ©2000, Minitab Inc. Statistical guidance for many of MINITAB's text-based and graphical analyses—from basic statistics, to quality assurance, to design of experiments—so you get the most from your data analysis efforts. The MINITAB StatGuide uses preselected examples to help you understand and interpret output.

Meet MINITAB, ©2000, Minitab Inc. Rather than fully document all features, this book explains the fundamentals of using MINITAB—how to use the menus and dialog boxes, how to manage and manipulate data and files, how to produce graphs, and more. This guide includes five step-by-step sample sessions to help you learn MINITAB quickly.

MINITAB User's Guide 1: Data, Graphics, and Macros, ©2000, Minitab Inc. This guide includes how to use MINITAB's input, output, and data manipulation capabilities; how to work with data and graphs; and how to write macros.

MINITAB User's Guide 2: Data Analysis and Quality Tools, ©2000, Minitab Inc. This guide includes how to use MINITAB's statistics, quality control, reliability and survival analysis, and design of experiments tools.

Online tutorials. The same tutorials available in *Meet MINITAB*, designed to help new users learn MINITAB, are now available in the Help menu.

Session Command Quick Reference, ©2000, Minitab Inc. A Portable Document Format (PDF) file, to be read with Acrobat Reader, that lists all MINITAB commands and subcommands.

The CD-ROM distribution of MINITAB Release 13 includes our printed documentation—*Meet MINITAB*, *MINITAB User's Guide 1*, and *MINITAB User's Guide 2*—in Portable Document Format (PDF) files along with the Acrobat Reader for you to use these publications electronically. You may view them online with the Reader, or print portions of particular interest to you.

Related Documentation

Companion Text List, 1996, Minitab Inc., State College, PA. More than 300 textbooks, textbook supplements, and other related teaching materials that include MINITAB are featured in the *Companion Text List*. For a complete bibliography, the *Companion Text List* is available online at http://www.minitab.com.

MINITAB Handbook, Third Edition, 1994, Barbara F. Ryan, and Brian L. Joiner, Duxbury Press, Belmont, CA. A supplementary text that teaches basic statistics using MINITAB. The Handbook features the creative use of plots, application of standard statistical methods to real data, in-depth exploration of data, simulation as a learning tool, screening data for errors, manipulating data, transformation of data, and performing multiple regressions. Please contact your bookstore, Minitab Inc., or Duxbury Press to order this book.

Typographical Conventions Used in this Book

C	denotes a column, such as C12 or 'Height'.
K	denotes a constant, such as 8.3 or K14.
M	denotes a matrix, such as M5.
Enter	denotes a key, such as the Enter key.
Alt + D	denotes pressing the second key while holding down the first key. For example, while holding down the Alt key, press the D key.
File ➤ Exit	denotes a menu command, such as choose Exit from the File menu. Here is another example: **Stat ➤ Tables ➤ Tally** means open the Stat menu, then open the Tables submenu, then choose Tally.
Click **OK**.	Bold text clarifies dialog box items and buttons.
Type *Pulse1*.	Italic text specifies text to be entered by you.

Examples

Note the special symbol for examples.

Examples are designed so you can follow along and duplicate the results. Here is an example with both Session window and Graph window output:

▶ Example of displaying descriptive statistics

You want to examine characteristic of the height (in inches) of male (Sex = 1) and female (Sex = 2) students who participated in the pulse study. You choose to display descriptive statistics with the option of a boxplot of the data.

1 Open the worksheet PULSE.MTW.

2 Choose **Stat ➤ Basic Statistics ➤ Display Descriptive Statistics**.

3 In **Variables**, enter *Height*. Check **By variable** and enter *Sex* in the text box.

4 Click **Graphs**. Check **Boxplot of data**. Click **OK** in both dialog boxes.

Session window output

Descriptive Statistics: Height by Sex

Variable	Sex	N	Mean	Median	TrMean	StDev
Height	1	57	70.754	71.000	70.784	2.583
	2	35	65.400	65.500	65.395	2.563

Variable	Sex	SE Mean	Minimum	Maximum	Q1	Q3
Height	1	0.342	66.000	75.000	69.000	73.000
	2	0.433	61.000	70.000	63.000	68.000

Graph window output

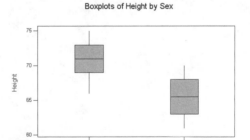

Boxplots of Height by Sex

Interpreting the results

The means shown in the Session window and the boxplots indicate that males are approximately 5.3 inches taller than females, and the spread of the data is about the same.

Sample Data Sets

For some examples you need to type data into columns. But for most examples, you can use data already stored in sample data set files in the DATA subdirectory of the main MINITAB directory.

MINITAB comes with a number of sample data sets that are stored in the DATA, STUDENT1, STUDENT8, STUDENT9, and STUDNT12 subdirectories (folders). For complete descriptions of most of these data sets, see the Help topic *sample data sets*.

part I

Managing Data

1

Data Overview

Chapter Overview

Analyses, of course, begin with data. You can enter data into MINITAB in various ways, edit the data values, save the data in a variety of formats, and print your output.

Before working with data, you should become familiar with some of the terminology and concepts used in MINITAB.

This chapter discusses the types of data you can work with in MINITAB, and the various forms those data types can take. The chapter then explains how to use the Data window and the Worksheet folder in the Project Manager.

First, here are the ways you can work with data, and the chapters that describe those procedures.

Entering and editing data

There are many ways for you to enter data into MINITAB. You can:

- type data or paste it from another application—see Chapter 2, *Typing and Editing Data in the Data Window*.

- open it from files. MINITAB can open many different types of files, including Excel and Lotus 1-2-3 files—see Chapter 3, *Opening, Saving, and Printing Files*. You can also bring in data from databases and unusually formatted text files—see Chapter 4, *Using ODBC and Special Text Files*.

- generate it from within MINITAB. You can create patterned data (see Chapter 5, *Generating Patterned Data*) or random data (see Chapter 9, *Random Data and Probability Distributions*).

Saving and printing data

When you are finished working with the data, you can save it to use later in MINITAB or another application. Or you can print a hard copy. See Chapter 3, *Opening, Saving, and Printing Files*.

Worksheets

In MINITAB, all the data associated with a particular data set are contained in a *worksheet*. A project can have many worksheets—the number of worksheets is limited only by your computer's memory.

Worksheets are not visible, but you can view your data in the Data and Session windows, and in the Worksheet folder in the Project Manager. Each worksheet will have its own Data window. There is only one Session window, but it can display information on any open worksheet.

Commands act on the current worksheet

When you are working in MINITAB, any command you use works on the *current worksheet*. The current worksheet is the worksheet associated with the *active Data window*. You make a window active by clicking on it, choosing it from the Window menu, or right clicking on the Worksheet folder and bringing it to the front. If no Data window is active, the command acts on the Data window that was most recently active.

Tip | You can tell which Data window contains the current worksheet by looking at the window's title bar. The current worksheet will have three asterisks in the title, like this:

Available memory and worksheet size

The number of worksheets you can have open at one time in a project is limited only by your computer's memory. But MINITAB also allocates a special section of memory for the current worksheet. Memory for the current worksheet is affected by the available system memory, and by settings in your MINITAB preferences.

MINITAB dynamically allocates memory to hold the data for the current worksheet. If the data in the current worksheet grows, MINITAB will allocate more memory.

If you ever run out of memory, MINITAB will display error messages about "insufficient memory" or "insufficient storage space." The messages will advise you on how to immediately increase available memory.

If you receive memory error messages frequently, you can change your preferences for memory allocation. There are advantages and disadvantages to doing this. For a discussion and instructions on changing memory preferences, choose **Edit ➤ Preferences ➤ General ➤ Select** and click **Help**.

Data Types and Forms

A worksheet can contain three types of data — numeric, text, and date/time — in three forms: columns, constants, or matrices.

Three types of data: numeric, text, and date/time

- *Numeric* data are numbers. See *Using Numeric Data* on page 1-8.

- *Text* data are characters that can consist of a mix of letters, numbers, spaces, and special characters, such as "Test Number 4" or "North Carolina." See *Using Text Data* on page 1-9.

- *Date/time* data can be dates (such as Jan-1-1997 or 3/17/97), times (such as 08:25:22 AM), or both (such as 3/17/97 08:25:22 AM). MINITAB internally stores dates and times as numbers, but displays them in whatever format you choose. See *Using Date/Time Data* on page 1-10.

Data can take three forms: column, stored constant, or matrix

Form	Contains...	Referred to by Number	Name	Number available
Column	numeric, text, or date/time data	C + a number, as in C1 or C22	'Sales' or 'Year'	Limited only by system memory, up to a maximum of 4000
Stored Constant	a single number or a text string (e.g., "New York")	K + a number, as in K1 or K93	'First' or 'Counter'	1000
Matrix	a rectangular block of cells containing numbers	M + a number, as in M1 or M44	'Inverse'	100

Columns, constants, and matrices are all:

- affected by menu and session commands

- named with the session command NAME (documented in Session Command Help), though columns can also be named in the Data window—see *Changing Column Names, Fonts, and Descriptions* on page 2-18

- saved to a file when you choose **File ➤ Save Current Worksheet (As)** or **File ➤ Save Project (As)**—see Chapter 3, *Opening, Saving, and Printing Files*

- summarized in the Worksheet folder

Three Windows to Work with Data

The Data window

This window contains the columns of data that are in the worksheet. When you have multiple worksheets open, each worksheet has its own Data window.

Each column generally represents a variable.

Each row generally represents an individual case, or observation.

	C1	C2	C3	C4	C5	C6	C7-T	C8-D
	Index	Quarter	Year	Sales	Advertis	Capital	AdAgency	Date
1	1	1	1991	94	17	8	Omega	1Q91
2	2	2	1991	99	10	6	Omega	2Q91
3	3	3	1991	98	9	12	Alpha	3Q91
4	4	4	1991	92	22	16	Alpha	4Q91
5	5	1	1992	106	24	29	Alpha	1Q92
6	6	2	1992	116	18	32	Alpha	2Q92
7	7	3	1992	113	13	33	Omega	3Q92

Marketd.mtw ***

In each Data window, you can

- view the columns of data that are in the worksheet
- enter values and edit them in various ways (see Chapter 2, *Typing and Editing Data in the Data Window*)
- rearrange your data in complex ways (see Chapter 6, *Manipulating Data*)

Note Although the Data window has rows and columns, it is not a spreadsheet like Microsoft Excel or Lotus 1-2-3. See *The Data window is not a spreadsheet* on page 1-7.

The Worksheet folder

The Worksheet folder in the Project Manager summarizes the columns, stored constants, and matrices used in the current worksheet. You can look at information for other worksheets in your project by clicking on their Worksheet folders. This summary is especially handy as a reference when you are trying to spot unequal column lengths or columns that contain missing values. The Worksheet folder content window is updated automatically.

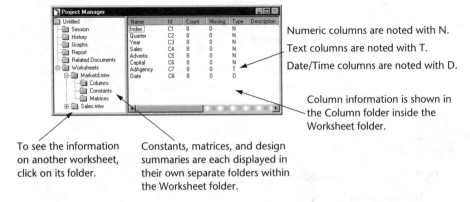

Numeric columns are noted with N.

Text columns are noted with T.

Date/Time columns are noted with D.

Column information is shown in the Column folder inside the Worksheet folder.

To see the information on another worksheet, click on its folder.

Constants, matrices, and design summaries are each displayed in their own separate folders within the Worksheet folder.

The Session window

You can display columns, constants, and matrices in this window when you choose **Manip ➤ Display Data**. For details on this command, see *Display worksheet data* on page 6-4. For more information on the Session window, see Chapter 11, *Using the Session Window*.

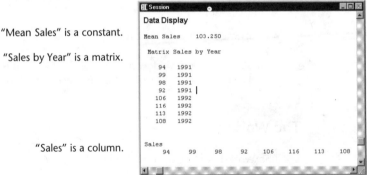

"Mean Sales" is a constant.

"Sales by Year" is a matrix.

"Sales" is a column.

Meet the Data Window

Choose **Window ➤ *worksheet*** to open the Data window.

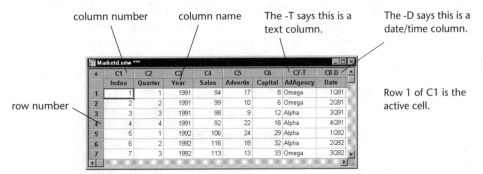

column number   column name   The -T says this is a text column.   The -D says this is a date/time column.

row number

Row 1 of C1 is the active cell.

In the Data window you can

- enter columns of data into the worksheet

- name, resize, and format columns

- move quickly to different cell locations

- cut, copy, or paste cells to and from the Clipboard

One Data window for each worksheet

You can have many worksheets open at a time, and each worksheet will have its own Data window. Information on each worksheet is contained in the Worksheet folder—see *Using Numeric Data* on page 1-8.

The Data window is not a spreadsheet

Although the Data window has rows and columns, it is not a spreadsheet like Microsoft Excel or Lotus 1-2-3. In MINITAB, cells contain values that you type or generate with commands. Cells do not contain formulas that update based on other cells.

For example, if you want column C3 to equal the values in C1 plus the values in C2, you would use the Calculator (**Calc ➤ Calculator**, described on page 7-2) to generate the values for C3. If you change the values in C1, C3 does not change until you use the Calculator again or use some other command to change C3's contents.

However, you can create a Dynamic Data Exchange (DDE) link between cells that will let cells update when other cells change. See *Recalculating MINITAB Columns Automatically* on page 10-12.

Using Numeric Data

Numeric data consist of number characters (0 1 2 3 4 5 6 7 8 9 10) and *, the missing value symbol (see *Missing Values* on page 1-12). The number can have positive and negative signs (+ and −) and can contain a decimal separator. If you are entering data in exponential (scientific) notation, numeric values also contain the letter E, as in 3.2E12 (see *Exponential notation* below). If a column or constant contains any character other than numbers or *, MINITAB interprets the entire column as text (see *Using Text Data* on page 1-9).

Very large or very small numbers

In the worksheet, you may store negative or positive numbers up to $\pm 1 \times 10^{18}$ (one million times one million times one million). MINITAB converts any number which exceeds this limit to missing, and prints an error message indicating that this has been done. In the (unlikely) event that you have data which exceed this limit, rescale the data before entering it into MINITAB.

Very large or very small numbers can be entered and displayed in exponential notation (below).

Exponential notation

Numbers can be entered in the Data window using decimal notation or exponential notation (also called scientific notation). The Data window can display numeric columns in decimal or exponential notation. The way you enter a number does not affect its display; the display is set by the column's format.

For instructions on typing data in exponential notation, see *To enter a number in exponential notation* on page 2-6.

By default, MINITAB automatically changes the format of columns based on their contents. When the contents change, the format may change. For example, if a column contains a number that is very large or very small, MINITAB changes the column format to use exponential notation, and all numbers will appear in that format. As long as the column contains that very small or large number, the column's format will be exponential. When that extreme number is removed, the column's format will switch back to decimal notation.

You can turn off automatic formatting and set the format of the column to use decimal or exponential notation—see *To change column format to exponential* on page 2-24.

Numerical precision

MINITAB stores and computes numbers in double precision, which means that numbers can have up to 15 or 16 digits (depending on the number) without round-off error.

Round-off error is an unavoidable problem that can occur with any computer program. Every computer operates in binary code—strings of zeros and ones—and so must convert decimal numbers to binary numbers. When the conversion is not exact, you get round-off error. The error may or may not be significant, depending on the number of significant digits in your data and the types of computations you are doing.

More | For more information on numerical precision, and how MINITAB handles binary and decimal numbers, see Help.

Using Text Data

Text data is often used to specify the levels of a categorical variable. For example, a column containing the gender of a participant in an experiment may use the text values "Male" and "Female" for the two levels of gender. Most commands where it makes sense handle text data.

Text values can be

- up to 80 characters long
- made up of any characters (letters, numbers, punctuation marks, blanks)
- stored in columns and stored constants, but not matrices

When you want to use text data in a function in which only numeric data are supported, choose **Manip ➤ Code ➤ Text to Numeric** (page 6-38) to convert the text values into numeric values. For example, if you have a column containing the gender of a participant in an experiment that has the values "Male" and "Female," you can convert all the values in the column to 1 and 2 respectively and store the results in another column.

Tip | To input text data from the keyboard, you may want to first input the data as numeric, then convert it to text to save time and avoid typographical errors. For example, say you are recording the year in school of fifty high school students in a study. Instead of typing "Freshman," "Sophomore," "Junior," or "Senior" for each student, you could type 1's, 2's, 3's, and 4's. Afterward, use **Manip ➤ Code ➤ Numeric to Text** to change the numbers to the words.

Using text data in stored constants

- You cannot use a stored constant in a dialog box item which accepts a text string. MINITAB will assume the constant (number or name, depending on what you type) is the text string, rather than the content of the stored content. For example, if K1 contains the text string "Graph Title" and you enter K1 in the Title option for **Graph ➤ Plot**, MINITAB will display "K1" as the title of your graph.

- You can use a text stored constant in all session commands that accept a text string, with two exceptions. You cannot use a text stored constant as
  - a file name in CD or TYPE.
  - a column name in the NAME command. See individual commands for details.

- You may use text constants in a local macro. For details, see Chapter 29, *Advanced Macros*.

▶ To store a text value in a constant

1 Choose **Calc ➤ Calculator**.

2 In the **Store result in variable** text box, enter the name of the stored constant (for example, *K1*).

3 In the **Expression** text box, type the text value, enclosed in double quotes (for example, "Green").

For more details on using the Calculator, see *Calculating Mathematical Expressions and Transformations* on page 7-2.

Using Date/Time Data

Although date/time variables appear in date/time format in the Data window, they are stored *internally* as numbers. Thus they can be used in any calculation or statistical procedure that accepts numbers.

The internal number consists of an integer and a fraction: the integer represents the number of days since December 30, 1899; the fraction represents the fraction of the day completed. For example, the date/time value January 1, 1990 6:00 AM is stored internally as the number 32874.25 since there are 32874 days since December 30, 1899, and 6:00 AM is one quarter of a day.

December 30, 1899, 12 midnight is stored as 0. Dates and times before that date and time are negative numbers. For example, December 29, 1899 12 midnight is −1. Valid date/time values range from January 1, 1000 A.D. to December 31, 4000.

Calculations are always based on the internal number of the date/time variable. Some commands will display results in the Session and Graph windows as a number, and not as a formatted date/time value. Date/time values that are stored in constants display as numbers.

Some commands will give you unexpected results when using date/time data. For example, consider an analysis of variance with a date/time variable as a factor. Two values in the date column, 1/1/95 and 1/1/95, may *appear* in the Data window to be the same value because the column is formatted to display just the date portion. But the two values may have different time portions (for example, 10:30 PM and 8:20 AM) and therefore have different internal numbers. The analysis of variance will treat each value as a different factor level.

Just as with numeric and text data, date/time data can be entered, imported, exported, and converted to another data type. Here are some other date/time functions you can perform:

Format date/time data in the Data window

You can change the format of a date/time column in the Data window to display the information you want. For example, you can change 1/31/97 to 1-31-1997 or 31-Jan-1997. For details, see *Formatting Columns and Changing Data Types* on page 2-23.

The variable's format in the Data window will be used when results are displayed on graphs and in Session window output. In the Session window, only the first eight characters are displayed.

Tip | For less cluttered results on graphs, or for more coherent labels on Session window output, format the date/time column to show only the most significant information. For example, 01/31/1999 would display as 01/31/19 in the Session window. Instead, you could format the column to display 1/31 or 1/99.

Use date/time data on graphs

- **Place labels on control charts and time series plots** Place date/time labels on the x-axis with quality control charts and Time Series Plot. For details, see *Options Shared by Quality Control Charts* in the *Variables Control Charts* chapter and *Options for Attributes Control Charts* in the *Attributes Control Charts* chapter of MINITAB *User's Guide 2*; *Time Series Plots* in Chapter 14, *Core Graphs* of this guide.

- **Use a date/time variable on the x and/or y axis for a plot** See *Plots* in Chapter 14, *Core Graphs* of this guide.

- **Make a chart, histogram, and boxplot on a date/time column** For general details on creating these graphs, see Chapter 14, *Core Graphs* of this guide.

- **Use a date/time variable as a categorical variable** Any graph that can use a categorical variable can use a date/time variable. For example, you could do a chart or boxplot with a date/time variable as a categorical variable.

Note | Some %macros that manipulate data before creating graphs will display date/time variables as numbers.

Use date/time data in analyses

- **Use a date/time variable in any analyses that use categorical variables** For example, date/time data could be used in analysis of variance, cross tabulation, or descriptive statistics.

- **Use a date/time variable in analyses that use continuous data** In cases where date/time data are considered continuous, the Session window output displays the internal number of the date/time value, not the Data window format.

Manipulating and calculating with date/time data

- **Subset your data based on a date/time variable** See *Subsetting: Copy Data to a New Worksheet* on page 6-9.

- **Extract components of a date/time variable** Use **Calc ➤ Extract from Date/Time to Numeric** or **Calc ➤ Extract from Date/Time to Text** to take a portion of a date/time variable and store it in another column. For example, perform an analysis by month by extracting the month name of each date/time value—"Feb" from 2/3/95 and 2/15/99, "Mar" from 3/5/95 and 3/24/99, etc.

- **Create mathematical expressions with special date/time functions** Use **Calc ➤ Calculator** to return the current date or time, or to evaluate an expression that involves a date/time value. See *Calculating Mathematical Expressions and Transformations* on page 7-2.

- **Create a column of patterned date/time data** Use **Autofill** or **Calc ➤ Make Patterned Data** as described in Chapter 5, *Generating Patterned Data*.

Missing Values

MINITAB uses an asterisk (*) in numeric and date/time columns and a blank in text columns to represent missing values. When you enter * as a value in the Data window or in a dialog box, you do not have to enclose it in single quotation marks, but when it is part of a session command you do.

Most commands exclude from analysis all cases (individual rows) with a missing value and display the number of excluded points. For example, plots exclude points where either the x- or y-coordinate is missing.

When an arithmetic command operates on a missing value, the result is set to *. In many commands, you can use * just as you would use a number. For example, when you copy columns, you can use or omit rows equal to *.

For details on how to handle missing values during data transfer to and from MINITAB, see *Opening Worksheets* on page 3-5.

2

Typing and Editing Data in the Data Window

Typing and Editing Data Overview

If your data is not already stored in a file, MINITAB makes it is easy to enter data into the Data window. You can type data or copy and paste it from other applications.

Once your data is in the Data window, it is also easy to edit it. You can correct individual observations in cells, or rearrange the columns and rows to get your data ready for analysis. You can select cells, rows, and columns, then delete them, insert new ones, or move them around.

Columns can be customized in various ways. You can name them, write descriptions of them, apply fonts, resize them, and even hide unused columns.

Finally, you can apply formats to your columns of data. The column's format depends on its data type: numeric, date/time, or text. The data type is set when you first enter the data. For each data type, you can change the way data is displayed. For example, numeric columns can show just the number of decimal places that you like, and date/time columns can show dates and times in forms such as "January 1, 1999" or "1/1/99."

Data window editing vs. manipulation commands

You can duplicate the results of some of the procedures in this chapter by using the manipulation commands described in Chapter 6, *Manipulating Data*. For example, you could duplicate some of the copy and paste functionality by using the **Manip ➤ Stack** command.

Copying and pasting using the mouse can be quicker and easier than filling out the manipulation dialog boxes. However, the commands in Chapter 6 allow you to perform complex actions that would be difficult or tedious to replicate in other ways. For example, not only can **Manip ➤ Stack** stack the contents of multiple columns on top of each other, but the command also allows you to simultaneously create a column of subscripts (identifier codes) so you can see which values in the new column came from which source column.

The choice of which methods to use—Data window editing commands or manipulation commands—depends on the complexity of your task.

Moving Around the Data Window

When you use your mouse to click on a cell, it becomes the *active cell*. You can also use the menus and your keyboard to move the cursor and make other cells the active cell.

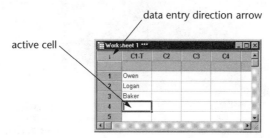

active cell

data entry direction arrow

▶ To move the active cell to...	Do this
any cell location	Choose **Editor ➤ Go To.**
to the next cell down (if the data entry direction arrow is pointing down) or across (if the data entry direction arrow is pointing right)	Press [Enter].
the beginning of the next row (if the data entry direction arrow is pointing right) or column (if the data entry direction arrow is pointing down)	■ Press [Ctrl]+[Enter], or ■ Choose **Editor ➤ Go To ➤ Next Row/Column.**
change the direction of the data entry direction arrow (this changes the behavior of [Enter] and [Ctrl]+[Enter])	■ Click the data entry direction arrow, or ■ Choose **Editor ➤ Worksheet ➤ Change Entry Direction.**
return to the active cell when it is located off the display	Choose **Editor ➤ Go To ➤ Active Cell.**

▶ **To open a new (empty) Data window**

1 Choose **File ➤ New.**

2 Select **Minitab Worksheet** and click **OK**.

Selecting Areas of the Data Window

You can perform a variety of actions on cells, rows, and columns in the Data window.

Before performing an action, you often select the area you want to affect. If you do not select a row or column before doing an operation that affects the entire row or column (such as insert column), the column that contains the active cell is considered selected. The active cell is always selected or is part of a selected area.

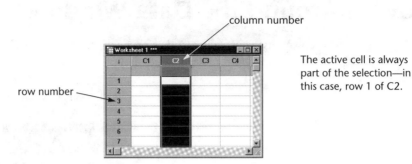

column number

The active cell is always
part of the selection—in
this case, row 1 of C2.

row number

To select...	Do this
a block of cells	drag across the cells
one or more entire rows	drag across the row numbers
one or more entire columns	drag across the column numbers
all the cells	choose **Edit ➤ Select All Cells**

Typing Data into the Data Window

To enter a value in a Data window cell, just click on the cell, type a value, and press
⌊Enter⌋. You can enter multiple values in any order you wish: column by column, row by
row, or in blocks.

Each column of cells generally
represents a variable.

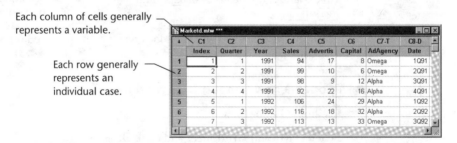

Each row generally
represents an
individual case.

When you type an entry into an empty column, MINITAB assigns a data type to the
column: numeric, text, or date/time. If the data type is not numeric, MINITAB also adds
an identifier next to the column number: D for date/time data and T for text data. For
details, see *Entering data automatically assigns a data type to the column* on page 2-6.

More | You can also

- enter numeric data in exponential notation—see *Exponential notation* on page 1-8.
- change data from one type to another—see *Changing Columns from One Data Type to Another* on page 6-42.

Entering data in columns, rows, or blocks

▶ To enter data columnwise

1 Click the data entry direction arrow to make it point down.

2 Enter your data, pressing [Tab] or [Enter] to move the active cell. Press [Ctrl]+[Enter] to move the active cell to the top of the next column.

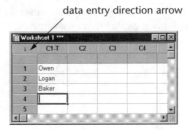

data entry direction arrow

For example, click in row 1, column 1, then type:
Owen [Enter]
Logan [Enter]
Baker [Enter]
Notice that after you type a value and press [Enter], the active cell moves down.

▶ To enter data rowwise

1 Click the data entry direction arrow to make it point to the right.

2 Enter your data. Press [Ctrl]+[Enter] to move the active cell to the beginning of the next row.

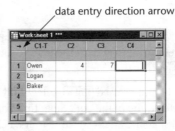

data entry direction arrow

For example, click in row 1, column 2, then type:
4 [Enter] *7* [Enter]

Notice that after you type a value and press [Enter], the active cell moves right.

▶ To enter data within a block

1 Highlight the area you want to work in.

2 Enter your data. The active cell moves only within the selected area.

3 To unselect the area, press an arrow key or click anywhere in the Data window.

For example:
– With the mouse, point to the cell at row 2, column 2.
– Drag down and to the right. This selects the block.
– Type:
  5 [Enter] *8* [Enter]
  6 [Enter] *9* [Enter]

Notice that if you select a block before typing values, pressing [Enter] moves the active cell to the next cell in the block. Pressing any arrow key unselects the block.

▶ **To enter a number in exponential notation**

    1 In a cell in a numeric or empty column, type three elements: a number (which can be an integer or decimal number), the letter E (which substitutes for multiplying by 10), and the exponent.

    For example, the number 3200 is equal to 32×10^2 or 3.2×10^3, so you could type 32E2 or 3.2E3.

Note | Entering a number using exponential notation does not necessarily mean that the number will display in that notation. To explicitly set that format, see *To change column format to exponential* on page 2-24. For general information on very large and very small numbers and exponential notation, see *Using Numeric Data* on page 1-8.

If you make a mistake

▶ **To correct a value in a cell**

- To delete the old value and enter a new one, click the cell, type the correct value, and press ⟨Enter⟩.

- To change a portion of the cell contents, double-click the cell, then use the arrow, ⟨Backspace⟩ and ⟨Del⟩ keys to make the changes.

▶ **To undo/redo a change**

- If you have just typed a new value in a cell, and have not yet pressed ⟨Enter⟩, press ⟨Esc⟩ or ⟨Ctrl⟩+⟨Z⟩ to restore the previous value of the cell. If you decide to reinstate the changed value, press ⟨Ctrl⟩+⟨Z⟩ again.

- If you have just changed a cell, and pressed ⟨Enter⟩, select **Edit ➤ Undo** (or press ⟨Ctrl⟩+⟨Z⟩) to restore the previous value of the cell. Selecting **Edit ➤ Redo** (or pressing ⟨Ctrl⟩+⟨Z⟩) at this point will reinstate the changed value in the cell (undo the last undo).

Entering data automatically assigns a data type to the column

When you type an entry into an empty column, MINITAB assigns a data type to the column, and adds an identifier next to the column number. Which data type is assigned depends on what you type:

When you enter...	The type is set to...	Identifier	Example
a number or *	numeric	nothing	C20
characters that match a built-in date/time format (such 1/31/97 or 11:10:14.22 PM)	date/time	–D	C20–D
any other characters	text	–T	C20–T

Notes

■ All data in one column must be all the same type, either all numeric, all date/time, or all text. MINITAB treats numbers and dates that appear in a text column (such as a street address or month name) as text. In numeric or date/time columns, MINITAB will not allow you to enter an invalid value.

■ You can convert a column from one data type to another by choosing **Manip ➤ Change Data Type**. See *Changing Columns from One Data Type to Another* on page 6-42.

Find and Replace in the Data Window

You can use the **Find** or **Replace** commands to search for and update data in the Data window. You can search for numerical, text, or date/time data, or search for any group of numerical or text strings.

▶ To find data in a worksheet

1 With the worksheet active, choose **Editor ➤ Find**.

2 In **Find what**, enter a number, text, or date/time string.

3 Use any of the options listed below.

4 Click **Find Next**. If you wish to update a cell once you have found the string you are looking for, click the **Replace** button to bring up the Replace dialog box. Click **Close** when done.

Note | Use Ctrl+Break to interrupt a **Find** search.

Options

Match case

■ When determining matches, consider the case.

Find entire cells only

■ When determining matches the number, text, or date/time string in the **Find what** box must match the entire displayed cell in the worksheet.

Direction

- Set the search to move upward or downward in the column from the active cell. When searching upward, the search will move to the bottom of the previous column when the top of the column is reached. When searching downward, the search will move to the top of the next column when the bottom of the column is reached.

► To find and replace data in a worksheet

1 With the proper worksheet active, choose **Editor ► Replace**.

2 In **Find what**, enter a number, text, or date/time string.

3 In **Replace with**, enter a number, text, or date/time string.

4 Use any of the options listed below.

5 Click **Find Next**. Once a number, text, or date/time string has been located, click **Replace** to replace the data in the current cell and find the next occurrence.

6 To automatically find and replace all occurrences of the number, text, or date/time string in **Find what** with the string in **Replace with**, click **Replace All**. Click **Close** when done.

Note | Use ⌈Ctrl⌉+⌈Break⌉ to interrupt a **Replace** search.

Options

Match case

- When determining matches, consider the case.

Find entire cells only

- When determining matches, the number, text, or date/time string in the **Find what** box must match the entire displayed cell in the worksheet.

Direction

- Set the search to move upward or downward in the column from the active cell. When searching upward, the search will move to the bottom of the previous column when the top of the column is reached. When searching downward, the search will move to the top of the next column when the bottom of the column is reached.

Note | The Find and Replace commands will ignore hidden columns when searching a worksheet.

Copying and Pasting Data

Copying and pasting is a quick way to exchange data between MINITAB windows or between MINITAB and other applications.

Using the **Edit ➤ Copy** and **Edit ➤ Paste** commands, you can copy from and paste to the Data window from a variety of sources:

- cells, rows, and columns in the same Data window

- cells, rows, and columns in another Data window

- documents in another application, such as a spreadsheet package or a word processor

- text in the History folder (though you cannot paste into the History folder)

- text in the Session window—see *Copying Session Window Output into Your Worksheet* on page 11-3

Clipboard replication

You can use the **Edit ➤ Copy** and **Edit ➤ Paste** commands to fill large groups of worksheet cells with patterned data by copying a section of data and pasting repeating blocks of the copied data over a larger area of cells. For details, see *Clipboard Replication* on page 5-7.

Other ways to copy data

The **Edit ➤ Copy** and **Edit ➤ Paste** commands copy Data window cells that are *contiguous*, that is, next to each other. But there are other methods for copying other types of data.

- To copy columns and rows that are not contiguous, use the **Manip ➤ Copy Columns** command. Columns copied this way can only be pasted within the same Data window, but this method gives you a great deal of control over which rows within those columns are copied. For details, see *Copying Non-Contiguous Columns and Rows Within a Data Window* on page 2-12.

- To copy matrices, use the **Calc ➤ Matrices ➤ Copy** command. See *Copying a Matrix* on page 8-6.

- To copy stored constants, use the **Calc ➤ Calculator** command. See *Example expressions* on page 7-3.

- To copy and paste data "links" that update automatically, use Dynamic Data Exchange (DDE). See Chapter 10, *Using Dynamic Data Exchange (DDE)*.

▶ To copy cells, rows, or columns from the Data window

1 Select the cells you want. See *Selecting Areas of the Data Window* on page 2-3.

2 Choose **Edit ➤ Copy Cells** or press Ctrl+C.

▶ To paste cells by replacing

1 Select the same number of cells that are on the Clipboard.

2 Choose **Edit ➤ Paste Cells** or press Ctrl+V.

3 If data are separated by spaces, MINITAB will ask you how to interpret the data—see *If data are separated by spaces* below.

▶ To paste cells by inserting

1 Click on a cell.

2 Choose **Edit ➤ Paste Cells**.

3 A dialog box appears. Choose **Insert above the active cell, shifting cells down to make room.** and click **OK**.

4 If data are separated by spaces, MINITAB will ask you how to interpret the data—see *If data are separated by spaces* below.

If data are separated by spaces

After you use a paste command, if the data are separated by tabs, MINITAB automatically puts each value into its own cell. But if the data are separated by spaces, MINITAB displays a dialog box that shows the first line of data and asks how MINITAB should interpret the spaces. Do one of the following:

- If the line of data looks right, click **Use spaces as delimiters**

- If you would prefer to paste all the data into one column, click **Paste as a single column**

Copying and pasting missing values

In the Data window, missing values in text columns are represented by blanks and missing values in numeric and date/time columns are represented by an asterisk (*). By default, when you copy from the Data window to the Clipboard, missing values remain blanks and asterisks. Also by default, when you copy from the Clipboard and paste into the Data window, MINITAB automatically interprets blanks and asterisks as missing values.

Some applications, however, denote missing numerical values by characters other than the asterisk, such as a space or a zero. When you copy from the Data window, you can have MINITAB automatically convert missing values to the character that application uses. You can also tell MINITAB how to convert those characters when they are pasted from the Clipboard to the Data window.

You control the conversion by changing the *Clipboard settings character*. The table following the instructions shows how MINITAB converts missing values when you copy and paste.

▶ **To set the Clipboard settings character**

1 Choose **Editor ➤ Clipboard Settings**.

2 In **String for Missing Value**, type any character. Click **OK**.

How missing values are converted

Direction	Missings and Blanks	Text	Numeric	Date/Time
From the Clipboard to MINITAB	Characters that = Clipboard settings character import as	blanks	*	*
	Blanks import as	blanks	*	*
From MINITAB to the Clipboard	Characters that = Clipboard setting character export as	unchanged	unchanged	unchanged
	Blanks or * export as	blanks	Clipboard setting character	Clipboard setting character

Note | If the Clipboard setting character is a number, it is ignored when importing numeric data.

How the Clipboard settings character affects data types

A string of data is imported as numeric if the data are all numbers except for the Clipboard settings character. Likewise, a string of data is imported as date/time if all the data except the Clipboard setting character match one of the pre-set date/time formats.

The string is imported as text if it contains any non-number characters besides the Clipboard settings character.

For example, say that the Clipboard settings character is set to "m." Three columns of data would be interpreted like this:

Clipboard data	Interpreted as this column type		
	numeric	text	date/time
1	1		
2	2		
m	*		
3	3		
1		1	
2		2	
m			
3		3	
x		x	
10/15/95			10/15/95
m			*
10/16/97			10/16/97

Copying Non-Contiguous Columns and Rows Within a Data Window

In the Copy Columns dialog box, you can select any columns you want in the active Data window, and copy them to another part of the same Data window. You can copy all the rows in those columns, or just certain rows.

More | If you are copying only certain rows in order to create subsets of your data, you may find it easier to use the subsetting and splitting functions. These functions can copy data to a new worksheet. For details, see *Subsetting: Copy Data to a New Worksheet* on page 6-9 and *Subsetting: Split the Active Worksheet* on page 6-14.

▶ To copy non-contiguous columns

1 Choose **Manip ➤ Copy Columns**.

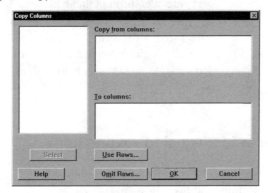

2 In **Copy from columns**, enter the column(s) you want to copy from.

3 In **To columns**, enter the columns you want to copy to.

4 If you like, use or omit certain rows (described below), then click **OK**.

▶ To use or omit selected rows

The instructions below are written in terms of using rows. To omit rows, follow the same instructions, substituting **Omit Rows** every time you see **Use Rows**.

1 In the Copy Columns dialog box, click **Use Rows**.

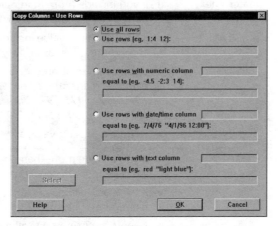

2 Do one of the following:

- To copy rows by row numbers:
  - Choose **Use rows**.
  - Enter the row numbers of the rows you want to copy. Use a colon to abbreviate a range of row numbers.

- To copy rows according to their value:
  - Choose **Use rows with numeric column, date/time column,** or **text column** and enter a column of that type.
  - In **equal to**, enter a value (to copy only rows that have that value), multiple values (to copy rows that have one value or another), or a range of values (to copy all rows from the first value to the second value, inclusive). See the *Rules for "equal to" expressions* below.

3 Click **OK** in each dialog box.

Rules for "equal to" expressions

Follow these rules for using or omitting rows. Some of the rule examples, however, are written in terms of using rows.

Column type	Rules
numeric	■ If you include more than one value, put a space between each value. For example, entering *15.98 16.02* will copy rows that contain either 15.98 or 16.02. ■ Use a colon to abbreviate a range. For example, entering *15.98:16.02* will copy all rows that have values from 15.98 to 16.02, inclusive. ■ Denote a missing value as '*'.
date/time	■ If you include more than one date, put a space between each date, as in *10/15/97 10/16/97*. ■ If the date/time value includes a blank space, use double quotes around the value, as in, *"10/15/97 3:30"*. ■ Use a colon to abbreviate a range, but you must include a space before and after the colon. For example, both of these are valid: *10/15/97 : 11/15/97* *"10/15/97 3:30" : "11/15/97 5:30"* ■ Denote a missing value as '*'.
text	■ If you include more than one word, put a space between each word, as in *Morristown Dothan*. ■ If the word includes a blank space, use double quotes around the word, as in, *"New York"*. ■ Denote a missing text value as two double quotes with no space in between, like this: "".

Deleting Data

Deleting cells, rows, and columns in the Data window

You can delete rows, cells, and columns, or just clear their contents. Before deleting, select an area of the Data window, or click on the cell you want to make active.

▶ To delete...	Do this
cells and put them on the Clipboard (following rows or columns move up or left)	Choose **Edit ➤ Cut Cells**. After cutting cells, you can paste them—see *Copying and Pasting Data* on page 2-9.
cell contents only (empty cells remain)	Choose **Edit ➤ Clear Cells**, or press `Backspace`. In a numeric column, MINITAB inserts ∗ in a cleared cell (unless it is the last cell in a column).
cells (following rows or columns move up or left)	Choose **Edit ➤ Delete Cells** or press `Delete`.

Deleting constants, matrices, and non-contiguous columns

Using the **Manip ➤ Erase Variables** command, you can erase any combination of constants, matrices, and columns.

If you want to delete a single column, or a contiguous block of columns, it would probably be easier and quicker to use the techniques covered under *Deleting cells, rows, and columns in the Data window* on page 2-15. But if you want to delete any collection of columns, you can use the Erase Variables command.

Because constants and matrices do not appear in the Data window, the Erase Variables command is the only way to erase them.

Caution | If you delete constants, matrices, or columns using the Erase Variables dialog box, you cannot undo the action.

▶ **To erase constants, matrices, and non-contiguous columns**

1 Choose **Manip ▶ Erase Variables**.

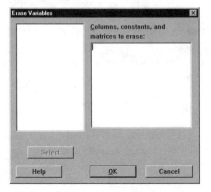

2 In **Columns, constants, and matrices to erase**, enter any combination of columns, constants, and matrices, then click **OK**.

Deleting non-contiguous rows

You can delete rows from any columns you select and move the remaining rows up to close the gap.

If you want to delete a single row, or a contiguous series of rows, it would probably be easier and quicker to use the techniques covered under *Deleting cells, rows, and columns in the Data window* on page 2-15. But if you want to delete any collection of rows, you can use the Delete Rows command.

Caution | If you delete rows using the Delete Rows dialog box, you cannot undo the action.

▶ **To delete non-contiguous rows**

1 Choose **Manip ▶ Delete Rows**.

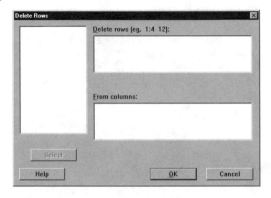

2 In **Delete rows**, enter the rows you want to delete. Use a colon to abbreviate a list of consecutive rows; for example, 2:4 6 means to delete rows 2, 3, 4, and 6.

3 In **From columns**, enter the columns you want to delete rows from, then click **OK**.

Inserting Empty Cells, Rows, and Columns

▶ **To insert cells, rows, or columns**

1 Select one or more cells.

2 Choose **Editor ➤ Insert Cells/Insert Rows/Insert Columns**.

Cells and rows are inserted above the selection, columns are inserted to the left of the selection.

MINITAB inserts the same number of items that are selected. For example, if cells in three rows are selected when you choose **Editor ➤ Insert Rows**, three rows are inserted.

For example, click in row 3.   When a row is inserted, the data in row 3 moves to row 4, and row 3 is filled with missing values.

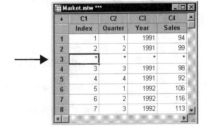

Moving Columns

▶ **To move columns**

1 Select one or more columns.

2 Choose **Editor ➤ Move Columns**.

3 Select one of the following and click **OK**.

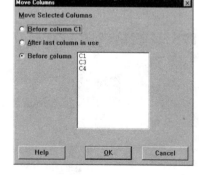

- **Before column C1** inserts the selected columns before C1 (pushing other columns to the right).

- **After last column in use** places the selected columns after the last non-empty column.

- **Before column** inserts the selected columns before whatever column you click in the list box.

Changing Column Names, Fonts, and Descriptions

▶ **To name a column**

1 Click a column name cell.

2 Type the name. Names cannot:

- be longer than 31 characters

- begin or end with a space

- include the symbol ' or #

- start with or consist entirely of the symbol *

3 Press ⌐Enter⌐.

More | To name constants or matrices, you must use the NAME session command. For example, to give the constant K2 the name 'MyConstant,' you would choose **Edit ➤ Command Line Editor**, type *NAME K2 'MyConstant'*, and click **Submit Command**. See Help for details.

Changing Data window fonts

You can set the font for labels (column numbers, like C1, column names, and row numbers), and one font for data (values in the cells). The fonts apply to all the columns in the Data window, not just the current column.

▶ **To change Data window fonts**

1   Choose **Editor ➤ Worksheet ➤ Select Data Font** or **Select Label Font**.

2   Set font properties, then click **OK**.

Setting column descriptions

Descriptions are useful for recording the source of the column's data, or for recording how the data have been modified from the source.

▶ **To create or edit a column description**

1   Click anywhere in the desired column.

2   Choose **Editor ➤ Column ➤ Description**.

3   Enter the information you want, then click **OK**

Note | Columns with descriptions have a red triangle displayed in the upper right corner of their column name cell. Column descriptions can be viewed in the Columns folder of the Project Manager.

Tip | In the Column Description dialog box, or any dialog box that accepts text, you can paste characters that are on the Clipboard by pressing Ctrl+V.

Changing Column Widths

You can change the width of one or more columns or all columns in the Data window. You can also hide unused columns or columns with less relevant data, so that you can see more of your data.

▶ To...	Do this
manually change the width of one or more columns	1 Select the column(s). 2 Point to the top of a line dividing two columns until you see two arrows with a solid line between them ◄|►. 3 Drag the border until the column is the desired width.
change the widths of all columns that have not been changed manually	1 Choose **Editor ➤ Column ➤ Standard Width**. 2 In **Standard column width**, type a number, then click **OK**. The number is the number of characters you want to display. The column will widen according to the typical width of a character in the current Data window font. If you set a standard width of 0, then MINITAB will hide worksheet columns that have not been changed manually.
change the widths of all columns	1 Choose **Editor ➤ Column ➤ Standard Width**. 2 In **Standard column width**, type a number. 3 Check **Change widths that were set individually**, then click **OK**. The number is the number of characters you want to display. The column will widen according to the typical width of a character in the current Data window font. If you set a standard width of 0, then MINITAB will hide all worksheet columns.

▶ **To...**

	Do this
choose between automatic widening or set a fixed width for selected columns	**1** Choose **Editor ➤ Column ➤ Width** or right-click on the selected columns and choose **Column ➤ Width**.
	2 Select **Automatic widening** or **Fixed width**, then click **OK**.
	If you select **Fixed width**, the number is the number of characters you want to display. The column will widen according to the typical width of a character in the current Data window font.
	If you set a fixed width of 0, then MINITAB will hide the selected columns.
change MINITAB's default standard width	**1** Choose **Edit ➤ Preferences** and select **Data Window**.
	2 In **Data window default column width:**, type a number, then click **OK**.
	3 Click **Save** in the Preferences dialog box.
	The number is the number of characters you want to display. The column will widen according to the typical width of a character in the current Data window font.
	If you set a standard width of 0, then MINITAB will hide all worksheet columns.

Hiding columns

If you have many columns of data spread out over a worksheet and you want to more easily view relevant data, you may want to hide columns with less relevant data, or hide any empty columns. You can hide and unhide columns manually or through the Hide/Unhide Columns dialog box.

▶ **To hide and unhide columns**

1 Make sure the worksheet is active and choose **Editor ➤ Column ➤ Hide/ Unhide Columns**.

2 Select the columns you wish to hide and move them to **Hidden Columns** with ⌐ `>` ⌐, or use ⌐ `»` ⌐ to move all columns.

3 Unhide columns by moving them to **Unhidden Columns**.

4 If you like, you have the option, using **Columns to display in list boxes**, to display all columns, data columns, or empty columns in the **Unhidden/ Hidden Columns** list boxes. Click **OK**.

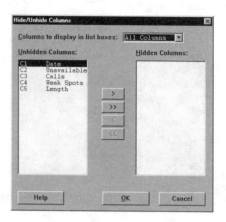

▶ **To hide columns manually by clicking and dragging**

1 Select the column(s) you wish to hide.

2 Point to the top of a line dividing two columns until you see two arrows with a solid line between them ◄|►.

3 Drag the border until the selected columns are no longer visible.

▶ **To unhide columns manually by clicking and dragging**

1 Point to the top of a column line where there is a hidden column (or columns) until you see two arrows with a double-spaced line between them ◄||►.

2 Drag the border until the hidden column (or columns) becomes visible.

▶ **To hide columns manually by right-clicking**

1 Select the column(s) you wish to hide.

2 Right-click on one of the selected columns and choose **Column ➤ Hide Selected Columns**.

▶ **To unhide columns manually by right-clicking**

1 Select two columns surrounding the hidden column(s).

2 Right-click on one of the selected columns and choose **Column ➤ Unhide Selected Columns**.

Options

You can choose to have all dialog boxes display or ignore hidden columns. You can set this option for each worksheet in a project or have dialogs display or ignore hidden columns by default.

▶ **To set dialog boxes to display or ignore hidden columns in a project**

1 Make sure the proper worksheet is active.

2 Select or deselect **Editor ➤ Column ➤ Use Hidden Columns in Dialog Boxes**. A check will appear in front of the menu item when the option is selected.

▶ **To set dialog boxes to display or ignore hidden columns by default**

1 Choose **Edit ➤ Preferences** and select **Dialog Box**.

2 Under **Columns Displayed**, choose **Use all columns in dialog boxes** or **Use only unhidden columns in dialog boxes**.

3 Click **OK** and then click **Save**.

Formatting Columns and Changing Data Types

There are three data types: numeric, text, and date/time (for more discussion of these types, see Chapter 1, *Data Overview*). If a column contains data, the column must be one of those three types. Once a column has a data type, you can specify format characteristics for that column. For example, a numeric column can be set to display two decimal places or three.

If a column is empty, you can begin typing and MINITAB will automatically assign a data type and format based on the characters you type into that first cell. You can also assign data types and formats to empty columns, and any data you enter in that column will display in the format you choose.

You can change a column's data type. When you change the data type of a column that contains data, that data is converted from one type to another. For example, when you convert a numeric column to a text column, a number (such as 1.23) becomes a text string ("1.23"). Text strings cannot be analyzed in most statistical procedures.

Once a column has a data type, MINITAB can automatically assign a format, or you can assign a specific format. By default, MINITAB automatically changes the format of columns based on their contents. When the contents change, the format may change.

For example, say that you have a column of numbers that all have one digit after the decimal (as in 3.2, 4.3, 5.4). If you type a number with four significant digits after the decimal (as in 1.1234), MINITAB changes the column format to use four decimal places, and all numbers will appear in that format (3.2 will appear as 3.2000). When that four-digit number is removed, the column's format will switch back to a single decimal place. If you like, you could then set the column to always display four digits after the decimal.

Date/time columns have additional formatting issues, which are covered in *Formatting Date/Time Columns* on page 2-25.

Note | When you modify the format characteristics of a column, you are only changing the way that column is displayed in the Data window—you are not modifying the underlying value. For example, if the number in a cell is 1.2345678 and you change the format to display only two decimals, all calculations will still use 1.2345678.

▶ To format an empty column

1 Click in the column you want to format and choose **Editor** ➤ **Format Column**.

2 Choose **Numeric**, **Text**, or **Date/Time**.

3 Complete the dialog box (for **Numeric** or **Date/Time**) to your specifications and click **OK**.

▶ To change the data type of a non-empty column

1 Click in the column you want to change and choose **Manip** ➤ **Change Data Type**.

2 Choose the conversion type you want.

3 Complete the dialog box and click **OK**.

For details on dialog box options, see *Changing Columns from One Data Type to Another* on page 6-42.

▶ To change the number of decimals displayed in a numeric column

1 Click in the column you want to format and choose **Editor** ➤ **Format Column** ➤ **Numeric**.

2 Select **Fixed decimal with** _____ **decimal places**.

3 In the text box, type the number of decimals and click **OK**.

▶ To change column format to exponential

1 Click in the column you want to format.

2 Choose **Editor** ➤ **Format Column** ➤ **Numeric**.

3 Select **Exponential with _____ decimal places**. In the text box, enter the number of decimal places you want to display before the E, then click **OK**. For example, you could display 3.2E3 (one decimal place) or 3.20E3 (two decimal places).

More | For instruction on typing exponential data, see *To enter a number in exponential notation* on page 2-6. For more information on very large or very small numbers and exponential notation, see *Using Numeric Data* on page 1-8.

Formatting Date/Time Columns

In MINITAB, values in a date/time column are stored internally as numbers. You can change the way those internally stored numbers are displayed in a date/time column by applying a date/time format. You can apply one of several default formats, or you can create your own.

A single date/time value can be a date, a time, or both. For example, all of the following are valid date/time values:

1/1/99
3:04 PM
1/1/99 3:04PM

As with all MINITAB columns, all the values in a column must share the same format.

Tip | To automatically format an empty column when you enter data, just begin typing. If the first entry matches a default date/time format, the column will assume that format. (To use a custom format, you must first create the format, apply the format to the column, then begin typing.)

▶ **To format a column with a default or previously-defined format**

1 Select one or more columns. The columns must be empty (unformatted) or already in a date/time format.

2 Choose **Editor ➤ Format Column ➤ Date/Time**.

3 From the **Current Date/Time Formats** box, select a format (default formats are shown on the next page). If the format you need is not available, you can create a new one (see *Creating and Deleting Custom Date/Time Formats* on page 2-26). Click **OK**.

Default date/time formats

The symbols in the Format column below—such as m, d, and yy—are date/time components. For a list, see *Date/time format components* on page 2-27.

Format	Description	Example
m/d/yy	American date	1/5/99
d-mmm-yy	International date	5-Jan-99
mmm-yy	Month and year	Jan-99
h:mm:ss.ss	24-hour time (military time)	23:10:14.22
h:mm:ss.ss AM/PM	12-hour time	11:10:14.22 PM

Default date (not time) components can be separated by (/), (-), or (.). All components must be separated by the same symbol. For example, 1/1/99 is valid; 1/1-99 is invalid.

Default 12-hour time components can be AM/PM, am/pm, A/P, or a/p.

Note | If Windows regional settings are changed in the Regional Settings control panel, Minitab will automatically update its default date/time settings to reflect the change. Minitab will retain any original default date/time settings unless an ambiguity could be created. For instance, if the regional settings change to d.m.yy, Minitab will remove m/d/yy from the list of default date/time settings.

Creating and Deleting Custom Date/Time Formats

You can combine the components in the Date/Time Component table (page 2-27) to build custom date/time formats. A format can consist of a date part, a time part, or both. Custom formats are saved when you exit MINITAB.

▶ To define a date/time format

1 Select one or more columns. The columns must be empty (unformatted) or already in a date/time format.

2 Choose **Editor ➤ Format Column ➤ Date/Time**.

3 In the **New format** text box, type a new format using the *Date/time format components* on page 2-27 and *Rules for defining formats* on page 2-28. Click **OK**.

Tip | Select a previously defined format from the **Current Date/Time Formats** list box, then edit it in the **New format** text box.

▶ **To delete a date/time format**

1 Select an empty column.

2 Choose **Editor ➤ Format Column ➤ Date/Time**.

3 Select a format from the **Current Date/Time Formats** scroll list.

4 Click **Delete**.

5 Click **Cancel**.

Note You can only delete default formats for the length of your session; when you restart MINITAB, the default formats will be back again.

Date/time format components

The following are valid components of date/time formats:

Format components	Displays...	Example
m	month as a number without leading zero (1–12)	1, 2, ...
mm	and with leading zero (01–12)	01, 02, ...
	1 = January, 2 = February, etc.	
mmm	month as a three-letter name or	Jan, Feb, ...
mmmm	unabbreviated name	January, February
d	day of month as a number without leading	1, 2, ...
dd	zero (1–31) or with leading zero (01–31)	01, 02, ...
yy	year as a two-digit or	99, 00, ...
yyyy	four-digit number	1999, 2000, ...
h	hour without leading zero (0–23) or	7, 8, ...
hh	with leading zero (00–23)	07, 08, ...
mm	minute with leading zero (00–59)	08:01, 08:02, ...
	Can only be used if hour (hh) is specified.	
ss	second with leading zero (00–59)	08:01:01
	Can only be used if minute (:mm) is specified.	08:01:02 ...
ss	hundredths of a second with leading zero (00–99)	08:01:01.01 08:01:01.02
	Can only be used if seconds (:ss) is specified.	...

Format components	Displays...	Example
AM/PM A/P am/pm a/p	the hour using 12-hour time Can only be used if time is specified.	08:01 AM 08:01:01.02 PM
Qq qQ	quarter as "Q" and a number (1–4) Q1 = January 1–March 31 Q2 = April 1–June 30 Q3 = July 1 –September 30 Q4 = October 1–December 31 Quarters can only be used in combination with years, as in qQyy (1Q99) or yyyyQq (1999Q1). "Q" is punctuation that must always come between the year number and the quarter number.	Q1, Q2, Q3, Q4 1Q, 2Q, 3Q, 4Q
Wkw Wkww wWk wwWk	week as "Wk" and a week number, without leading zero (1–54) or with leading zero (01–54) Wk1 = January 1 to the first Sunday in January. Wk2 = Sunday to Saturday, and so on. Wk53 = From the last Sunday in December to January 1. Weeks can only be used in combination with years, as in yyWkw (99Wk1) or wWkyyy (1Wk1999). "Wk" is punctuation that must always come between the year number and the week number.	Wk1, Wk2, ... Wk01, Wk02, ... 1Wk, 2Wk, ... 01Wk, 02Wk, ...

Rules for defining formats

The rules for defining a format depend on whether you are defining day/month/year formats, quarter and week formats, or time formats. The rules for each are listed below.

Defining day/month/year date formats

■ Specify one or more of the following, in any order: day, month, year.

■ Separate components with (/), (–), or (.). All components must be separated by the same symbol. For example, 1/1/99 is valid; 1/1-99 is invalid.

■ A format consisting of only "mm" will be assumed to be months, not minutes.

If day/month/year components are missing

MINITAB always internally stores a full date which includes a month, day, and year component. When you enter a value in a column, and the column's date format does not include one of the components, MINITAB assumes the following:

If format is missing this component	MINITAB assumes...
day	the first day of the month
month	the current month
year	the current year

Implicit century

Minitab interprets two digit years as follows:

- 00 to 29 as 20xx (for example, 1/1/20 would be interpreted as 2020).

- 30 to 99 as 19xx (for example, 1/1/56 would be interpreted as 1956).

Defining quarter and week formats

- Quarter (Qq) and week (Wkw) components can only be used in combination with year components—not with day, month, or time components. Quarters and weeks cannot be used together.

- The "Q" and "Wk" are punctuation that must always come between the year number and the quarter/week number; for example, yyQq and wWkyy are valid, but yyqQ and Wkwyy are invalid.

If quarter or week components are missing

MINITAB always internally stores a full date which includes a month, day, and year component. When you enter a quarter or week value in a column, you cannot specify a day or month, and year components are optional. When components are missing, MINITAB assumes the following:

If format is	MINITAB assumes...	For example, when you type...	MINITAB stores
Qq	the first day of the quarter, the first month in the quarter, and the current year	Q1	January 1st of the current year
Wkw	the first day of the week, the month that the week falls in, and the current year	Wk1	January 1st of the current year

Defining time formats

- Specify one or more of the following, in this order: hour, minute, second, and hundredth of a second. Larger time unit components must appear to the left of smaller time unit components. For example, hh:mm is valid, but mm:hh is invalid.

- Components must be contiguous: hours next to minutes, minutes next to hours or seconds, etc. For example, hh:mm and mm:ss are valid, but hh:ss is invalid.

- Components are always separated as follows:
  hh:mm:ss.ss AM/PM
  Notice that a period must separate seconds from hundredths of seconds, and a space must precede AM/PM.

- A format consisting of only "mm" will be assumed to be months, not minutes.

- A format consisting of only "ss" will be assumed to be seconds, not hundredths of seconds.

Combining dates and times in one format

- The date part must always appear first.

- A space must separate the date part from the time part.

3

Opening, Saving, and Printing Files

Chapter Overview

Projects contain Session window output, graphs, and worksheets. Worksheets contain all your data: columns, constants, and matrices. You can have multiple worksheets open in one project. When you open a project file, all the worksheets that were inside that project when you last saved are available to you. When you save a project, the worksheets are saved within that project file.

You can add worksheets to your project by copying data from a file. Note that data are *copied*. That means that when you change the data within a project, you do not affect the original file. You can open a project, change data, and save the project over and over, and the original file will not be affected.

If you like, you can also save a worksheet as a separate file that can be used in other MINITAB projects or other applications.

Most of the time, the data files you will bring into your project and save from your project will be MINITAB worksheets. Those worksheets may be stand-alone files (files with the extension MTW), or parts of a project (MPJ) file. You can preview a project file to see a list of all the worksheets in the file, then copy one of the worksheets from that project to your own.

You can also open and save data files in the formats of many applications, like Excel and Lotus 1-2-3. To exchange data with other applications, such as mainframe computer programs, you can open and save text files. Finally, you can exchange data with versions of MINITAB on other platforms using MINITAB portable worksheets (MTP files).

Other tools for importing and exporting data

You can also exchange data with other applications using tools described in other chapters:

- If you want to import data from a database, use the Open DataBase Connectivity (ODBC) tools. See Chapter 4, *Using ODBC and Special Text Files*.

- If the data are in text format but arranged in unusual ways, you can use the special text import and export commands. For a discussion of what text formats can be problematic, see *When to Use the Import Special Text command* on page 4-9. For details on the special text commands, see Chapter 4, *Using ODBC and Special Text Files*.

- If the data are on another Windows program on your system, you can use Dynamic Data Exchange (DDE) to establish a link with that program. When data in the source program change, the data can be automatically updated in MINITAB. DDE has other uses as well. See Chapter 10, *Using Dynamic Data Exchange (DDE)*.

Opening Projects

When you start MINITAB, a new, empty project will be opened for you. You can create a new project at any time or open existing projects.

▶ **To open a new project**

This closes the current project and opens a new one.

1 Choose **File ➤ New**.

2 Choose **Minitab Project** and click **OK**.

Opening a new project closes the current project. If your current project has been changed since it was last saved, MINITAB will prompt you to save all or part of the project before closing it. See *Saving and Closing Projects* on page 3-4.

▶ **To open a project**

1 Choose **File ➤ Open Project**.

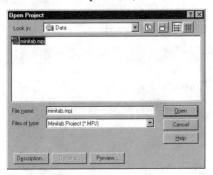

The appearance of this dialog box may be different on your computer, depending on which operating system you are using. For details, see your system documentation.

2 Select a directory and file.

3 If you like, use any of the options below, then click **Open**.

Options

Description subdialog box

■ Read the project description. The **Description** button is available only if the selected file contains a description. See *Project and Worksheet Descriptions* on page 3-11.

Preview subdialog box

■ View a list of the worksheets and graphs in a project before you open it. See *Previewing Projects and Worksheets* on page 3-9.

Saving and Closing Projects

Saving projects

When you save the project, you save all the information about your work:

- the contents of all the windows, including
  - the columns of data in each Data window
  - the stored constants, matrices, and design objects (used with the design of experiments commands) that are summarized in the Worksheet folders
  - the complete text in the Session window and History folder
  - each Graph window
- the description of each project created with **File ➤ Project Description**
- the description of each worksheet created with **Editor ➤ Worksheet ➤ Description**
- the size, location, and state of each window
- the contents of each dialog box you used

▶ To save a project

1 Choose **File ➤ Save Project (As)**.

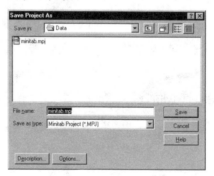

2 In **File name**, enter a name for the project.

3 If you like, choose any of the options below, then click **Save**.

Options

Description subdialog box

- Enter a description for this project. See *Project and Worksheet Descriptions* on page 3-11.

Options subdialog box

- Choose which parts of the project to save. You can save or ignore Session window content, graphs, dialog box settings, and History folder content. Data window content (the worksheets in the project) are always saved with the project.

Closing projects

In MINITAB, a project of one type or another is open at all times. The project may be a new project or a project file that was saved earlier. There is no "Close Project" command. To close a project, you open a new project, open a saved project, or exit MINITAB.

▶ **To close a project**

1 Do any of the following:

- Choose **File ➤ New ➤ Minitab Project**.
- Choose **File ➤ Open Project**.
- Choose **File ➤ Exit**.

Note │ If you close a project before saving it, MINITAB will prompt you to save the project.

Opening Worksheets

You can open a new, empty worksheet at any time. You can also open a file that contains data. When you open a file, you copy the contents of the file into the current MINITAB project. Any changes you make to the worksheet while in the project will not affect the original file.

Most often you will open new worksheets or open MINITAB files: MINITAB worksheet (MTW) files, or worksheets contained within MINITAB project (MPJ) files. This section describes how to open those two types of files.

You can also open other types of files, described elsewhere in this chapter. You can open:

- non-MINITAB files, such as Excel worksheets, Lotus 1-2-3 worksheets, and text files. See *Opening Files from Other Applications* on page 3-12.
- files from other older releases of MINITAB, including versions of MINITAB on other platforms. See *Exchanging Data with Other Versions of MINITAB* on page 3-19.

▶ **To open a new worksheet**

1 Choose **File ➤ New**.

2 Choose **Minitab Worksheet** and click **OK**.

▶ **To open a MINITAB worksheet (MTW) file**

1 Choose **File ➤ Open Worksheet**.

The appearance of this dialog box may be different on your computer, depending on which operating system you are using. For details, see your system documentation.

Options is disabled because those options are only used when opening non-MINITAB files.

2 Select a directory and file.

3 If you like, use any of the options (described under *Options* on page 3-7), then click **Open**.

A message box will appear, telling you that a copy of the content of this file will be added to the worksheet.

4 If you do not want this message to appear every time you open a file, check **Do not display this message again**. Click **OK**.

▶ **To open a MINITAB worksheet contained in a MINITAB project**

1 Choose **File ➤ Open Worksheet**.

2 In **Files of type**, choose **Minitab Project**.

3 Select a directory and a project file.

4 Click **Preview** or **Open**.

5 Under **Available items**, select a worksheet.

6 If you like, click **Preview** or **Description** (described under *Options* on page 3-7). Click **OK**.

7 In the Open Worksheet dialog box, click **Open**.

8 Select a worksheet to be opened and click **OK**.

Options

Open Worksheet dialog box

- **Open** creates a new worksheet and displays the data in its own Data window. This is the default.

- **Merge** adds the columns of data to the current worksheet. See *Merging worksheets* below.

Description subdialog box

- When you select a MINITAB file, click **Description** to read the worksheet description. **Description** is available only if the selected file contains a description. See *Project and Worksheet Descriptions* on page 3-11.

Preview subdialog box

- View the selected file before you open or merge it. If you are merging the file, you can also change how the data are interpreted by MINITAB and where the data are placed in the worksheet. See *Merging worksheets* below.

Merging worksheets

When you select a file, instead of putting the file's data in its own Data window, you can add columns of data to the current worksheet. If you are opening a new worksheet, you can merge two worksheets using the **Merge** option in the Open Worksheet dialog box. If you already have two worksheets open, you can use the **Manip ➤ Merge Worksheets** command. The Merge Worksheets command gives you more control over how the data in the two worksheets will be merged. For more information on the Merge Worksheets command, see *Merging Worksheets* on page 6-4.

If you use the Merge option in the Open Worksheets dialog box, data are added to the worksheet like this:

- Columns are added to the right of existing columns. If the current worksheet is empty, Merge copies data into the current worksheet, beginning with C1.

- Data are always put into new columns. Data cannot be inserted at the top or bottom of existing columns.

- When merging a MINITAB worksheet file, constants, matrices, and column descriptions are ignored. Worksheet descriptions are added to the current worksheet's comments.

- If a file contains column names that duplicate column names in the current worksheet, MINITAB will automatically add a numbered suffix to the name of each duplicate column that will be added. For example, MYDATA will become MYDATA_1.

You can change many of these defaults in the **Open Worksheet ➤ Preview** subdialog box. Most usefully, you can choose where the added columns will go, select which columns should not be added at all, and edit the default column names. See the following procedure for details on when to use the Preview subdialog box.

▶ To merge worksheets

1 In the Open Worksheet dialog box, click **Merge**.

2 Select a directory and file.

3 If you like, click **Preview**, make changes in how MINITAB should interpret the file, and click **OK**.

In the Preview subdialog box, you can make all the changes to the merge file that could normally be made only to a non-MINITAB file. For details, see *Previewing non-MINITAB files* on page 3-13.

4 Click **Open**.

Saving and Closing Worksheets

When you save a project, all the worksheets in your project are also saved within the project file. But if you want to use your worksheet in another project, another application, or another version of MINITAB, you can save the worksheet into a separate file. The worksheet can be saved as

- a Release 13 worksheet that can be used in other MINITAB projects. See below for the procedure.

- a file that can be used in another application, such as Excel. See *Saving Files to Use in Other Applications* on page 3-17.

- a file that can be used in other versions of MINITAB. These other versions can be older or newer releases of MINITAB for Windows, or versions of MINITAB on other platforms. For details, see *Exchanging Data with Other Versions of MINITAB* on page 3-19.

Note | Saving a worksheet saves only the data; to save your *analysis,* including graphs and output in the Session window, use **File ➤ Save Project**, described on page 3-4.

▶ **To save data as a Release 13 worksheet**

1 Choose **File** ➤ **Save Current Worksheet**.

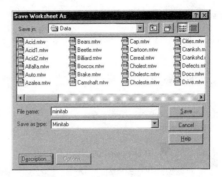

2 In **File name**, type a file name.

3 In **Save as type**, choose **MINITAB**.

4 If you like, click **Description** to create a description for the worksheet. For details, see *Project and Worksheet Descriptions* on page 3-11.

5 Click **Save**.

▶ **To close a worksheet**

1 Make the Data window for that worksheet active.

2 Choose **File** ➤ **Close Worksheet**.

Previewing Projects and Worksheets

Previewing shows you the contents of a file before you open it. The preview dialog box has different capabilities, depending on the type of file you have selected to preview:

- When you select a MINITAB project file, previewing shows you which worksheets and graphs are contained in the file. Those worksheets can in turn be previewed. You can also view descriptions for each worksheet.

- When you select a MINITAB worksheet file, previewing shows you the columns of data in that file.

- When you select a non-MINITAB file, previewing shows you how MINITAB will interpret the rows and columns. If you want the rows and columns to be interpreted differently, click **Options** to change how MINITAB will read the file.

▶ **To preview a project file**

1 Do one of the following:

- Choose **File ➤ Open Project**.

- Choose **File ➤ Open Worksheet**, then under **Files of type**, choose **Minitab Project**.

2 Click **Preview**.

If you chose **File ➤ Open Project**, this
list shows the worksheets and graphs
in the project.

If you chose **File ➤ Open Worksheet**,
this list shows just the worksheets.

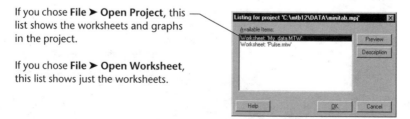

3 If you like, highlight a worksheet in the list and do the following:

- To preview the worksheet, click **Preview**. See *To preview a worksheet file* below.

- To see a description of the worksheet, click **Description**. If the worksheet does not have a description, the button will be disabled. Click **OK**.

▶ **To preview a worksheet file**

1 In the Open Worksheet dialog box, click **Preview**.

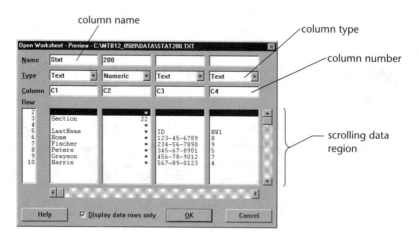

When opening a MINITAB file, you can only view the data—the columns are already set to open correctly. If you are opening a non-MINITAB file, or merging any kind of file, you can use the Preview subdialog box to change how MINITAB will interpret the data. See *Previewing non-MINITAB files* on page 3-13.

2 Click **OK**.

Project and Worksheet Descriptions

You can store comments about your project, and about each worksheet in your project. You can also view the descriptions of projects and worksheet files that are not open.

Note | A worksheet's description will not be saved if you save the worksheet as a non-MINITAB file type, such as an Excel worksheet.

▶ **To create or view a description for the current project or worksheet**

1 Open the Description dialog box:

- To create a project description, choose **File ➤ Project Description** or, click on the Project folder in the Project Manager.

- To create a worksheet description, make the appropriate Data window active and choose **Editor ➤ Worksheet ➤ Description** or, click on the Worksheet folder in the Project Manager.

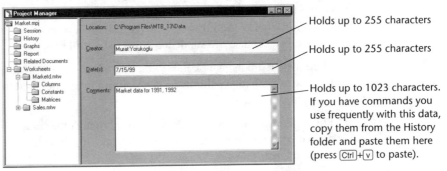

Holds up to 255 characters

Holds up to 255 characters

Holds up to 1023 characters. If you have commands you use frequently with this data, copy them from the History folder and paste them here (press Ctrl + v to paste).

2 Enter information in **Creator**, **Date(s)**, and/or **Comments**.

3 Click **OK**. If you are creating a project or worksheet description in the Project Manager, you do not have to click **OK**.

More | Project descriptions can also be created when you save a project (see *Saving and Closing Projects* on page 3-4). Worksheet descriptions can be created when you save a worksheet as a MINITAB worksheet (MTW) file (see *Saving and Closing Worksheets* on page 3-8).

▶ **To view descriptions of files**

You can view descriptions for other files when you are about to open those files.

1 Choose **File ➤ Open Project** or **File ➤ Open Worksheet**.

2 Select the file and click **Description**. You will not be able to edit the description. Click **OK** when you are finished.

Opening Files from Other Applications

You can get data not only from MINITAB worksheets, but from files created by many other applications. MINITAB can directly read and write Excel, Quattro Pro, Lotus 1-2-3, and dBASE files.

If the data you want to use are not from an application in that list, try using a text file. MINITAB can open plain text (ASCII) files, which usually have an extension of TXT (for text) or DAT (for data). Most applications can create text files, and many can import them as well.

Files created by other applications may have data arranged in ways different from the row and column format used by MINITAB worksheets. For example, the data may not appear until the third row of the file, or the fifteenth column. Variable names may not always be in the first row, or be present at all. You can open the file as is, then clean it up in MINITAB, or you can use options in the Open Worksheet dialog box to control how MINITAB will interpret the data before you open the file.

To open files from other applications, you use the same command you use to open MINITAB worksheets, the **File ➤ Open Worksheet** command. In the Open Worksheet dialog box, you can use two subdialog boxes to control how the data will be interpreted:

■ The Preview subdialog box shows you how MINITAB will interpret the file, and allows you to change column names, column data types, and the location of columns

■ The Options subdialog box lets you control many other aspects of the conversion, such as what rows contain the names and data, or what character separates columns (used in text files)

Opening a non-MINITAB file may involve previewing the file, changing options, previewing again, and so on, until you see that MINITAB will interpret the data exactly as you want.

▶ To open a non-MINITAB file

1 Choose **File ➤ Open Worksheet**.

2 In **Files of type**, choose the type of file you are looking for: Excel, 1-2-3, Text, etc.

3 Select a directory and file. Click **Preview**.

4 Change any of the preview settings and click **OK**. For details, see *Previewing non-MINITAB files* on page 3-13.

5 Click **Options**.

6 Change any of the options and click **OK**. For details, see *Setting options for non-MINITAB files* on page 3-14.

7 If you like, preview the file again. The data should appear as you want it. Click **OK**.

8 Click **Open**. If a message box appears telling you that a copy of the file contents will be added to the worksheet, click **OK**.

Previewing non-MINITAB files

When opening a non-MINITAB file, or when merging any kind of file (see *Merging worksheets* on page 3-7), you can use the Preview subdialog box not only to view the data, but also to change several aspects of how MINITAB will interpret the data.

1 In the Open Worksheet dialog box, select a file and click **Preview**.

When checked, name rows appear only in the **Name** row—any rows between the name row and the first data row are not shown.

When unchecked, every row of the file shows in the scrolling data region—and names will appear in both the **Name** row and in the data region.

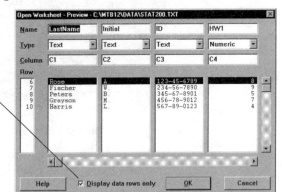

2 To change a column's name, type a new name in the **Name** row.

MINITAB assumes that the first row of the file contains the column names. You can specify another row as the name row, or choose to have no column names at all—see *Setting options for non-MINITAB files* on page 3-14.

3 To change the data type for a column, choose **Text**, **Numeric**, or **Date/Time** in the **Type** row.

If a value in a column does not match the data type—for example, if the word "Smith" appears in a column set to Numeric—the previewer will display that value as missing, and MINITAB will import the value as missing. Numeric and date/time missing values are represented by the symbol *; text missing values are represented by blanks.

If the previewer does not recognize a column of date/time data as being Date/Time type, you can either (a) create a new date/time format so MINITAB will recognize the column, or (b) reformat the column after you open the file. For details, see *Opening non-MINITAB files containing date/time data* on page 3-17.

4 To change a column's position in the worksheet, change the column number in the **Column** row. If you do not want to bring in a column at all, delete its column number.

5 Click **OK**.

Setting options for non-MINITAB files

▶ **To set options**

1   In the Open Worksheet dialog box, click **Options**.

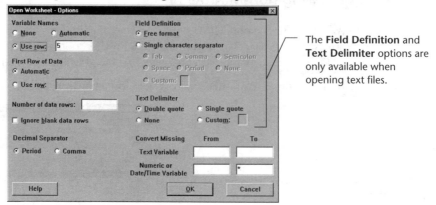

The **Field Definition** and **Text Delimiter** options are only available when opening text files.

2   Under **Variable Names**, choose one of the following:

- **None** tells MINITAB that no rows contain variable names. Column names in the new worksheet will be blank.

- **Automatic** tells MINITAB to assign the first row of data it finds to be variable names. Even if the first row contains all numbers, if Automatic is selected, those numbers are still used as column names.

- **Use row** tells MINITAB to use the names in a row number you provide. Use the Preview dialog box to find the correct row number, then enter that number in the text box.

3   Under **First Row of Data**, choose one of the following:

- **Automatic** tells MINITAB to begin reading data from the first row *after* the variable names row. For example, if in step 2 you chose **Use row** and entered 5, MINITAB will begin reading data starting with row 6. If in step 2 you choose **None**, MINITAB will begin reading data starting with the first row in the file.

- **Use row** tells MINITAB to use the data in a row number you provide. Use the Preview dialog box to find the correct row number, then enter that number in the text box.

4   Set any other options—see Help for details. Click **OK**.

▷ Example of opening a space-delimited text file

Suppose the grades for a statistics course you taught are kept on a mainframe computer. The computer lab gave you the course information in a text file named STAT200.TXT that looks like this:

```
Stat 200

Section 22

LastName    Initial    ID             HW1    HW2    Test1    Test2    Total
Rose        A.         123-45-6789    8      7      20       23       58
Fischer     W.         234-56-7890    9      10     23       21       63
Peters      B.         345-67-8901    5      4      15       18       42
Grayson     M.         456-78-9012    7      8      21
Harris      L.         567-89-0123    4      6      13       18       41
```

Columns are separated by at least one space. Note that Grayson's last two scores are missing.

1 Choose **File ➤ Open Worksheet**.

2 Under **Files of Type**, select **Text (*.txt)**.

3 Go to the Data folder, which is in your main MINITAB folder.

4 Select the file Stat200.txt.

5 Click **Preview**.

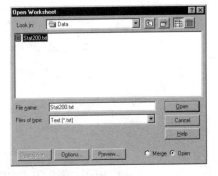

You see some problems. MINITAB read the title at the top of the file, Stat 200, as the first column name. You can see from the screen that column names do not begin until row 5, and all the information is crammed into one column.

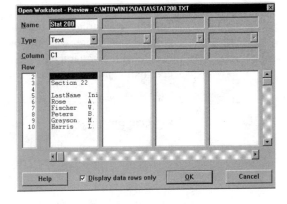

6 Click **Cancel**.

7 In the Open Worksheet dialog box, click **Options**.

8 Under **Variable Names**, click **Use row** and enter the number 5.

9 Under **Field Definition**, click **Free Format**. Click **OK**.

10 In the Open Worksheet dialog box, click **Preview** again.

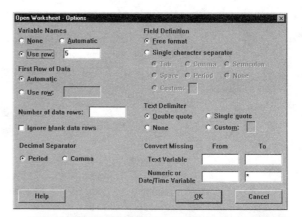

The column names now appear correctly, and the information is separated correctly into columns.

Everything looks correct in the data region. You might want to scroll to the right to make sure Grayson's missing scores came in okay.

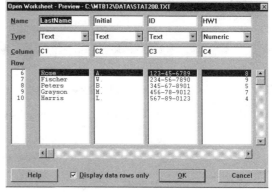

11 Click **OK**. In the Open Worksheet dialog box, click **Open**.

Limitations of using Open Worksheet to open text files

Text files can be formatted in as many different ways as there are software programs. You may encounter a text file that the Open Worksheet command cannot import correctly, no matter what options you select. For example, if the text file contains rows of data with no character to separate the rows into columns, the Open Worksheet command will place all the data in one column.

There are several ways to work around format problems:

- Open the file as is and fix any problems in the Data window.

- Open the file in a text editor and reformat the file.

- Use the **File ➤ Other Files ➤ Import Special Text** command and specify a custom format. Custom formats can be more difficult to create, but they are very powerful. For details, see *Importing Special Text Files* on page 4-9.

For a list of common text format problems, and the suggested way around them, see *When to Use the Import Special Text command* on page 4-9.

Opening non-MINITAB files containing date/time data

Most of the time, MINITAB automatically recognizes date/time data and assigns the correct data type in the previewer. If your data is not in a format that MINITAB automatically recognizes, you can create a new date/time format before you open the file, or reformat the column after you open the file.

Note | With Quattro Pro files, date/time values enter the worksheet as numbers. Reformat the column after you open the file (described below).

▶ **To create a new date/time format before you open the file**

1 If you are in the Preview subdialog box or the Open worksheet dialog box, click **Cancel**.

2 Create the new date/time format. For instructions, see *Creating and Deleting Custom Date/Time Formats* on page 2-26.

3 Open and preview the file again. MINITAB should now recognize that the column has a type of Date/Time.

▶ **To reformat the column after you open the file**

1 Open the file. MINITAB will probably interpret the column as Text.

2 Choose **Manip ➤ Change Data Type ➤ Text to Date/Time** and fill out the dialog box. For instructions, see *Example of changing a column from text to date/time* on page 6-44.

Saving Files to Use in Other Applications

If you want to use your data in another application, you can save your worksheet in the format of that application. If the application you want is not supported directly by MINITAB's Save Worksheet command, you can save the data as a text file. Text files can be imported by many applications.

▶ **To save a worksheet in a non-MINITAB format**

1 Choose **File ➤ Save Current Worksheet As**.

2 In **File name**, type a file name.

3 In **Save as type**, select the format you want: Excel, 1-2-3, etc.

4 Click **Options**.

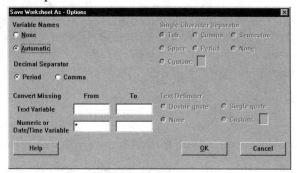

See Help for details on specific options.

5 Set any options. For example, to save only the data and ignore column names, set **Variable Names** to **None**. Click **OK** and then click **Save**.

Saving worksheets containing date/time columns

Suppose a worksheet column contains date and time information, for example: *1/15/00 3:30 AM*. Now suppose you format the column, using **Editor ➤ Format Column ➤ Date/Time**, so that it displays in the Data window as the date only, for example: *1/15/00*.

When you save your worksheet as a text file, MINITAB saves date/time data in the same format in which it appears in the Data window. Thus, in our example, the column in the text file would include only the characters that make up the date, "*1/15/00*." The column would not contain the characters "*3:30 AM*."

When you save your worksheet as any other type of file, MINITAB saves the entire date/time information. Thus in our example, if you saved the worksheet as an Excel file and opened that file in Excel, your spreadsheet would include both the date and time information: *1/15/00 3:30 AM*. The date and time would display in whatever format was applied to that cell in Excel.

Saving worksheets as text files with unusual formatting

When saving your worksheet as a text file with Save Worksheet As, you cannot save non-contiguous columns. You also cannot use the special format statements that allow you to (for example) create line breaks after certain columns, or combine columns into one field. If you want to do either of these operations, choose **File ➤ Other Files ➤ Export Special Text**. For details, see *Exporting Special Text Files* on page 4-11.

Exchanging Data with Other Versions of MINITAB

You can open and save worksheets that are compatible with older versions of MINITAB, newer versions, and even versions on other computer platforms.

Opening worksheets saved by older versions of MINITAB

MINITAB worksheets are upwardly compatible, which means that you can always open a worksheet saved by the release of MINITAB immediately previous to the current one. You can open that file just as you would a Release 13 worksheet—see *To open a MINITAB worksheet (MTW) file* on page 3-6.

If the file is from an even older release, try opening the file normally. If that does not work, use the same method as when exchanging data with a version of MINITAB on another computer platform. See *Exchanging data with computers on different platforms* on page 3-20.

Opening worksheets saved by newer versions of MINITAB

If you have a worksheet file created by a version of MINITAB newer than Release 13, you can probably open the file. Opening the file may generate an error message stating that there are unknown objects in the worksheet. MINITAB will try to ignore unknown objects and copy the data that it does recognize, such as rows and columns.

To avoid an error message, start the newer version of MINITAB, save the data as a Release 13 or portable worksheet, then open the file in MINITAB Release 13.

Saving worksheets compatible with an older version of MINITAB

You can save your worksheets as Release 12, Release 11, or Release 10 worksheets. Project files cannot be saved as an older format.

Some worksheet features are also new to Release 13. When you save a worksheet in an older format, features that are not compatible will not be saved. When you save the file, MINITAB will warn you which features are not being saved.

▶ **To save a worksheet in MINITAB Release 12, Release 11, or Release 10 format**

1 Choose **File ➤ Save Worksheet As**.

2 In **File name**, enter a file name.

   If a Release 13 file of this worksheet already exists, make sure to enter a different name so that you do not accidentally overwrite the Release 13 file (remember, both files will have the extension MTW).

3 Under **Save as type**, choose **Minitab 12, Minitab 11, or Minitab 10**.

4 Click **Save**.

   MINITAB will display a message dialog box telling you which Release 13 worksheet features will not be saved with the Release 12, 11, or 10 worksheet. For more information, click the Help button in this dialog box. Click **OK**.

Exchanging data with computers on different platforms

The portable worksheet format allows you to transfer worksheets from MINITAB on one type of computer, such as an IBM-compatible PC, to MINITAB on another computer, such as a Macintosh or mainframe.

▶ **To transfer a portable worksheet**

1 Choose **File ➤ Save Worksheet**.

2 In **Save as type**, choose **Minitab Portable**.

3 Enter a name and click **Save**.

4 Transfer the file to the other computer. The method you use depends on the target computer platform:

   ■ To transfer data to a Macintosh computer, you can use a utility that comes with that operating system, PC Exchange. For details, see the Help topic *files: transfer*.

   ■ To transfer to another type of computer, you can often use FTP (file transfer protocol) software, or file conversion software. For details, see the target computer's documentation.

5 On the target computer, start MINITAB and open the file (see below).

▶ **To open a portable worksheet**

1 Choose **File ➤ Open Worksheet**.

2 In **Files of type**, choose **Minitab Portable (*.mtp)**.

3 Select the directory and file. Click **Open**.

Printing Data

You can print columns and rows of data by printing the Data window. Print constants and matrices by first displaying them in the Session window, then printing that section of the Session window.

▶ **To print the Data window**

1 Make the Data window active.

2 Choose **File ➤ Print Worksheet**.

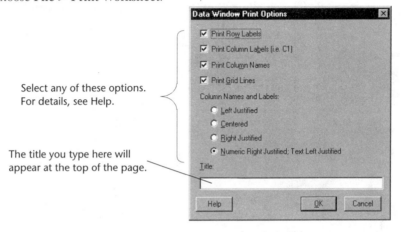

Select any of these options.
For details, see Help.

The title you type here will
appear at the top of the page.

3 In the Data Window Print Options dialog box, select the options you want, and click **OK**.

4 In the Print dialog box, click **OK**.

Tip | To print a selected block of cells, first select the cells you want (see *Selecting Areas of the Data Window* on page 2-3), then print as above.

▶ **To print constants and matrices**

1 Choose **Manip ➤ Display Data**.

2 Under **Columns, constants, and matrices to display**, select the desired items. Click **OK**.

3 In the Session window, select the lines containing the constants and matrices.

4 Choose **File ➤ Print Session Window**. Under **Print Range**, make sure **Selection** is selected. Click **OK**.

More | You can also print the contents of the Session window and the History folder. Right-click on the Session folder or History folder in the Project Manager and select **Print [window/ folder name]**. If the Session window is active, you also can select **File ➤ Print Session Window**.

Print setup

You can change which printer to print to, what paper size to use, and other print specifications.

The settings you select will affect printing from MINITAB only. They will not override settings you may have selected in other applications or in your main Windows Control Panel printer setup.

▶ **To change your print setup**

1 Choose **File ➤ Print Setup**. This opens the standard Microsoft Windows Print Setup dialog box.

2 Change any of the specifications. See your Microsoft Windows or printer documentation for information.

3 Click **OK**.

4

Using ODBC and Special Text Files

Using ODBC and Special Text Files Overview

Much of the time, you will exchange data with other applications by using the **File ➤ Open Worksheet** and **File ➤ Save Worksheet** commands, described in Chapter 3, *Opening, Saving, and Printing Files*.

However, there are many software programs that have file types that MINITAB does not understand. You may need to get data from large databases, or from applications that can only share data with other programs using plain text.

To import data from database files, you can use the **File ➤ Query Database** command, which imports data using ODBC. ODBC stands for Open DataBase Connectivity, a protocol that is used by many applications. With ODBC, you can import data from a database file, such as one saved by Microsoft Access, Oracle, Sybase, or SAS. You can import the entire database file, or just the subset of data you are interested in.

To exchange data with other types of applications, use the Import Special Text and Export Special Text commands. MINITAB can import text files that are formatted in unusual ways: you tell MINITAB how to interpret characters and lines, and the program will place the data correctly. You can also export text files in custom formats, so the other application receives data in the form it can understand.

More | You can also exchange data with applications using Dynamic Data Exchange (DDE). DDE allows you to establish a link with the other application. When data in the source program change, the data can be automatically updated in MINITAB. DDE has other uses as well. See Chapter 10, *Using Dynamic Data Exchange (DDE)*.

Understanding ODBC

ODBC lets you import data from database files. Often, you will not want to import the entire database file. Instead, you can import just the subset of data you are interested in analyzing, such as the data collected during a certain month.

ODBC is a protocol shared by many applications. To use ODBC in MINITAB, you may have to first install ODBC software on your system. Once ODBC is set up correctly, in MINITAB you can use the Query Database command to connect to the database file you want and import the subset of data you want.

More | If you run into problems, read *ODBC troubleshooting tips* on page 4-8.

How data is converted

MINITAB imports fields as columns of data. Records in the fields become rows in the columns. The table below shows how field types are converted to column types.

Database field type	Imported as column type	Notes
Memo Text	Text	Values longer than 80 characters are truncated.
Numeric Currency Counter	Numeric	
Yes/No	Numeric	"Yes" values converted to 1, "No" values converted to 0.
Logical (true/false)	Numeric	True values converted to 1, False values converted 0.
Date/time	Date/time	

The columns of database data are inserted in the current MINITAB worksheet, to the right of any existing data.

Setting Up ODBC

To use ODBC in MINITAB, you must have a the following items installed on your system:

- The 32-bit ODBC manager. MINITAB will not work with the 16-bit ODBC manager that ships with some 16-bit database programs (such as Access 2.0), or that comes with older versions of Windows.

- ODBC drivers. You must have the driver for the type of database you want to connect to. These drivers are added using the driver's setup program. Drivers are not added within the ODBC manager.

- A data source. Data sources specify which database file to connect to, which driver to use for that connection, and which options to use when opening that file (such as login name and password). Data sources are defined in the ODBC manager. You can start the ODBC manager from the Windows Control Panel, or from within MINITAB when you use the **File ➤ Query Database** command.

▶ **To check for the ODBC manager and drivers**

1 Open the Control Panel. From the task bar, choose **Start ➤ Settings ➤ Control Panel**.

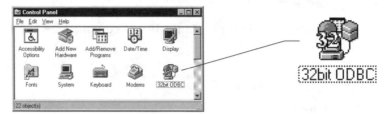

2 Make sure you have the 32bit ODBC icon.

3 To see which ODBC drivers and data sources are installed, double-click the ODBC icon. See your ODBC documentation for details on adding drivers.

If you do not have the 32-bit OBDC manager or drivers

If you do not have the 32-bit OBDC manager or drivers, MINITAB's ODBC features will not work. You may need help from your system administrator in finding the ODBC software and drivers. The ODBC manager is available from the Microsoft web site at www.microsoft.com. ODBC drivers can be obtained from disks supplied by your database application vendor, or from your vendor's web site.

Querying a Database

▶ **To import database data in MINITAB**

1 Make the desired Data window active. (When the query is executed, columns of database data will be added to the right of any existing columns in this Data window.)

2 Choose **File ➤ Query Database (ODBC)**.

The ODBC manager dialog box will appear. This dialog box may appear differently, depending on which version of the manager you are using.

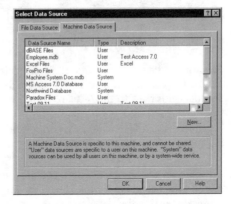

3 Pick from the list of data sources (if any exist) or create a new data source.

The method you use for creating a data source depends on the ODBC manager you have installed. See your ODBC manager's documentation for details.

4 Click **OK**.

5 Depending on data source, you may be prompted to provide login name, password, directory, and/or file information. Provide whatever information is requested, then click **OK**. (To get this information, you may need help from your system administrator.)

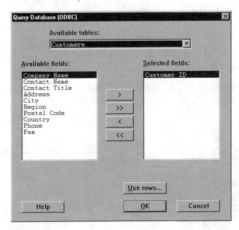

6 In **Available tables**, select the table you want (click the down arrow to see available tables).

7   Use the arrow buttons to move items from the **Available fields** box to the **Selected fields** box. Note that each selected field will become a column in MINITAB.

-   ▭ > and ▭ < move the highlighted field

-   ▭ >> and ▭ << move all the fields to the other box

Tip | If you want to select most, but not all of the fields in the database, it is quicker to click ▭ >> to move all the available fields to the Selected box, then click ▭ < to move individual fields back to the Available box.

8   If you like, click **Use rows** to set conditions for which subset of the data you want to import—see *Specifying a Subset of Database Data* below.

Tip | Depending on the amount of data you are importing and your network's performance, importing data can take a while. Once the import is complete, save your project so you can quickly retrieve the data later.

Specifying a Subset of Database Data

Instead of importing the entire database file (which may be huge), you can import just the fields (which are converted to MINITAB columns) and records (rows) you are interested in.

▶ **To specify a subset of data to import**

1   In the Query Database dialog box, click **Use rows**.

Field list. "D" denotes date/time fields. "T" denotes text fields.

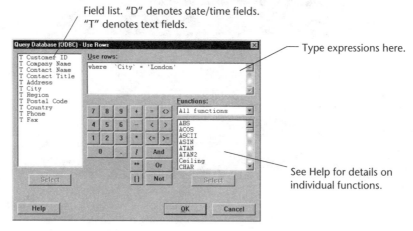

Type expressions here.

See Help for details on individual functions.

2   In **Use rows**, enter an expression that defines which records from the fields will be imported (becoming rows in MINITAB).

Expressions start with the keyword "where" and contain field names, logical operators (such as "And" and "="), ODBC functions, and values. Use this dialog box much as you would the MINITAB calculator (the **Calc ➤ Calculator** command).

These expressions are Structured Query Language (SQL) strings. SQL is used in many database applications. If you are familiar with SQL and know the SQL string you want, you can paste it into the **Use rows** text box.

3 Click **OK** in each dialog box.

Syntax rules for ODBC expressions

Caution | Syntax rules vary from one database application to another; there is no standard. We provide some information here, but you may need help from your database administrator to find out the appropriate syntax to use.

Expression element	Syntax rule
Text values	For many databases, such as Microsoft Access, enclose text values in single quotes, as in *'Morristown'*. (Note that this syntax differs from the rest of MINITAB, where text values should be enclosed by double quotes. This syntax must follow ODBC rules, not MINITAB rules.)
	For Oracle or SQL Server databases, enclose text values in two sets of double quotes, as in, *""Morristown""*
Numeric values	Do not enclose numbers, such as 300, with any special characters.
Date/time values	For Access and dBASE databases, enclose dates in pound signs, as in #12/31/99#. For other databases, see the application's documentation. Or, use a date/time function (explained in Help).
Field names	Field delimiters vary according to the ODBC driver. If you enter the field name by selecting it from the field list, MINITAB will enclose the field in the delimiter appropriate for your ODBC driver.
Functions	Enclose functions with braces and the characters "fn" as follows: *{fn SQRT(128)}*. This syntax identifies the function as an ODBC function, as opposed to a function native to the database application you are importing from. If you select functions from the list, MINITAB automatically adds the necessary enclosure characters.

Sample expressions

All of these examples are for importing data from an Access database. The syntax for other databases may be different, as noted in the syntax rules above.

To import...	Use this expression
records for the first quarter of 1995	where DATE >= #1/1/95# And DATE < #4/1/95#
records for employees hired since January 1, 1990 who are in the Finance Department	where DATE_HIRED > #1/1/90# And DEPT = 'Finance'
records logged during the last 30 days	where DATE > ({fn CURDATE} - 30) Note that CURDATE is an ODBC function. If your ODBC driver supports that function, it should work with any database.

ODBC troubleshooting tips

An error message indicates a problem with my ODBC driver

This could occur if there is an incompatibility between the ODBC driver you are using and its associated data source, because the path to the data source is specified incorrectly, because you do not have the specified network drive mounted correctly, or because the ODBC driver you need is not installed or set up properly. You may need assistance from your system administrator, since the solution will probably depend on knowing details about your particular network and data source files. Something to try: Reinstall ODBC, and make sure there are no duplicate ODBC files on your computer.

Performance is slow

Performance will vary depending on performance on your network while you are using ODBC and on the size of the data source file you are accessing.

Syntax error in query expression

Several problems could prompt this message:

- A selected field name contains an embedded blank space or some other illegal character. "Illegal" is defined by the ODBC driver you are using, not MINITAB.

- The expression in the Use Rows subdialog box contains incorrect syntax. See the *Syntax rules for ODBC expressions* on page 4-7, or get help from your database system administrator.

Importing Special Text Files

Most of the time, the **File ➤ Open Worksheet** command is the best way to open a text file. However, the Import Special Text command can do two things that the Open Worksheet command cannot. You can

- create a format statement that gives MINITAB very specific instructions for interpreting the file. This can solve import problems when the text file is formatted in an odd way.

- append data from a file to the bottom of existing columns. The Open Worksheet command places data in a new worksheet, or, when used with the merge option, places data in new columns in the current worksheet.

When to Use the Import Special Text command

Do not automatically use the Import Special Text command to solve text format problems; there may be an easier way to solve the problem. Here are the three methods you can use:

- Open the file with Open Worksheet and fix any problems in the Data window

- Open the file in a text editor and reformat the file

- Use the **File ➤ Other Files ➤ Import Special Text** command and specify a custom format

The following table lists some common text format problems and suggests which method to use to solve them.

Note | For every problem that suggests you use the Import Special Text command with a format statement, there is an example of that format statement in *Sample format statements* on page 4-14.

Format problem	Open Worksheet command will...	Suggested solution
No spaces or other characters separate columns of data (columns are delimited by the number of characters in each field). For example, *12142* is meant to be five separate values.	place the entire file in one column.	Use the Import Special Text command with a format statement that specifies a fixed width for each column.
Each row of data is on two or more lines.	place each line in its own row.	Use the Import Special Text command with a format specifying a carriage return.

Format problem	Open Worksheet command will...	Suggested solution
Blank cells are scattered randomly throughout a space-delimited file.	skip blanks; the next non-blank character is assumed to be the next value in the row. Skipping blanks creates rows that are shorter than the rows without blank cells. In shorter rows, remaining columns are filled with the missing value symbol (*).	1 In a text editor, enclose blank cells with a delimiter such as double quotes. 2 Open the file with **File ➤ Open Worksheet**.
Blank cells occur at known intervals in a space-delimited file. For example, there is always a blank between first and second value, as in *85 67 32*	skip blanks (described above).	Open the file with **File ➤ Open Worksheet**, then in the Data window insert empty columns. Or, use the Import Special Text command with a format statement that specifies a fixed width for each column.
Values in a character column contain an embedded delimiter such as a space. For example, "Jones, John Paul" (without the quotes) contains two spaces.	create a new column every time a space is encountered. For example, "Jones, John Paul" (without the quotes) would be read into three columns.	Use the Import Special Text command with a format statement that specifies exact length of the text column.
Numbers in the file that look like integers (for example, 10056) need to be interpreted as decimal numbers (100.56 or 10.056).	interpret numbers as integers.	Use the Import Special Text command with a format statement that specifies decimal places for each column.

▶ **To import a special text file**

    1 Choose File ➤ Other Files ➤ Import Special Text.

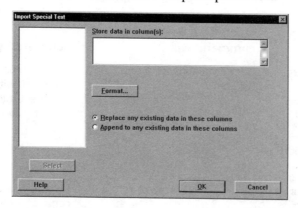

2 In **Store data in column(s)**, enter the column(s) where you want the data to be entered.

3 If you like, specify a format for how you want the data interpreted. See *To give custom instructions for importing a special text file* below.

4 If you want the data to be added to the end of these columns, click **Append to any existing data in these columns**. Click **OK**.

▶ **To give custom instructions for importing a special text file**

1 In the Import Special Text dialog box, click **Format**.

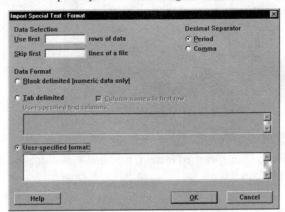

Complete this dialog box to give special instructions on how to read the file. See Help for details.

2 In **User specified format**, enter a format statement. See *Format Statement Syntax* on page 4-12. Click **OK** in each dialog box.

Exporting Special Text Files

Most of the time, the command Save Worksheet As is best for saving your worksheet in a text file. But if you want to save your data in a custom format, or if you want to save non-contiguous columns, you must use Export Special Text.

More | To macro writers: The session command WRITE has more functionality than is available from the Export Special Text menu command. See Session Command Help for details.

How data is exported

Column names are not saved, only the data.

If all columns do not fit on one line, the continuation symbol (&) is put at the end of the line and the data continues onto the next line.

When exporting columns of unequal length, MINITAB adds missing value symbols (∗) to the shorter numeric column(s).

▶ **To export to a text file**

1 Choose **File ➤ Other Files ➤ Export Special Text**.

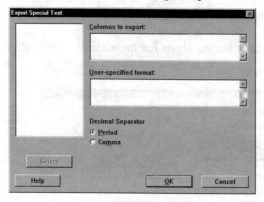

2 In **Columns to export**, enter the columns you want to export.

3 If you like, in **User-specified format**, type the format statement that describes how you want to export the data. For details, see *Format Statement Syntax* below.

   If you do not specify a format, MINITAB saves the columns of data in a file, separated by spaces.

4 If you like, choose a decimal separator of **Period** or **Comma**. Commas are used for decimal separators in some countries.

5 Click **OK**.

Format Statement Syntax

When you import or export special text, you can use a format statement. Format statements are made up of one or more format items. Here are the most common format items:

Format item	Stands for
F	Numeric data
A	Text (alpha) data
DT	Date/time data
X	Blanks
/	Carriage return

Syntax notes

Syntax for F, A, and DT

The format items F, A, and DT are always followed by a number that tells MINITAB how many characters make up one column. For example, a format statement that begins with A20 means that the first 20 characters go in one column, and are given the text format. Do not put a space between the format item and the number.

Additional syntax for F: decimal places

With numeric data, you can specify the number of digits before and after a decimal point. After F, specify the total number of digits in the number, type a period, then specify the number of digits in that number that should appear after a decimal. For example, F5.2 interprets the value 12345 as 123.45. F5.1 interprets 12345 as 1234.5.

If your Windows regional settings are not set to United States English, use the decimal separator character for your chosen region.

Additional syntax for DT: date/time formats

DT may also be followed by a date/time format, such as mm/dd/yy (to create a date like 01/29/97) or mm/yyyy (01/1997). The date/time format immediately follows the character number, as in *DT8mm/dd/yy*. For a list of available date/time formats, see *Formatting Date/Time Columns* on page 2-25.

Syntax for X

X is always preceded by a number. The number equals the number of characters to skip.

Combining format items

Separate format items with a comma. For example, *A5,1X,F2* tells MINITAB to read the first five characters into a text column, skip one space, and read the next two characters into a numeric column.

If your Windows regional settings are not set to United States English, use the list separator character for your chosen region.

Repeating a sequence

F, A, and DT *may* be proceeded by a number which specifies how many times to repeat that format item. For example, 5A20 means that the first 20 characters will be entered into a text column, the next 20 characters entered into another text column, and so on, until there are five columns of 20 characters. MINITAB then proceeds to the next format item in the format statement.

You can also repeat sequences of format statements by enclosing the sequence in parentheses, then placing the repeater number before the parentheses. For example, say that you have five columns of text data, separated by spaces, and each column contains 20 characters. The base sequence is A20,1X. To repeat this sequence five times, you would enter *5(A20,1X)*.

Sample format statements

Problem	Example	Format statement
No spaces or other characters separate columns of data	12142 should be read as five separate columns: 1 2 1 4 2	5F1
Each row of data is on two or more lines	10 14 12 87 28 23 should be read as: 10 14 12 87 28 23	4(F2,1x),/,2(F2,1x)
Numbers in the file that look like integers need to be interpreted as decimal numbers	10056 328 9687 should be: 100.56 32.8 96.87	F5.2,1X,F3.1,1X,F4.2
Blank cells occur at known intervals in a space-delimited file	85 67 32 should be read as four values, with a missing value between 85 and 67: 85 * 67 32	F2,F1,F2,F2
Values in a character column contain an embedded delimiter, such as a space	Jones, John Paul should be read as one value: "Jones, John Paul"	A16

Note | The session command INSERT has more functionality than is available from the Import Special Text menu command. See Session Command Help for details.

There are more sample format statements in Help.

5

Generating Patterned Data

Generating Patterned Data Overview

The commands in this chapter fill columns with patterned data.

You can easily fill columns with numbers, text, or date/time values that follow a pattern, such as:

- 1 through 100
- five sets of 1, 2, and 3
- 1/1/97, 1/2/97, 1/3/97, …
- yes, no, maybe, …

This is very useful for entering factor levels for analysis of variance designs.

With numbers and date/time values, the patterns can be equally spaced, such as 10 20 30, or 12:00 AM, 6:00 AM, 12:00 PM, 6:00 PM. You can also specify patterns that are not equally spaced, such as 10 20 50, or 6:00 AM, 10:00 AM, 1:00 PM, 4:00 PM.

MINITAB gives you several methods of creating patterned data:

- **Autofill** fills user-defined columns with equal or unequally spaced patterns of numbers, text, or dates/times, based on already existing data. Autofill is the quickest, easiest, and most interactive method of creating patterned data—see *Creating Patterned Data with Autofill* below.

- **Clipboard Replication** fills large groups of cells with patterned data using the **Edit ► Copy** and **Edit ► Paste** commands by allowing users to copy a section of data (for example, 1, 2, 3, …) and paste repeating blocks of the copied data over a larger area of cells—see *Clipboard Replication* on page 5-7.

- **Make Patterned Data** fills a column with equal or unequally spaced patterns of numbers, text, or dates/times. The Make Patterned Data command is not as easy to use as the Autofill command, but it does allow you to more easily create large data sets with repeated values—see *Creating Patterned Data with Make Patterned Data* on page 5-7.

- **Make Indicator Variables** creates indicator or dummy variables, which are typically used for regression analysis—see *Making Indicator (Dummy) Variables* on page 5-12. In textbooks, indicator variables may be called binary variables.

Creating Patterned Data with Autofill

You can easily create a variety of different data patterns with **Autofill.** By highlighting existing data cells and clicking and dragging with the mouse, you can:

- fill cells with a pattern of values (1, 2, 3, 1, 2, 3, …)
- fill cells with a series of values (1, 2, 3, …, 100)
- delete values in cells

Autofill's functionality changes depending on the number of data cells selected, the type of data present, and whether or not Ctrl is active. In all cases, multiple columns can be selected, although differences in data type between columns can affect how Autofill will behave.

Note | Because data in MINITAB are column oriented, you can use Autofill to fill one or more columns with patterned data (dragging up or down), but you cannot create patterned data across rows (dragging horizontally).

▶ To Autofill cells

1 Highlight one or more cells in one or more columns.

2 Place the mouse cursor over the Autofill handle in the lower-right corner of the highlighted cells. When the mouse is over the handle, a cross symbol (+) will appear.

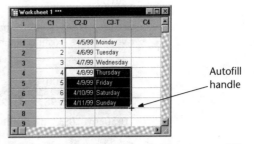

Autofill handle

For some tasks, you can hold Ctrl down to change the way Autofill operates. When you hold Ctrl down, a superscript cross will appear above the Autofill cross symbol ($+^+$). For details on Autofill functionality, see *To create patterned data with Autofill* below.

3 Left click and drag outside the highlighted cells to create patterned data, and inside the selection to delete cells (if more than one cell is highlighted).

Note | When Autofill is activated, MINITAB's status bar provides feedback on Autofill's current operation.

▶ To create patterned data with Autofill

To do this:	Do this...
Repeat a single value For example: 1, 1, 1, ... blue, blue, blue, ... 1/1/99, 1/1/99, 1/1/99, ...	■ For text and numeric data, highlight one cell and drag to fill cells with the repeated value. ■ For date/time data, highlight one cell and press Ctrl and drag to fill cells with the repeated value.
Repeat a pattern of values For example: 1, 2, 3, 1, 2, 3, ... red, green, blue, red, green, blue, ... Jan-99, Feb-99, Jan-99, Feb-99, ...	Highlight the cells containing the desired pattern, press Ctrl, and drag outside the selection to fill cells with the repeated pattern.

To do this:	Do this...
Create a series of values from a single value For example: from 1, make 1, 2, 3, …,100 from 1/1/99 make 1/1/99, 1/2/99, 1/3/99, …, 2/3/99 from day 1, make day1, day2, …, day100	■ For numeric data, highlight one cell, press Ctrl, and drag to fill cells with the new series. ■ For date/time data and text data that includes integers, highlight one cell and drag to fill cells with the new series. For more information, see *Notes on Autofill and data types* below.
Create a series of values based on two or more existing values For example: 5, 10, 15, …,100 1/31/98, 2/28/98, 3/31/98, … 10:30am, 10:33am, 10:36am, …	Highlight two or more cells and drag outside the selection to fill cells with a series of predicted values. For more information, see *Notes on Autofill and data types* below.
Create a text series from a custom list For example: Mon, Tue, Wed, …, Sun Qtr1, Qtr2, Qtr3, Qtr4 Jan, Feb, Mar, Apr, …, Dec	Highlight one or more cells and drag outside the selection to fill cells with the next predicted item in a custom list or subset of a custom list. For more information on custom lists, see *Custom lists* on page 5-6.

Notes on Autofill and data types

The following Autofill behavior is specific to these data types.

Numeric

If...	Then Autofill...
1 cell is highlighted	repeats the value in subsequent cells
multiple columns are selected (1 cell selected per column), and at least one cell is not numeric	will add (drag down) or subtract (drag up) 1 unit per cell
1 cell is highlighted with Ctrl active	will add (drag down) or subtract (drag up) 1 unit per cell

Date/Time

If...	Then Autofill...
1 cell containing only date data is highlighted	will determine the smallest date unit and add (drag down) or subtract (drag up) 1 unit per cell
1 cell containing only time data is highlighted	will add (drag down) or subtract (drag up) 1 hour per cell
1 cell containing *both* date and time data is highlighted	will add (drag down) or subtract (drag up) 1 day per cell
2 or more cells are highlighted and the data is monthly For example: 2/28/98, 3/31/98...	will add (drag down) or subtract (drag up) 1 month per cell
2 or more cells are highlighted and the data is yearly For example: 1/2/98, 1/2/99...	will add (drag down) or subtract (drag up) 1 year per cell
2 or more cells are highlighted and the data is not monthly or yearly data	predicts subsequent values based on the selected values Missing values are not included in the prediction

Text

If...	Then Autofill...
2 or more cells containing text with evenly spaced integers are highlighted For example: Day5, Day10	predicts subsequent values based on the selected values
2 or more cells containing text with non-evenly spaced integers are highlighted For example: Day1, Day3, Day10	repeats the pattern in subsequent cells
2 or more cells containing text in a custom list are highlighted	continues the custom list, going forward (drag down) or backwards (drag up) Custom list values that are reversed (for example, Dec, Nov) will be continued in reverse order (Oct, Sep).
2 or more cells containing text in a subset of a custom list are highlighted For example: Jan, Mar, May, Jul	continues the subset of the custom list, going forward (drag down) or backwards (drag up)

Custom lists

You can define your own custom lists of ordered text data to use with the Autofill command. Autofill will automatically recognize and continue custom lists in the order in which they are defined. For example, Strongly Disagree, Disagree, No Opinion, Agree, Strongly Agree.

MINITAB comes with the following default set of pre-defined custom lists (these cannot be edited or deleted):

- Sunday, Monday, Tuesday, …, Saturday

- Sun, Mon, Tue, …, Sat

- January, February, March, …, December

- Jan, Feb, Mar, …, Dec

▶ To add a new list

1 With a Data window active, choose **Editor ➤ Define Custom Lists**.

2 In **Custom lists**, select NEW LIST.

3 In **Define a list (one value per line)**, type in a series of text values, entering only one value per line.

4 Click **Add List**. Click **OK**.

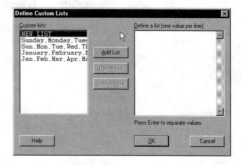

▶ To edit a custom list

1 With a Data window active, choose **Editor ➤ Define Custom Lists**.

2 In **Custom lists**, select the list you want to edit.

3 In **Define a list (one value per line)**, type in or delete text values.

4 Click **Replace List**. Click **OK**.

▶ To delete a custom list

1 With a Data window active, choose **Editor ➤ Define Custom Lists**.

2 In **Custom lists**, select the list you want to delete.

3 Click **Delete List**. Click **OK**.

Clipboard Replication

With Clipboard replication, you can easily fill large groups of worksheet cells with patterned data by copying a section of data (for example 1, 2, 3…) and pasting repeating blocks of the copied data over a larger area of cells. Any data type or mix of data types can be copied and used to fill a larger selection of cells.

▶ **To use Clipboard replication**

1 Highlight one or more cells in a Data window.

2 Right-click and select **Copy Cells**.

3 Highlight any number of data cells.

4 Right-click and select **Paste Cells**.

The original pattern of copied data will be repeated throughout the highlighted area.

Note | If the paste region is smaller than the copied region, Clipboard replication truncates the data and fills only the paste region.

Creating Patterned Data with Make Patterned Data

You can use Make Patterned Data to create a variety of data patterns. The Make Patterned Data command is not as quick and interactive as Autofill, but it allows you to more easily create large data sets with repeated values (for example, 1, 1, 1, 2, 2, 2, …):

To use Make Patterned Data to fill a column with…	See page…
an equally spaced pattern of numbers	5-8
an unequally spaced pattern of numbers	5-9
text that follows a pattern	5-10
an equally spaced pattern of dates/times	5-11
an unequally spaced pattern of dates/times	5-12

▶ **To fill a column with an equally spaced pattern of numbers**

    1 Choose **Calc ➤ Make Patterned Data ➤ Simple Set of Numbers**.

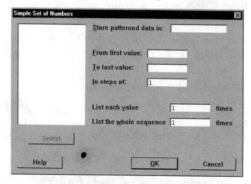

    2 In **Store patterned data in**, enter the column you want to fill.

    3 In **From first value**, enter the number with which you want the sequence to begin.

    4 In **To last value**, enter the number with which you want the sequence to end.

    5 In **In steps of**, enter the increments between each number.

    6 In **List each value**, enter the number of times you want to repeat each number within the sequence.

    7 In **List the whole sequence**, enter the number of times you want to repeat the entire sequence, then click **OK**.

▷ **Example of creating an equally spaced pattern of numbers**

Suppose you want to put the numbers 1, 2, 3, ..., 100 into a column named ID.

    1 Choose **Calc ➤ Make Patterned Data ➤ Simple Set of Numbers**.

    2 In **Store patterned data in**, enter *ID*.

    3 In **From first value**, enter *1*. In **To last value**, enter *100*. Click **OK**.

More examples of creating equally spaced patterns of numbers

From first value	4	1	1	1	1
To last value	1	3	2	3	3
In steps of	1	0.5	1	1	1
List each value	1	1	3	1	2
List the whole sequence	1	1	1	2	2
Stores these numbers	4, 3, 2, 1	1, 1.5, 2, 2.5, 3	1, 1, 1, 2, 2, 2,	1, 2, 3, 1, 2, 3	1, 1, 2, 2, 3, 3, 1, 1, 2, 2, 3, 3,

▶ **To fill a column with an unequally spaced pattern of numbers**

1 Choose Calc ➤ Make Patterned Data ➤ Arbitrary Set of Numbers.

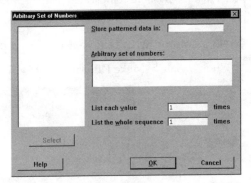

2 In **Store patterned data in**, enter the column you want to fill.

3 In **Arbitrary set of numbers**, enter the pattern of numbers. See *More examples of creating unequally spaced patterns of numbers* on page 5-9 for examples.

4 In **List each value**, enter the number of times you want to repeat each number within the sequence.

5 In **List the whole sequence**, enter the number of times you want to repeat the entire sequence, then click **OK**.

▷ **Example of creating an unequally spaced pattern of numbers**

In this example, we put the numbers 10, 10, 20, 20, 50, 50, 10, 10, 20, 20, 50, 50, 10, 10, 20, 20, 50, 50 into a column named PSI.

1 Choose Calc ➤ Make Patterned Data ➤ Arbitrary Set of Numbers.

2 In **Store patterned data in**, enter *PSI*.

3 In **Arbitrary set of numbers**, enter *10 20 50*.

4 In **List each value**, enter *2*.

5 In **List the whole sequence**, enter *3*, then click **OK**.

More examples of creating unequally spaced patterns of numbers

Here are some more ways to enter numbers in the **Arbitrary Set of Numbers** box:

Entering this set of numbers...	Fills the column with these numbers
10 20 50	10 20 50
10 20 50:52	10 20 50 51 52
10 20 50:52/0.5	10 20 50 50.5 51 51.5 52
10 20:17 50	10 20 19 18 17 50

Note | Using the session command SET, documented in Session Command Help, you can create data that follow more complicated patterns. You can also use SET to import text files and give a user-specified format for the data.

▶ **To fill a column with text that follows a pattern**

1 Choose **Calc ➤ Make Patterned Data ➤ Text Values**.

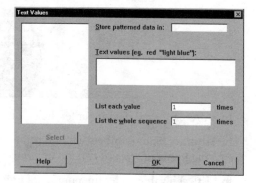

1 In **Store patterned data in**, enter the column you want to fill.

2 In **Text values**, type the base pattern for the text. If the text contains a blank, surround the entire value by double quotes.

3 In **List each value**, enter the number of times you want to repeat each text value within the sequence.

4 In **List the whole sequence**, enter the number of times you want to repeat the entire sequence. Click **OK**.

Note | Using the session command TSET, documented in Session Command Help, you can create data that follow more complicated patterns. You can also use TSET to import text files.

▷ **Example of creating a pattern of text**

Suppose you want to fill a column with the following text: red, blue, green, dark blue, and yellow. You want to repeat the series of colors 10 times.

1 Choose **Calc ➤ Make Patterned Data ➤ Text Values**.

2 In **Store patterned data in**, enter C1.

3 In **Text values**, enter *red blue green "dark blue" yellow*.

4 In **List each value**, enter *1*.

5 In **List the whole sequence**, enter *10*, then click **OK**.

▶ To fill a column with an equally spaced pattern of dates/times

1 Choose **Calc ➤ Make Patterned Data ➤ Simple Set of Date/Time Values**.

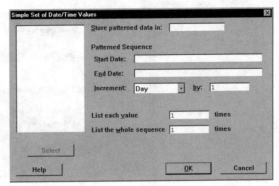

2 In **Store patterned data in**, enter the column you want to fill.

3 In **Start Date**, enter the starting date/time. In **End Date**, enter the end date/time. The starting and ending date/time values must be in a default format (see page 2-26).

4 From **Increment**, choose a date/time increment from the list.

5 In **List each value**, enter the number of times you want to repeat each date/time within the sequence.

6 In **List the whole sequence**, enter the number of times you want to repeat the entire sequence, then click **OK**.

➤ Example of creating dates and/or times that follow a pattern

Suppose you want to put the dates 1/1/99, 1/2/99, ..., 1/31/99 into a new column named January.

1 Choose **Calc ➤ Make Patterned Data ➤ Simple Set of Date/Time Values**.

2 In **Store patterned data in**, enter *January*.

3 In **Start Date**, enter *1/1/99*. In **End Date**, enter *1/31/99*. Click **OK**.

What you can enter in the Start Date and End Date boxes

You may type a date, a time, or a date/time combination in the **Start Date** and **End Date** boxes in a default date/time format that MINITAB recognizes. See page 2-26 for a list of these formats.

Note | Using the session command DSET, documented in Session Command Help, you can use text constants for start and end dates. With DSET, you can also specify a custom format for displaying the new date/time data, or for specifying the start and end date/time values.

▶ **To fill a column with an unequally spaced pattern of dates/times**

1 Choose **Calc ➤ Make Patterned Data ➤ Arbitrary Set of Date/Time Values**.

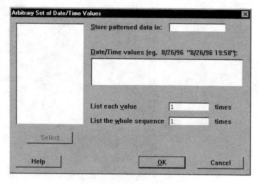

2 In **Store patterned data in**, enter the column you want to fill.

3 In **Date/Time values**, enter the pattern of dates/times.

4 In **List each value**, enter the number of times you want to repeat each date/time within the sequence.

5 In **List the whole sequence**, enter the number of times you want to repeat the entire sequence, then click **OK**.

Making Indicator (Dummy) Variables

You can create indicator (dummy) variables.

A typical use of this command is for regression analysis. You can do a regression analysis on an independent (x) variable which is a qualitative variable, such as color of package where there are only 3 colors, if that variable is first transformed into dummy variables. This command allows you to create those dummy variables. In textbooks, these are also called binary variables.

▶ **To create indicator variables**

1 Choose **Calc ➤ Make Indicator Variables**.

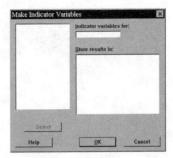

2 In **Indicator variables for**, enter a column on which to base the indicator variables.

3 In **Store results in**, enter one or more columns in which to store the indicator variables. Enter as many columns as there are distinct values in the Input column. Click **OK**.

▷ **Example of creating indicator variables**

Suppose you want to create four indicator variables in C2 through C5, as shown below. (Notice that the third row of Color is missing):

Color		C2	C3	C4	C5
red		1	0	0	0
red	→	1	0	0	0
		*	*	*	*
blue		0	0	1	0
green		0	0	0	1

1 In the Data window: Create a column, *Color*, which contains the values *red, red, **, *blue, green*, as shown above.

2 Choose **Calc ➤ Make Indicator Variables**.

3 In **Indicator variables for**, enter *Color*.

4 In **Store results in**, enter *C2-C5*, then click **OK**.

We specified four columns in which to store the indicator variables because Color has four distinct values: red, missing, blue, and green. If Color contains a missing value, all indicator variables will have the missing value symbol * in the corresponding row. The first indicator variable, C2, contains 1's for the first distinct value in Color, red, and 0's for the other rows. C3 contains no 1's because the next distinct value in Color is missing. C4 contains a 1 for the next distinct value, blue. And C5 contains a 1 for the last distinct value, green.

If the source column is numeric, MINITAB creates indicator columns for each distinct numeric value.

part II

Manipulating and Calculating Data

6
Manipulating Data

Manipulating Data Overview

You can duplicate the results of some of the procedures in this chapter by directly editing cells, rows, and columns, as described in Chapter 2, *Typing and Editing Data in the Data Window*. For example, you could duplicate some of the functionality of the **Manip ➤ Stack** command by selecting cells in one column and pasting them into another.

Copying and pasting using the mouse can be quicker and easier than filling out the manipulation dialog boxes. However, the commands in this chapter allow you to perform complex actions that would be difficult or tedious to replicate in other ways. For example, not only can **Manip ➤ Stack** stack the contents of multiple columns on top of each other, but the command also allows you to simultaneously create a column of subscripts (identifier codes) so you can see which values in the new column came from which source column.

The methods you use—Data window editing commands or manipulation commands—depend on the complexity of your task.

Merging Worksheets

You can merge two open worksheets into a new worksheet, according to your specifications. You can merge using several options:

- The default settings combines the two worksheets in their original format side by side in a new worksheet. See *Merging Worksheets* on page 6-4.

- **By Columns** combines the two worksheets side by side in a new worksheet, according the length and order of specified columns. See *Using By Columns to standardize merged worksheets* on page 6-6.

- **Include Columns** allows you to choose which columns you would like to include in the new worksheet. See *Using Include Columns* on page 6-9.

Subsetting data

You can subset data several ways:

- copy specified rows from the active worksheet to a new worksheet using Subset Worksheet—see *Subsetting: Copy Data to a New Worksheet* on page 6-9.

- split the active worksheet into two or more new worksheets based on one or more "By" variables—see *Subsetting: Split the Active Worksheet* on page 6-14.

Sorting, value ordering, and ranking data

You can organize your data several ways:

- **sorting** alphabetizes or numerically orders one or more specified columns, and carries along associated columns. The ordering appears in the worksheet. See *Sorting Data* on page 6-15.

- **ranking** assigns rank scores to values in a column: 1 to the smallest value in the column, 2 to the next smallest, and so on. Ties are assigned the average rank for that value. Missing values are left as missing. See *Ranking Data* on page 6-17.

- **value ordering** organizes one or more text columns according to a defined ordering, such as months of the year, or color. The ordering isn't visible in the worksheet, but is used in subsequent statistical analyses. You can choose a standard MINITAB ordering, or define your own ordering. See *Ordering Text Categories* on page 6-19.

Switching columns to rows and rows to columns

You can rearrange your data by switching columns to rows (transposing columns) or by using the Stack command to switch rows to columns.

Stacking and unstacking (splitting) columns

You can stack and unstack data in the following manner:

- stack one or more columns on top of each other

- stack one or more blocks of columns on top of each other

- unstack columns or blocks of columns into conveniently sorted data

More | You can also stack rows to create a single column—see *Switching Rows to Columns* on page 6-25.

Combining text columns

You can combine (concatenate) two or more text columns to create a new wider column—see *Combining Text Columns Side-by-Side* on page 6-37.

Recoding data

You can replace a value or set of values with new values.

- You can replace numeric data with text data and vice versa—see *Recoding Data* on page 6-38.

- You can also recode date/time data, you need to use a conversion table—see *Using a conversion table to recode data* on page 6-40.

Changing columns from one data type to another

In MINITAB, there are three types of columns: text, numeric, and date/time. MINITAB provides six commands that allow you to change your data from one type to another. See *Changing Columns from One Data Type to Another* on page 6-42.

Display worksheet data

You can display worksheet data (including columns, constants, and matrices) in the Session window. See *Displaying Worksheet Data in the Session Window* on page 6-45.

Merging Worksheets

You can combine any two open worksheets using Merge Worksheets. Unlike the merging option available when opening additional worksheets, Merge Worksheets duplicates, and then combines, the information from two original worksheets into a new worksheet. The default setting combines the worksheets, side by side and with their existing attributes, into the new worksheet, named *Merge Worksheet* by default.

You can also customize the merged worksheet using the main dialog box options. You can use By Columns to combine the worksheets according to the order and length of one or more columns. In addition, you can specify whether or not to include unmatched values, missing values or multiple values from one or both of the By columns. You can also specify which columns will be included from each original worksheet using Include Columns.

Note | Stored constants, matrices, DOE objects, and worksheet descriptions do not transfer into the merged worksheet.

▶ To merge worksheets using the default settings

1 Click on, or activate, one of the two worksheets you want to merge.

2 Choose **Manip ➤ Merge Worksheets**.

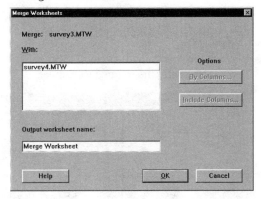

3 In **With**, click on the name of the worksheet that you want to merge with the active worksheet.

4 If you like, use any of the options listed below and click **OK**.

Options

By Columns subdialog box

The By Columns subdialog box contains several options for combining worksheets according to the order and length of one or more pairs of columns in either of the merging worksheets. By Columns options will affect all of the data contained in the opposing worksheet. See *Using By Columns to standardize merged worksheets* on page 6-6.

- include or exclude rows based on missing observations in the By columns. See *Missing observations* on page 6-9.

- include or exclude rows based on unmatched observations within the specified By columns from either of the merging worksheets. See *Multiple observations* on page 6-8.

- include or exclude rows based on multiple observations, or duplicate values, within the specified By columns from either of the merging worksheets. See *Multiple observations* on page 6-8.

Include Columns subdialog box

- specify columns that should be included in the merged worksheet. See *Using Include Columns* on page 6-9.

► Example of merging worksheets using the default settings

1 Open the worksheet SURVEY2.MTW and then open the worksheet SURVEY1.MTW.

2 Choose **Manip ➤ Merge Worksheets**.

3 In **With**, click on SURVEY2.MTW.

4 Click **OK** to accept the default settings. The following displays both the original worksheets and the merged worksheet:

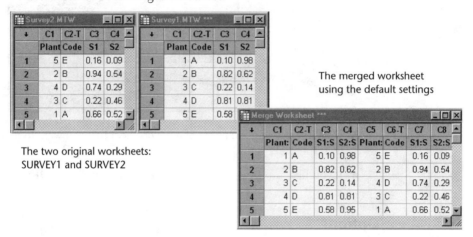

The two original worksheets:
SURVEY1 and SURVEY2

The merged worksheet
using the default settings

Using By Columns to standardize merged worksheets

You can standardize the combination of two worksheets using By Columns. The order of the data within the By columns becomes ascending. The length and order of the remaining columns in the merged worksheet are manipulated according to the By column adjustments, no matter the order or length of the original columns.

The length of the columns also depends on how you would like to handle multiple, unmatched, and missing observations within the By columns. The adjusted length of the By column(s) will still be applied to the order and length of the remaining columns. For more information, see the following sections.

Requirements for By Columns

- The column names for each of the two worksheets do not have to be unique. MINITAB will create a unique name for the columns in the merged worksheet based on the original worksheet names.

- You must specify at least one pair of By columns (one column from each worksheet) in the By Columns subdialog box. Additional By columns must also come in pairs.

- By columns must have the same data type (numeric, date/time, or text).

- When merging columns with value ordered text, the value orders in the By columns must be the same for both worksheets. For more information on value ordering, see *Ordering Text Categories* on page 6-19.

- Column lengths must be the same between multiple By columns.

- Columns that are not the same lengths as the By columns are excluded from the merged worksheet. A note in the session window documents the number of columns excluded.

▶ **To merge worksheets using By Columns**

1 Click on, or activate, one of the two worksheets you want to merge.

2 Choose **Manip ➤ Merge Worksheets**.

3 In **With**, click on the name of the worksheet that you want to merge with the active worksheet.

4 Click **By Columns**.

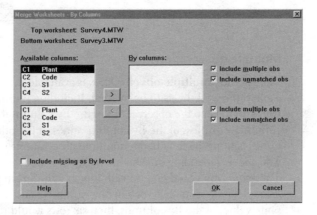

5 Click on a column number and/or heading in each of the **Available columns** fields (one column from each worksheet).

6 Click on [>] to use the highlighted columns as By columns.

7 Check the check boxes in the subdialog box to include missing observations, unmatched observations, or multiple observations. Click **OK** in each dialog box.

▷ **Example of using By Columns**

1 Open the worksheet SURVEY4.MTW and then open the worksheet SURVEY3.MTW.

2 Choose **Manip ➤ Merge Worksheets**.

3 In **With**, click on SURVEY4.MTW.

4 Click **By Columns**.

5 Click on "C1 Plant" in each of the **Available columns** fields.

6 Click on 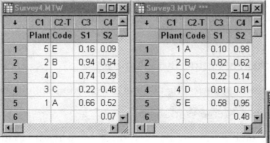 to use the highlighted columns as By columns.

7 Click **OK** in each dialog box. The following displays the original worksheets and the merged worksheet:

The merged worksheet using "Plant" as the By Column. Notice both of the data sets from the original worksheets are now in ascending order and with the same column length.

The original two worksheets: SURVEY3 and SURVEY4.

Multiple observations

The **Include multiple obs** checkbox is available in the By Columns subdialog box for each of the worksheets to be merged. Including multiple observations indicates that you wish to keep the observations of the By column that are repeated within the column, regardless of the By column values in the other worksheet. However, the values can still be matched to multiple observations in the By columns of the other worksheet, depending on whether or not the checkbox is active for the other worksheet. Therefore, you could end up with longer columns in the merged worksheet. For example, if there are two rows in one worksheet and three rows in the other, all with the same values of the By columns, then six rows would result.

If you were to choose to drop multiples for each worksheet, you would be ignoring all but the first row with the same values for the By columns. If more than one row in a worksheet has values for the By columns, then only the first such row is used.

Unmatched observations

The **Include unmatched obs** checkbox is available in the By Columns subdialog box for each of the worksheets to be merged. By default, **Include unmatched obs** is checked to include all of the rows in the opposite worksheet that do not have matching By column values. Missing value symbols would be added to the cells for the entire row associated with the unmatched By column values for the opposite worksheet. Consequently, padding rows with missing values will make all of the columns for both of the worksheets the same length as the By columns.

If a checkbox is left empty, unmatched By column rows would be removed from the merged worksheet. If any row in a worksheet has values for the By columns that are not matched in the By columns for the other worksheet, then that row is not used.

Missing observations

You can include missing values within By columns for both worksheets by checking **Include missing as By level** in the By Columns subdialog box. The missing observations within both worksheets will then be treated as distinct values. The missing By column value will be matched with a missing By column value in the other worksheet. Otherwise, by default, rows with missing values of By columns are omitted.

Note │ Missing values in text columns are represented by blanks and missing values in numeric and date/time columns are represented by an asterisk.

Using Include Columns

Whether you merge worksheets using the default settings or using By Columns, you can specify which columns you want to include from either worksheet.

▶ To exclude columns while merging worksheets

1 Click on, or activate, one of the two worksheets you want to merge.

2 Choose **Manip ➤ Merge Worksheets**.

3 In **With,** click on the name of the worksheet that you want to merge with the active worksheet.

4 Click on **Include Columns**.

5 Double-click the column names from the **Include Columns** fields to exclude the desired columns from either worksheet. Click **OK** in each dialog box.

Subsetting: Copy Data to a New Worksheet

You can use Subset Worksheet to copy specified rows from the active worksheet to a new worksheet. With Subset Worksheet, you can specify the subset based on row numbers, brushed points on a graph, or a condition such as unmarried males under 50 years old.

Split Worksheet (page 6-14) splits, or unstacks, the active worksheet into two or more new worksheets based on one or more "By" variables. Subset Worksheet and Split Worksheet always copy data to *new* worksheets. You can use Copy Columns (page 2-9) to replace data in the *current* worksheet with a subset.

Data

Data can be numeric, text, or date/time.

▶ To copy a subset of your current worksheet to a new worksheet

1　Choose **Manip ➤ Subset Worksheet**.

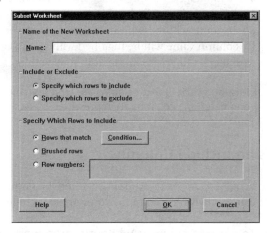

2　If you like, type a name for the new worksheet (instead of using the default name).

3　Under **Include or Exclude**, do one of the following:

- to copy specified rows to the new worksheet, choose **Specify which rows to include**

- to omit the specified rows, choose **Specify which rows to exclude**

4　Under **Specify Which Rows to Include/Exclude**, do one of the following:

- to base your subset on an expression, choose **Rows that match**. Then, click **Condition**, and complete the subdialog box to define the expression. Click **OK**.

- to base your subset on brushed points on a graph, choose **Brushed rows**.

- to base your subset on specific row numbers, choose **Row numbers** and type one or more row numbers (for example, 1:10).

5　Click **OK**.

▶ **To specify a subset based on a condition**

1 In the Subset Worksheet dialog box, choose **Rows that match**, then click **Condition**.

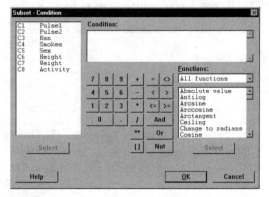

2 In **Condition**, enter an expression (such as *Sex = 1*) to specify the subset, and click **OK**.

Note | See the Calculator, page 7-2, for definitions of functions and syntax rules.

Exactly what is copied to the new worksheet?

Subset Worksheet copies columns to the new worksheet, but not stored constants or matrices. To copy stored constants and matrices as well, use the SUBSET session command (documented in Session Command Help).

If columns in the active worksheet are all the same length, then Subset Worksheet copies all columns to the new worksheet. But what if columns are not all the same length?

If you specify the subset with brushing, then MINITAB copies all columns that are the same length as the columns you brushed. If you specify the subset with a condition, then MINITAB copies all columns that are the same length as the result of the condition. If any columns are not copied to the new worksheet because of their length, MINITAB displays a note to that effect in the Session window.

If you specify the subset with row numbers, MINITAB will display a dialog box for you to select which columns to copy to the new worksheet.

▶ **Example of copying a subset of your current worksheet to a new worksheet**

In some of the following examples, a range of rows or values are indicated using two special punctuation marks. Use a colon to abbreviate a range, and a slash to indicate a step. For example, in the case for including every second row, the range 2:6/2 means to copy every row from 2 to 6, by two's, resulting in rows 2, 4, and 6. If you entered 2:6/3, MINITAB would copy rows 2 and 5.

1 Open the worksheet DIAMETER.MTW.

2 Choose **Manip ➤ Subset Worksheet**.

3 Choose **Specify which rows to include**.

4 Do one of the following and click **OK**.

To include...	Do this
rows 1, 2, 3, and 6	Choose **Row numbers**, and type *1:3 6*.
every second row	Choose **Row numbers**, and type *2:6/2*.
rows where Diameter 1 is between 64 and 65	**1** Choose **Rows that match**, then click **Condition**. **2** In **Condition**, type *Diameter1 > 64 And Diameter1 < 65*. **3** Click **OK** in each dialog box.
rows from the Morristown plant	**1** Choose **Rows that match**, then click **Condition**. **2** In **Condition**, enter *Plant = "Morristown"*. (Enclose text values with double quotes.) **3** Click **OK** in each dialog box.
data collected from 10/15/95 to 11/1/95	**1** Choose **Rows that match**, then click **Condition**. **2** In **Condition**, type *LogDate >= DATE("10/15/95") And LogDate <= DATE("11/1/95")*. **3** Click **OK** in each dialog box. This condition uses the **Date (from text)** function.
data collected during the last 30 days	**1** Choose **Rows that match**, then click **Condition**. **2** In **Condition**, type *LogDate >= TODAY() - 30*. (Use the **Today** function.) **3** Click **OK** in each dialog box. This example produces an error message because the variable LogDate does not include a date within the last 30 days from today. (Of course, today is whenever you try this example.) If you replace one of the dates in LogDate with a date from the last 30 days, the example works without error.

To include...	Do this
data based on a mathematical expression	1 Choose **Rows that match**, then click **Condition**.
Suppose that the diameter was measured at each end of a cylindrical rod, which should be a uniform shape. You want to subset data where the second diameter minus the first diameter is greater in magnitude than 0.5.	2 In **Condition**, type *ABSO(Diameter2 - Diameter1) > 0.5*. 3 Click **OK** in each dialog box. This condition uses the **Absolute value** function.

▷ **Example of excluding rows corresponding to brushed points in a graph**

Suppose you brush an outlier, which you would like to omit from your analysis. For an explanation of brushing graphs, see Chapter 25, *Brushing Graphs*.

Step 1: Get the data, create the graph, and brush the outlier

1 Open the worksheet PULSE.MTW.

2 Choose **Graph ➤ Plot**.

3 In **Y**, type *Weight*. In **X**, type *Height*. Click **OK**.

4 With the Graph window active, choose **Editor ➤ Brush**.

5 Highlight the point shown below.

Graph window output

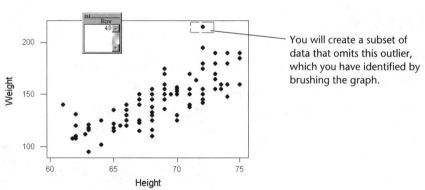

You will create a subset of data that omits this outlier, which you have identified by brushing the graph.

The Brushing palette indicates that row 40 is associated with that point.

Step 2: Create the subset

1 Choose **Manip ➤ Subset Worksheet**.

2 Choose **Specify which rows to exclude**.

3 Choose **Brushed rows** and click **OK**.

Data
window
output

The new worksheet contains a subset of data that omits row 40—the outlier that you identified by brushing the graph.

Subsetting: Split the Active Worksheet

Use Split Worksheet to split, or unstack, the active worksheet into two or more new worksheets based on one or more "By" variables. For instance, if you split your worksheet based on a By variable that contains the values "Yes" and "No," then Split Worksheet will create two new worksheets, one for the Yes's, and one for the No's.

Generally, Split Worksheet is most useful when it will create only a few new worksheets. Although there is no absolute limit to the number of worksheets you can create with Split Worksheet, numerous worksheets can be cumbersome to manage.

Use Subset Worksheet (page 6-9) to copy specified rows from the active worksheet to a new worksheet. With Subset Worksheet, you can specify the subset based on row numbers, brushed points on a graph, or a condition (such as unmarried males under 50 years old).

Subset Worksheet and Split Worksheet always copy data to *new* worksheets. You can use Copy Columns (page 2-9) to replace data in the *current* worksheet with a subset.

Data

Data can be numeric, text, or date/time. By columns must be of equal length.

▶ **To split your current worksheet into two or more new worksheets**

1 Choose **Manip ➤ Split Worksheet**.

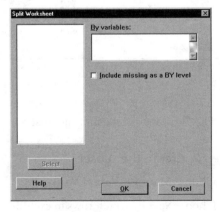

2   In **By variables**, enter at least one variable. MINITAB will create as many new worksheets as there are distinct values in the By column(s). By columns must be of equal length. Click **OK**.

Exactly what is copied to the new worksheets?

Split Worksheet copies data from columns to the new worksheets, but not stored constants or matrices. To copy stored constants and matrices as well, use the SPLIT session command (documented in Session Command Help).

Split Worksheet copies all columns that are the same length as the By variable(s). It ignores columns with lengths not equal to the By variable(s). If any columns are not copied to the new worksheets because of their length, MINITAB displays a note to that effect in the Session window.

Options

By default, Split Worksheet ignores rows where the By variable contains a missing value. To treat missing values as an additional distinct value, check **Include missing as a BY level**.

▷ **Example of splitting your current worksheet into two new worksheets**

Suppose you want to analyze data separately for smokers (Smokes = 1) and non-smokers (Smokes = 2) in the PULSE.MTW sample data set:

1   Open the worksheet PULSE.MTW.

2   Choose **Manip ➤ Split Worksheet**.

3   In **By variables**, enter *Smokes*. Click **OK**.

Data window output   MINITAB creates two new worksheets: Subset of Pulse.MTW(Smokes = 1) and Subset of Pulse.MTW(Smokes = 2).

Sorting Data

You can sort one or more columns of data according to the values in the column(s) you indicate. Sorting alphabetizes or numerically orders the column(s) you are sorting by and carries along associated columns. You can sort in ascending or descending order. The ordering appears in the worksheet.

The following data is sorted—first by Ad Agency (ascending order), then by Advertis (descending order).

Sales	Advertis	AdAgency	Sales	Advertis	AdAgency
94	17	Omega	106	24	Alpha
99	10	Omega	92	22	Alpha
98	9	Alpha	116	18	Alpha
92	22	Alpha	98	9	Alpha
106	24	Alpha	94	17	Omega
116	18	Alpha	108	14	Omega
113	13	Omega	113	13	Omega
108	14	Omega	99	10	Omega

The example on page 6-17 gives detailed instructions on how to sort the data as shown above.

For details on how MINITAB sorts text, special symbols, and missing data, see Help.

Note   To sort by more than four columns, use the session command SORT with the BY subcommand, documented in Session Command Help.

Data

Data can be numeric, text, or date/time. Columns must be of equal length.

▶ **To sort data**

1   Choose **Manip ➤ Sort**.

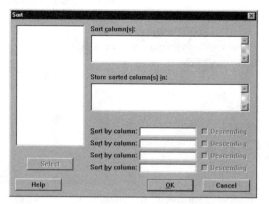

2   In **Sort column(s)**, enter the column(s) you want to sort.

3   In **Store sorted column(s) in**, enter the columns in which you want to store the sorted data. Type the same columns specified in step 2 if you don't want to save the unsorted columns.

4 In **Sort by column**, enter at least one and up to four columns to sort by. Rows are sorted by the first column listed, then the second column, and so on.

5 If you would rather sort a row from highest to lowest rather than lowest to highest, check **Descending** next to that row. Click **OK**.

Options

You can choose whether to sort the data in descending order instead of ascending (default) order.

▷ Example of sorting data

Suppose you want to view each of your ad agency's sales data. You want to list the ad agencies alphabetically, but you want each agency's advertising data shown in descending order.

1 Open the worksheet MARKET.MTW.

2 Choose **Manip ➤ Sort**.

3 In **Sort column(s)**, enter *Sales Advertis AdAgency*.

4 In **Store sorted column(s) in**, enter *Sales Advertis AdAgency*. This step replaces the unsorted data with the newly sorted data.

5 In the first **Sort by column**, enter *AdAgency*.

6 In the second **Sort by column**, enter *Advertis*, and check **Descending**. Click **OK**.

Data window output   The data is sorted first by AdAgency (ascending order), then by Advertis (descending order) as shown on page 6-16.

Ranking Data

You can assign rank scores to values in a column: 1 to the smallest value in the column, 2 to the next smallest, and so on. Ties are assigned the average rank for that value. Missing values are left as missing

In the following illustration, MINITAB assigns rank scores to the Sales column and stores them in a new column:

Sales	Rank
94	2
99	4
98	3
92	1
106	5
116	8
113	7
108	6

The example on page 6-18 gives detailed instructions on how to rank the data as shown above.

Data

Data must be numeric or date/time.

▶ **To calculate rank scores**

1 Choose **Manip ➤ Rank**.

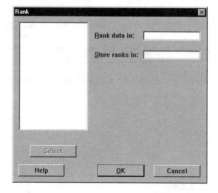

2 In **Rank data in**, enter the column for which you want to calculate ranks.

3 In **Store ranks in**, enter the storage column for those ranks. Click **OK**.

▷ **Example of calculating rank scores**

Here are the instructions for assigning rank scores to values in a column.

1 Open the worksheet MARKET.MTW

2 Choose **Manip ➤ Rank**.

3 In **Rank data in**, enter *Sales*.

4 In **Store ranks in**, enter *Rank*. Click **OK**.

*Data
window
output*

The rank assignments are stored in a new column as shown in the illustration on page 6-18.

Ordering Text Categories

Use Value Order to control the order in which you would like text categories to be processed by MINITAB commands. By default, text categories are processed in alphabetical order. However, this may not always be the most convenient way to process your data.

In the illustration below, the standard MINITAB order "Jan, Feb, Mar, …" was applied to the text column that produced the default (Before ordering) chart. The After ordering chart shows the reordered values.

Before ordering

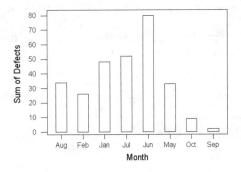

After ordering

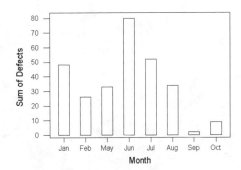

With Value Order, you can:

- check to see if an ordering has been previously applied to a column, and if so, what type of ordering.

Note | Unlike the Sort command (page 6-15), the order that you apply will not be visible in the Data window.

- choose a standard MINITAB order for the text values. Standard orders include common orders such as days of the week, months of the year, and so on.

- define your own order for the text values. For example, you may have Strongly Disagree, Disagree, No Opinion, Agree, Strongly Agree.

- maintain a list of orders that can be used in future sessions. The list includes the standard MINITAB orders. You can add your own orders to the list, and delete or replace them as needed. You cannot delete or replace any of the orders MINITAB provides.

- choose to process text categories in the order in which they appear in the worksheet column. The value in the first row becomes the first category, the next unique value becomes the second category, and so on.

- restore the default order (alphabetical) to the column.

Note | Once you have applied an order to a column, that information is saved in the worksheet until you reapply the default alphabetical order.

Data

Data must be text.

▶ To check the ordering status of text columns

1 In the Data window, click in at least one cell of the text column(s) you want to check.

2 Choose **Editor ➤ Column ➤ Value Order**.

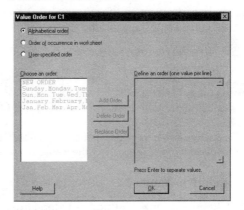

3 Look to see which button is chosen:

- **Alphabetical order** means that no ordering has been applied; the values will be processed alphabetically

- **Order of occurrence in worksheet** means that the value in the first row becomes the first category, the next unique value becomes the second category, and so on

- **User-specified order** means that the order highlighted in the **Choose an order** box was previously applied

4 Click **OK**.

▶ To order values in text columns using a previously-defined order

1 In the Data window, click on at least one cell in the text column(s) containing the values you want to order.

2 Choose **Editor ➤ Column ➤ Value Order**.

3 Choose **User-specified order** if it is not already selected. The text values from the column(s) appear in the **Define an order** box.

4 In the **Choose an order** list, highlight the order you would like to use, then click **OK**.

▶ To order values in a text column by defining your own order

1 In the Data window, click in at least one cell of the text column(s) you want to order.

2 Choose **Editor ➤ Column ➤ Value Order**.

3 Choose **User-specified order** if it is not already selected. The text values from the column(s) appear in the **Define an order** box. Change the order of those values, cutting and pasting as needed.

■ To cut: highlight the value and press Ctrl+X.

■ To paste: position the cursor where you want to paste and press Ctrl+V. The pasted value appears after the cursor.

■ To separate values so there is one value per line: press Enter to start each new line.

4 If you want to save the format for future use, click **Add Order**. The order will be added to the **Choose an order** box. Click **OK**.

Note | If a column contains values that are not included in the ordering scheme, those values are processed alphabetically after the values which do appear in the ordering.

▶ **To delete or replace an order in the Choose an order box**

1 Choose **Editor ➤ Column ➤ Value Order**.

2 In the Value Order dialog box, choose **User-specified order** if it is not already chosen.

3 In the **Choose an order** box, highlight the order you would like to delete or replace by clicking on it.

4 Do one of the following:

■ To delete an order, click **Delete Order**.

■ To replace an order, modify the text in the **Define an order** box as described below, then click **Replace Order**.
   – To cut: highlight the value and press Ctrl+X.
   – To paste: position the cursor where you want to paste and press Ctrl+V. The pasted value appears after the cursor.
   – To separate values so there is one value per line: press Enter to start each new line.

5 Click **OK**.

Note | You cannot delete or replace the standard MINITAB orders.

▶ **To process text values in their worksheet order**

1 In the Data window, click on at least one cell in the text column(s) containing the values you want to order.

2 Choose **Editor ➤ Column ➤ Value Order**.

3 Choose **Order of occurrence in worksheet**. Click **OK**.

▶ **To restore the default alphabetical ordering to a column**

1 In the Data window, click in at least one cell of the text column(s) to which you want to restore the default order.

2 Choose **Editor ➤ Column ➤ Value Order**.

3 Choose **Alphabetical order**. Click **OK**.

More | For an example in which Value Order is used with a data analysis command, see the Example of Cross Tabulation (Tables chapter) in MINITAB *User's Guide 2*.

▷ **Example of ordering values in a text column**

Suppose during your analysis of the cause of drill bit defects at your manufacturing plants, you decide to view the total number of defects that were reported each month. The first chart you create looks like the "Before ordering" chart on page 6-19. To easily analyze the data, you must reorder the Defects values and product a new chart.

1 Open the worksheet DEFECTS2.MTW.

2 In the Data window, click on at least one cell in the Month column.

3 Choose **Editor ➤ Column ➤ Value Order**.

4 Choose **User-specified order** if it is not already selected. The values from the Month column appear in the **Define an order** box.

5 In the **Choose an order** list, highlight "January, February, March, …," then click **OK**.

Data window output   The new value order that you apply is not visible in the Data window. However, when you regenerate the chart, your data appear in a more logical order as shown in the "After ordering" chart (illustrated on page 6-19).

Switching Columns to Rows

You can switch columns to rows (transpose columns) in your worksheet. For example, you may want to change the worksheet data structure as shown in the following illustration:

The columns that contain each student's exercise totals are switched to rows. This arrangement allows you to analyze the data by exercise type.

Task	Lyn	Bill	Sam	Marie
Pushups	50	69	70	57
Pullups	66	85	81	76
Situps	73	88	95	79

Labels	Pushups	Pullups	Situps
Lyn	50	66	73
Bill	69	85	88
Sam	70	81	95
Marie	57	76	79

The example on page 6-25 gives detailed instructions on how to rearrange the data as shown above.

Data

Data must be of the same type, and columns must be the same length.

▶ **To switch columns to rows**

1 Choose **Manip ➤ Transpose Columns**.

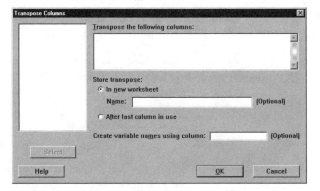

2 In **Transpose the following columns**, enter the columns you want to transpose.

3 Under **Store transpose**, choose the location for the transposed columns:

■ choose **In new worksheet** to place the transposed columns in a separate worksheet

■ choose **After last column in use** to place the transposed columns in the current worksheet after the last column that contains data

4 If you like, use any of the options listed below, then click **OK**.

Options

- name a new worksheet in which to store the transposed columns
- specify a column from which to extract values to be used as headers for the transposed columns

▷ Example of switching columns to rows

Suppose you are analyzing data based on students' progress in your exercise class. The current data is arranged in columns by student, but you need to rearrange the columns by the types of exercises your students are doing.

1 Open the worksheet EXERCISE.MTW.

2 Choose **Manip ➤ Transpose Columns**.

3 In **Transpose the following columns**, enter *Lyn-Marie*.

4 Under **Store transpose**, choose **After last column in use**.

5 In **Create variable names using column**, enter *Task*. Click **OK**.

Data window output

The four original columns are switched to four rows of data arranged into three columns containing the exercise data, as shown in the illustration on page 6-24.

Switching Rows to Columns

You can switch rows to columns in your worksheet.

Suppose you work at a plant that makes plastic trashbags. You have been having trouble with the seal at the bottom of the bag breaking apart. In an attempt to isolate the problem, you took four strength measurements on the first work day of each week from January 15th through February 24th. You originally entered each subgroup's data (four measurements) across a row in the worksheet. In addition, you entered the day on which the data was collected in a separate column.

Now you need to stack the row data to create a single column of data. For example, you may want to change the worksheet data structure in the following manner:

The first row of the columns Measure1 through Measure4 become the first four rows of the new data column named Strength. The Measure column stores the subscripts.

Day	Measure1	Measure2	Measure3	Measure4	Strength	Measure	SubgrpNumber
13	26.75	26.71	25.19	25.77	26.75	Measure1	13
20	26.74	27.30	27.15	27.05	26.71	Measure2	13
27	26.50	26.47	25.87	26.27	25.19	Measure3	13
3	25.33	27.17	27.33	26.89	25.77	Measure4	13
10	27.20	25.22	26.75	26.02	26.74	Measure1	20
17	25.30	27.92	28.10	27.03	27.30	Measure2	20
24	27.33	26.88	26.72	26.92	27.15	Measure3	20
					27.05	Measure4	20
					26.50	Measure1	27
					26.47	Measure2	27
					25.87	Measure3	27
					26.27	Measure4	27
					25.33	Measure1	3
					27.17	Measure2	3
					27.33	Measure3	3
					⋮	⋮	⋮

The values in the Day column have been expanded and serve as subgroup numbers.

The example on page 6-27 gives detailed instructions on how to rearrange the data as shown above.

Data

The data columns must be of the same type, and must be of equal length.

▶ **To switch rows to columns in your worksheet**

1 Choose **Manip ➤ Stack ➤ Stack Rows**.

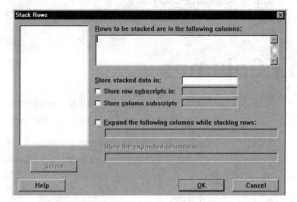

2 In **Rows to be stacked are in the following columns**, enter the columns that contain the data you want to appear in a single column.

3 In **Store stacked data in**, enter a column number or name.

4 If you like, use any of the options listed below, then click **OK**.

Options

- store the row subscripts

- store the column subscripts

- expand columns while stacking rows to create a subscript column using your own values—see the data described on page 6-26

▷ **Example of switching rows to columns**

Here are the step-by-step instructions for manipulating the trashbag data described on page 6-26.

1 Open the worksheet TRASHBAG.MTW.

2 Choose **Manip ➤ Stack ➤ Stack Rows**.

3 In **Rows to be stacked are in the following columns**, enter *Measure1–Measure4*.

4 In **Store stacked data in**, type *Strength*.

5 Check **Store column subscripts**, and type *Measure*.

6 Check **Expand the following columns while stacking rows**, and enter *Day*.

7 In **Store the expanded columns in**, enter *SubgrpNumber*. Click **OK**.

Data
window
output
The rows will be stacked into a single column as shown on page 6-26, the subscripts are stored in the column Measure, and the values in the Day column have been expanded and serve as subgroup numbers.

Stacking Columns

Use Stack Columns to move data from two or more columns to one longer column within your current worksheet or to a new worksheet.

When you stack columns, you can also create a column of subscripts, or identifier codes, that indicate which column an observation came from. You can use these subscripts to

- subset your data

- create graphs in which data points display differently depending on which group they are from

- unstack the columns

In the illustration below, the Sales column shows the combined sales data from stores in Denver, Boston, and Seattle. We know that the values 36, 32, 35, and 29 in the Sales column represent the sales figures from the Boston store because the subscript value (in the Store column) is Boston.

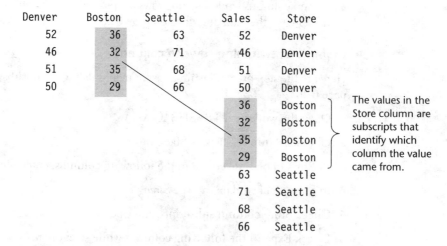

The data in the Boston column are stacked below the Denver data and on top of the Seattle data in the new Sales column.

Denver	Boston	Seattle	Sales	Store
52	36	63	52	Denver
46	32	71	46	Denver
51	35	68	51	Denver
50	29	66	50	Denver
			36	Boston
			32	Boston
			35	Boston
			29	Boston
			63	Seattle
			71	Seattle
			68	Seattle
			66	Seattle

The values in the Store column are subscripts that identify which column the value came from.

The example on page 6-30 gives detailed instructions on how to stack the data as shown above.

It is usually a good idea to store a subscript column so you can identify the data point associated with each group. For example, in this case, you could analyze the data in Sales, using the data in Store as a factor or a grouping variable.

More | To stack stored constants, use the session command STACK, documented in Session Command Help.

Data

Data can be numeric, text, or date/time. Columns are not required to be the same length.

▶ **To stack two or more columns into a new, longer column**

1 Choose **Manip ➤ Stack ➤ Stack Columns**.

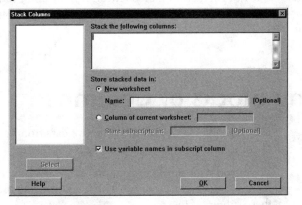

2 In **Stack the following columns**, enter the columns that contain the data you want to stack. The first column is stacked on top of the second column, the second on top of the third, and so on.

3 Under **Store the stacked data in**, choose the location for the new stacked data:

- choose **New worksheet** to place the stacked column into a separate worksheet

- choose **Column of current worksheet** to place the stacked column in the current worksheet in the column you specify

4 If you like, use any of the options listed below, then click **OK**.

Options

- name a new worksheet in which to store the stacked data

- use variable names in the subscript column

- specify where to store the subscripts

▷ **Example of stacking two or more columns into a new, longer column**

Suppose you want to analyze the quarterly sales data for one of your products. You focus on the sales at three outlet stores as shown in the following steps.

1 Open the worksheet SALES.MTW.

2 Choose **Manip ➤ Stack ➤ Stack Columns**.

3 In **Stack the following columns**, enter *Denver Boston Seattle*.

4 Under **Store the stacked data in**, choose **Column of current worksheet** and type *Sales*.

5 In **Store subscripts in**, type *Store*.

6 Choose **Use variable names in subscript column** and click **OK**.

Data window output   The sales figures from the Denver, Boston, and Seattle columns are now stacked in the Sales column as shown on page 6-28. The Store column contains the subscripts.

Stacking Blocks of Columns

Use Stack Blocks of Columns to move data from several columns to one longer block of columns in your current or a new worksheet.

When you stack blocks of columns, you can also create a column of subscripts, or identifier codes, that indicate which column an observation came from. You can use these subscripts to

- subset your data

- create graphs in which data points display differently depending on which group they are from

- unstack the blocks of columns

In the following illustration, the Qtr and Sales columns contain the quarterly sales figures from the Denver store stacked on top of the Boston store's quarterly totals, which are stacked on top of the figures from the Seattle store. The Store column contains the subscripts.

Quarter	Denver	Boston	Seattle		Sales	Qtr	Store
1	52	36	63		52	1	Denver
2	46	32	71		46	2	Denver
3	51	35	68		51	3	Denver
4	50	29	66		50	4	Denver
					36	1	Boston
					32	2	Boston
					35	3	Boston
					29	4	Boston
					63	1	Seattle
					71	2	Seattle
					68	3	Seattle
					66	4	Seattle

The data in the Quarter and Boston columns are stacked below the Quarter and Denver data and on top of the Quarter and Seattle data to form the new Qtr and Sales columns.

The values in the Store column are subscripts that identify which column the sales figures came from.

The example on page 6-32 gives detailed instructions on how to stack the data as shown above.

It is usually a good idea to store a subscript column so you can identify the data point associated with each group. For example, in this case, you could analyze the data in Sales, using the data in Qtr and Store as factor or grouping variables.

More | To stack blocks of stored constants or more than eight blocks of columns in one step, use the session command STACK, documented in Session Command Help.

Data

Data can be numeric, text, or date/time, but columns that are stacked together must be of the same data type. Columns are not required to be the same length.

▶ **To stack two or more blocks of columns into a new block of longer columns**

1 Choose **Manip ➤ Stack ➤ Stack Blocks of Columns**.

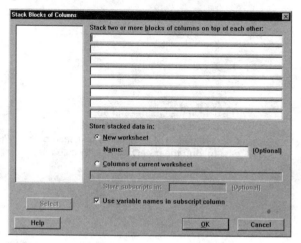

2 In **Stack two or more blocks of columns on top of each other**, enter each block of columns to be stacked. Each block of variables must be entered into a separate text box.

Note | All variables listed in a text box must have the same number of columns.

3 Under **Store stacked data in**, choose

- **New worksheet** to store the stacked blocks in a new worksheet, or

- **Columns of current worksheet** to specify the columns where you want to store the stacked blocks.

4 If you store the data in the current worksheet and you want to store the subscripts, specify a column where you want to store the subscripts. Click **OK**.

Options

- name a new worksheet in which to store the stacked data

- use variable names in the subscript column

- if you store the data in the current worksheet, specify where to store the subscripts

▷ **Example of stacking blocks of columns into a new block of longer columns**

Assume that you have accumulated the quarterly sales data for the Denver, Boston, and Seattle stores. Now, you want to stack blocks of sales data as shown on page 6-31.

1 Open the worksheet SALES.MTW.

2 Choose **Manip ➤ Stack ➤ Stack Blocks of Columns**.

3 In **Stack two or more blocks of columns on top of each other**, enter *Denver Quarter* in the first box, *Boston Quarter* in the second box, and *Seattle Quarter* in the third box.

4 Select **Columns of current worksheet**, and type *Sales Qtr* to indicate where the newly stacked data will be stored.

5 In **Store subscripts in**, type *Store* to identify the column that will contain the subscripts and click **OK**.

Data window output

The Qtr and Sales columns contain the quarterly sales figures from the three stores stacked on top of each other as shown in the example on page 6-30. The Store column contains the subscripts.

Unstacking Columns

Use Unstack Columns to split the contents of a stacked column or block of columns into two or more shorter columns within your current worksheet or copy the split columns to a new worksheet. For instance, you might unstack a data set so that the sales data for each store is stored in a separate column.

In the following illustration, the Sales column contains the stacked sales figures from stores in Boston, Denver, and Seattle. Unstack Columns splits this column into three separate columns based on the subscript in the Store column.

The data in the Sales column are unstacked (split) into the Sales_Boston, Sales_Denver, and Sales_Seattle columns.

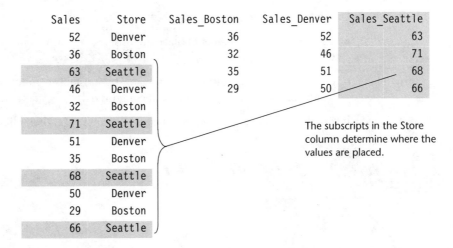

Sales	Store	Sales_Boston	Sales_Denver	Sales_Seattle
52	Denver	36	52	63
36	Boston	32	46	71
63	Seattle	35	51	68
46	Denver	29	50	66
32	Boston			
71	Seattle			
51	Denver			
35	Boston			
68	Seattle			
50	Denver			
29	Boston			
66	Seattle			

The subscripts in the Store column determine where the values are placed.

The example on page 6-36 gives detailed instructions on how to unstack the data as shown above.

More │ To unstack each value in a column into individual stored constants, use the session command UNSTACK, documented in Session Command Help.

Data

Data can be numeric, text, or date/time. Columns must be the same length.

▶ To unstack a column into two or more shorter columns

1 Choose **Manip ➤ Unstack Columns**.

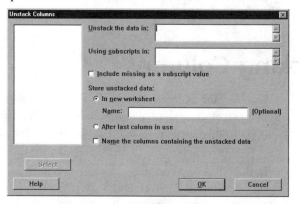

2 In **Unstack the data in**, enter the column you want to split.

3 In **Using subscripts in**, enter the column containing the subscripts. The values in this column determine how the column will be unstacked.

4 Under **Store unstacked data**, choose the location for the new unstacked columns:

■ choose **In new worksheet** to place the unstacked columns into a separate worksheet

■ choose **After last column in use** to place the unstacked columns in the current worksheet after the last column that contains data

5 If you like, use any of the options listed on the next page, then click **OK**.

▶ **To unstack a block of columns into two or more shorter columns**

1   Choose **Manip** ➤ **Unstack Columns**.

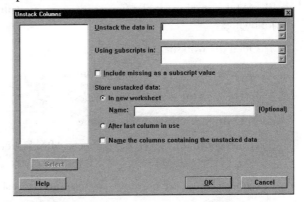

2   In **Unstack the data in**, enter the block of columns you want to split.

3   In **Using subscripts in**, enter the column(s) containing the subscripts. These values determine how the block of columns will be unstacked.

4   Under **Store unstacked data**, choose the location for the new unstacked block of columns:

  ■ choose **In new worksheet** to place the unstacked block of columns into a separate worksheet

  ■ choose **After last column in use** to place the unstacked block of columns in the current worksheet after the last column that contains data

5   If you like, use any of the options listed below, then click **OK**.

Options

  ■ unstack using single or multiple subscript columns.

  ■ include or exclude missing data values in the subscript column(s). If you include missing as a subscript value, MINITAB creates a column for all missing values. Otherwise, missing values are ignored during the unstack operation.

  ■ name a new worksheet in which to store the unstacked data.

  ■ name the columns containing the unstacked data.

▷ **Example of unstacking a column into two or more shorter columns**

Suppose you want to see the sales figures for your stores in Boston, Denver, and Seattle. To split the combined sales figures into separate columns for each store, do the following:

1 Open the worksheet SALES2.MTW.

2 Choose **Manip ➤ Unstack Columns.**

3 In **Unstack the data in**, enter *Sales.*

4 In **Using subscripts in**, enter *Store.*

5 Under **Store unstacked data**, choose **After last column in use** to place the unstacked column in the current worksheet after the Store column.

6 Choose **Name the columns containing the unstacked data** and click **OK.**

Data window output   The figures in the Sales column are split into three new columns as shown on page 6-33. The new columns of data are alphabetically arranged according to the subscripts contained in the Store column.

▷ **Example of unstacking a block of columns into shorter columns**

Suppose you want to analyze each store's sales figures by quarter.

1 Open the worksheet SALES2.MTW.

2 Choose **Manip ➤ Unstack Columns.**

3 In **Unstack the data in**, enter *Qtr Sales.*

4 In **Using subscripts in**, enter *Store.*

5 Under **Store unstacked data**, choose **After last column in use** to place the unstacked column in the current worksheet after the Store column.

6 Choose **Name the columns containing the unstacked data** and click **OK.**

Data window output   The figures in the Qtr and Sales columns are split into six new columns as shown below.

Qtr_Boston	Sales_Boston	Qtr_Denver	Sales_Denver	Qtr_Seattle	Sales_Seattle
1	36	1	52	1	63
2	32	2	46	2	71
3	35	3	51	3	68
4	29	4	50	4	66

Combining Text Columns Side-by-Side

Use Concatenate to combine two or more text columns and store them in a new, wider column as shown below.

Last	First	Student
Allen	Jo	Jo Allen
Charles	Dave	DaveCharles
Perkins	Max	Max Perkins
Richards	Bob	Bob Richards
Stephens	Mary	MaryStephens

The example on page 6-38 gives detailed instructions on how to combine the text columns as shown above.

Data

Data must be text and columns must be of equal length.

▶ **To concatenate two or more text columns**

1 Choose **Manip ➤ Concatenate**.

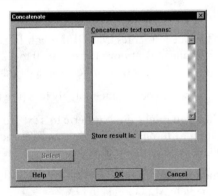

2 In **Concatenate text columns**, enter the text columns you want to combine side-by-side. Be sure to enter the columns in the order you want them to appear in the new concatenated column.

3 In **Store result in**, enter a column in which to store the concatenated text. Click **OK**.

▶ **Example of concatenating two text columns**

Suppose you have created a worksheet containing specific data for the students in your class. The students' names are currently arranged in two columns—last name and first name—but you want to have each student's complete name in one column.

1 Open the worksheet STUDENTS.MTW.

2 Choose **Manip ➤ Concatenate**.

3 In **Concatenate text columns**, enter *First Last* to display each student's first name, then last name.

4 In **Store result in**, enter *Student*. Click **OK**.

Data window output

The names from the first and second columns are combined into the Student column as shown on page 6-37. The text in this new, wider column is stored according to the order you specified in the Concatenate dialog box (see step 3 above).

Recoding Data

Use the Code commands in the Manip menu to search columns for a value or set of values and replace them with a new value.

When you might use Numeric to Numeric

- To code test scores from 91 through 100 to a 4 (grade of A), from 81 through 90 to a 3 (grade of B), from 71 through 80 to a 2 (grade of C), from 61 through 70 to a 1 (grade of D), and 60 or below to a 0 (grade of F)

- To code all occurrences of −99 to ∗ (the missing value symbol)

When you might use Numeric to Text To code test scores from 91 through 100 to an A, from 81 through 90 to a B, from 71 through 80 to a C, from 61 through 70 to a D, and 60 or below to an F.

When you might use Text to Text To code Tennessee to TN, North Carolina to NC, Alabama to AL, Georgia to GA.

When you might use Text to Numeric To code the letter grade A to a 4, B to a 3, C to a 2, D to a 1, F to a 0.

Note | If you want to recode date/time values, or if you want to recode values based on a conversion table, use the **Manip ➤ Code ➤ Use Conversion Table** command. See *Using a conversion table to recode data* on page 6-40.

Data

Data can be numeric, text, or date/time.

▶ **To recode numeric or text data**

1 Choose **Manip ➤ Code ➤ Numeric to Numeric, Numeric to Text, Text to Text**, or **Text to Numeric** depending on which type of column you want to change.

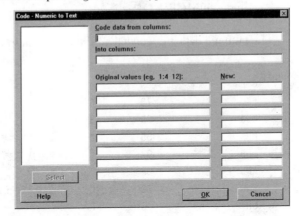

2 In **Code data from columns**, enter the column(s) containing data that you want to recode. When the cursor is in this box, the variable list box displays only those columns whose type corresponds to the command you chose.

3 In **Into columns**, enter the column(s) where you want to store the recoded data.

4 In **Original values**, enter the data values you want to recode.

You may type multiple values in one **Original values** box, such as *1:3 15 20* or *red white blue*; just separate the values with a space.

5 In **New**, specify the new value you want to replace the original value(s) with. Click **OK**.

To manipulate date/time data, use the Extract commands in the Calc menu and the Change Data Type commands in the Manip menu.

More | The session command CODE, documented in Session Command Help, lets you recode up to 50 new values, and works with text and numeric data types.

▷ **Example of recoding numeric data to text**

Suppose that you have calculated all test scores and arrived at each student's semester average. Now you must convert each numeric average into a final letter grade.

1 Open the worksheet GRADES2.MTW.

2 Choose **Manip ➤ Code ➤ Numeric to Text**.

3 In **Code data from columns**, enter *Scores*. Note that the variable list box displays only the columns that contain numeric data—in this case, Scores.

4 In **Into columns**, enter *Grades*.

5 In **Original values**, type *91:100* in the first row, *81:90* in the second, *71:80* in the third, *61:70* in the fourth, and *0:60* in the fifth.

6 In **New**, type *A* in the first row, *B* in the second, *C* in the third, *D* in the fourth, and *F* in the fifth. Click **OK**.

Data window output   The numeric data are recoded and stored as text in the new Grades column as follows:

Student	Scores	Grades
GMB	93	A
FKC	78	C
GUJ	88	B
NBK	65	D
LDN	97	A
FNN	83	B
FNR	72	C
GHT	0	F
VNW	85	B
FHI-W	80	C

Each value in the new Grades column corresponds to the numeric value in the Scores column. This new letter grade is based on the original values you entered in step 5 above.

Using a conversion table to recode data

Choose Use Conversion Table to recode numbers, dates, or text values to new values, based on a conversion table that you set up in the worksheet.

Note | You can also use the other Code commands, explained above, to recode data. However, they cannot recode date/time values or use a conversion table as this command can.

▶ **To recode data using a conversion table**

1 In the worksheet, enter a column of original values and a second column of corresponding codes.

↓	C1-T	C2
	StNam	StCod
1	AL	1
2	AK	2
3	AZ	3
4	AR	4

For example, these two columns might contain 50 names in C1, and 50 corresponding codes in C2.

2 Choose **Manip ➤ Code ➤ Use Conversion Table**.

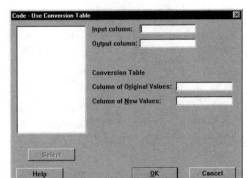

3 In **Input column**, enter the column that contains the values you want to recode.

4 In **Output column**, enter the storage column that will contain the new values.

5 In **Column of Original Values**, enter the column that contains the original values that you want to base the conversion on.

6 In **Column of New Values**, enter the column that contains the new values that you want to base the conversion on. Click **OK**.

➤ Example of recoding data using a conversion table

Suppose you want to recode the state names in an address list to the corresponding state ID numbers.

1 Open the worksheet STATES.MTW. Assume you have already entered a conversion table consisting of a column of original values (StNam) and a second column of corresponding codes (StCod).

2 Insert a new column after the State column and name it *StID* to store the new ID numbers next to the associated State data. If you do not insert a column for your new data, MINITAB will store the ID numbers after the last column in use.

3 Choose **Manip ➤ Code ➤ Use Conversion Table**.

4 In **Input column**, enter *State*.

5 In **Output column**, enter *StID*. If you inserted a new column in step 2, but did not name it StID, MINITAB ignores the newly inserted column and stores a new column named StID after the last column in use.

6 In **Column of Original Values**, enter *StNam*.

7 In **Column of New Values**, enter *StCod*. Click **OK**.

Data window output   MINITAB recodes the state names in the State column and stores them in a new column as shown below:

State	StID	StNam	StCod
MT	26	AL	1
CO	6	AK	2
CO	6	AZ	3
OR	37	AR	4
WA	47	CA	5
CA	5	CO	6
WA	47	CT	7
CO	6	DE	8
NV	28	FL	9
UT	44	GA	10

MINITAB applies a StCod value to each of the values in the State column. These codes are then stored in the StID column.

Changing Columns from One Data Type to Another

MINITAB provides six commands that allow you to change your data from one type to another.

Why would you want to use these commands? In MINITAB, there are three types of columns: text, numeric, and date/time. When you enter data into a column, MINITAB decides which type of column it is, depending on the data. In the Data window and Columns folder, MINITAB identifies text columns with T and date/time columns with D. Numeric columns are not identified in the Data window, but in the Columns folder, numeric columns are identified with an N.

Sometimes MINITAB sets a column as text when you want it to be numeric, and vice versa. For example, if you accidentally type a letter into the first row of a column in the Data window, MINITAB will identify that column as a text column. Similarly, if you accidentally type a number into the first row of a column, MINITAB will identify that column as numeric. The Text to Numeric and the Numeric to Text command can correct these problems.

There are a few commands that cannot use date/time columns. If you encounter this restriction, the Date/Time to Text command can help you work around it.

The menu commands summarized below are particularly useful when there is a problem with the format of date/time data which you have imported into MINITAB or you want to export from MINITAB. Since MINITAB recognizes and adheres to standard date/time formats, this should be a rare occurrence.

When you might use

Date/Time to Numeric   MINITAB, like most other applications, stores dates internally as serial numbers, and times as decimal fractions. This command changes your date/time data to the representative numeric values. This can be useful if you want to compare MINITAB's representation of date/time data with another application.

Numeric to Date/Time   Most software applications, including MINITAB, store dates and times internally as numbers. For example, the date 1/2/95 is represented internally as the number 34701. If you import date/time data into MINITAB and find that it displays in the Data window as numbers, use the Numeric to Date/Time command to change those numbers to a date/time format.

Text to Date/Time   Suppose you import a text file that contains date/time data which is not in a default format that MINITAB recognizes. In this case, MINITAB will identify that column as text. You can use the Text to Date/Time command to change this text column to a date/time column by specifying a user-defined format.

See *Using Date/Time Data* on page 1-10 for an overview of date/time data.

▶ **To change a column from numeric to text or date/time, from text to numeric or date/time, or from date/time to text or numeric**

1 Choose **Manip ➤ Change Data Type,** then choose one of the following depending on which type of column you want to change:

   ■ **Numeric to Text**

   ■ **Text to Numeric**

   ■ **Date/Time to Text**

   ■ **Date/Time to Numeric**

   ■ **Numeric to Date/Time**

   ■ **Text to Date/Time**

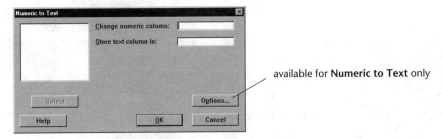

available for **Numeric to Text** only

2 In **Change column**, enter the column to change. When the cursor is in this box, the variable list box displays only those columns whose type corresponds to the command you choose.

3 In **Store column in**, enter the column where you want to store the changed data.

4 If you are changing numeric data to text data, choose any of the options listed below. Click **OK**.

Options

If you are changing numeric data to text data, you can specify

- the width of the column

- the number of digits and decimal digits

- a value for missing data; by default, MINITAB converts missing values (*) to a blank

▷ Example of changing a column from text to date/time

This will work only if the date/time values in the text column are in a default or a user-defined date/time format (see pages 2-25 and 2-26). MINITAB allows many different formats, but if your data do not follow any of these, you will need to edit the data, either in MINITAB or in another application.

Suppose your column of date/time data looks like the following (note the T, which indicates that MINITAB considers this to be a text column):

```
    C1-T
    Date
Nov-15-99
Nov-26-99
Dec-05-99
```

1 Open the worksheet DATES.MTW.

2 Choose **Manip ➤ Change Data Type ➤ Text to Date/Time**.

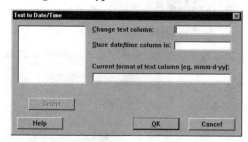

3 In **Change text column**, enter *Date*.

4 In **Store date/time column in**, enter *Date*.

5 In **Current format of text column**, type *mmm-d-yy*. Click **OK**.

Page 2-25 explains which date/time formats are allowable and how to specify those formats.

Data window output

The new column you just created looks the same as the original column, but it is now identified as a date/time column (labeled with D in the Data window and Columns folder) and will be treated as such by MINITAB.

```
     C1-D
     Date
Nov-15-99
Nov-26-99
Dec-5-99
```

Displaying Worksheet Data in the Session Window

Use Display Data to view data that you select from the current worksheet in the Session window, including any combination of columns, stored constants, or matrices.

Display Data is especially useful for viewing the contents of stored constants and matrices, since these variables are not displayed in the Data window. This information can also be viewed in the Constants and Matrices folders within the Project Manager.

▶ **To display worksheet data in the Session window**

1 Choose **Manip** ➤ **Display Data**.

2 In **Columns, constants, and matrices to display**, enter the items you want to print in the Session window. Click **OK**.

More | The session command PRINT is a useful way to display output in the Session window. Using the subcommand FORMAT, you can override the default format for display. See Session Command Help for details.

⮞ **Example of displaying worksheet data in the Session window**

Suppose you want to display the conversion table you used to recode data in the Session window.

1 Open the worksheet TRASHBAG.MTW.

2 Choose **Manip ➤ Display Data**.

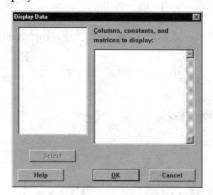

3 In **Columns, constants, and matrices to display**, enter *Day Measure1 Measure2 Measure3 Measure4*. Click **OK**.

Session window output

The data from the worksheet is copied into the Session window as shown below:

Row	Day	Measure1	Measure2	Measure3	Measure4
1	13	26.75	26.71	25.19	25.77
2	20	26.74	27.30	27.15	27.05
3	27	26.50	26.47	25.87	26.27
4	3	25.33	27.17	27.33	26.89
5	10	27.20	25.22	26.75	26.02
6	17	25.30	27.92	28.10	27.03
7	24	27.33	26.88	26.72	26.92

7

Calculations

Calculations Overview

With the commands in this chapter, you can:

- calculate mathematical expressions and transformations—see *Calculating Mathematical Expressions and Transformations* on page 7-2

- calculate individual row and column statistics—see *Calculating Individual Statistics for Columns and Rows* on page 7-13

- center and scale columns of data—see *Standardizing Data* on page 7-15

- extract one or more parts of a date/time column, such as the year or the hour—see *Extracting Components of a Date/Time Column* on page 7-16

Calculating Mathematical Expressions and Transformations

Use the Calculator to do arithmetic operations, comparison operations, logical operations, functions, and column operations. Expressions may include columns, stored constants, numbers, and text, but not matrices.

More | You can change an individual value in a column using the session command LET, documented in Session Command Help. This can be helpful when writing macros.

▶ **To calculate a mathematical expression**

1 Choose **Calc ➤ Calculator**.

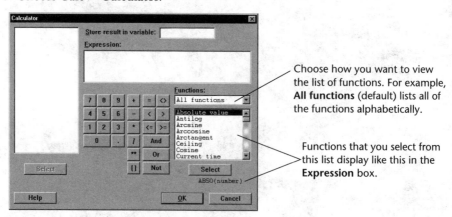

Choose how you want to view the list of functions. For example, **All functions** (default) lists all of the functions alphabetically.

Functions that you select from this list display like this in the **Expression** box.

2 In **Store result in variable**, enter the column or constant where you want to store the result of the expression.

If you are creating a new column, enter a column number, such as C10 or C11, or a name that does not yet exist in the current worksheet.

If you are creating a new constant, you must type the constant number, such as K2 or K3. If you type a name, such as *MyConstant*, MINITAB assumes that you want to create a column with that name. Later you can name constants using the NAME session command, as in NAME K2 'MyConstant'. See Session Command Help for details.

3 With the cursor in **Expressions**, select variable names, buttons, and functions to build your expression. To set functions to their default values, omit the arguments at the end of the functions. Descriptions of the functions begin on page 7-7. Click **OK**.

Example expressions

To...	Use this expression	For this result
Store a number in a column	5	The number 5 is stored in the first row of the column you specify.
Store a number in a constant	5	The number 5 is stored in the constant number (e.g., K2) you specify.
Copy the contents of one constant to another constant	K2	If K2 contains the number 5, 5 will be stored in the constant number you specify.
Compute a mathematical expression	MEAN(C10) / STDEV(C1)	Divides the mean of C10 by the standard deviation of C1.
Compute a mathematical expression	K1000 * C1**2	Stores the product of π (in K1000) and C1 squared. (By default, MINITAB stores the value of π in K1000, e in K999, and $*$ in K998.)
Compute a mathematical expression	5/9 * (Fahrenheit − 32)	Stores Celsius values. (The example assumes that Fahrenheit is the name of a column that contains temperature in degrees Fahrenheit.)
Store a text value in a column	"green"	Stores the text value green. Specific text values must be enclosed with double quotes.
Store a subscript (true/false) column based on values in a text column	C1 = "green"	Stores 0's for false, and 1's for true, where true is any row where C1 equals "green" (MINITAB is case sensitive when comparing text values. Thus, rows where C1 equals "Green" or "GREEN" would be considered false.)

To...	Use this expression	For this result
Store a subscript (true/false) column based on a logical expression	`C1 > C2`	Stores 0's for false, and 1's for true, where true is any row where C1 is greater than C2. "Greater than" means "larger than" if C1 and C2 are numeric columns, "later in the alphabet than" if C1 and C2 are text columns, or "later than" if C1 and C2 are date/time columns.
Store a subscript (true/false) column based on a logical expression	`(C1 < 10) or (C1 >= 15)`	Stores 0's for false and 1's for true, where true is any row where C1 is either less than 10, or greater than or equal to 15.

Example expressions using date/time data

Note | If the last operation evaluated in an expression is a numeric operation (such as minus (–) or MEAN), MINITAB stores the result as a number. If the last operation evaluated is a date/time function, such as NOW or WHEN, MINITAB stores the result as a date/time value. The fourth rule on page 7-6 lists the order in which MINITAB performs operations.

To...	Use this expression	To store this result
Subtract two date columns	`DateFailed — DateInstalled`	The difference in days between DateFailed and DateInstalled.
Subtract 30 days from today, and store the result as a number	`TODAY() — 30`	The numeric equivalent of today's date minus 30 days.
Subtract 30 days from today and store the result as a date	`DATE(TODAY() — 30)`	The date which equals today's date minus 30 days.
Extract the date from a date/time column	`DATE(DateFailed)`	Suppose the column DateFailed contains dates and times, such as *3/15/99 1:30 PM*. This expression, which uses the *DATE(from value)* function, stores just the date portion, *3/15/99*, in the new variable.
Store a subscript (true/false) column, based on the date and time in a date/time column	WHEN is both date and time: `DateFailed = WHEN("3/15/99")`	0's for false and 1's for true, where true is any row where DateFailed equals *3/15/99 12:00 AM*. The *WHEN* function includes both date and time. Since you did not supply a time within the double quotes, MINITAB assumes 12:00 midnight.

To...	Use this expression	To store this result

Store a subscript (true/false) column, based on the time in a column	This will work:
	`TimeFailed >= TIME("7:30") And`
	`    TimeFailed <= TIME("13:30")`
		Uses the *TIME(from text)* function. This expression stores 0's for false and 1's for true, where true is any row where TimeFailed is between 7:30 and 13:30, inclusive. (TimeFailed should contain times only, not date/time values.)
		
		Note: The time must be in double quotes and must be in a default time format (see page 2-26).

	This will not work:
	`TimeFailed >= 7:30 And`
	`    TimeFailed <= 13:30`
		If you reference a specific time as shown here, MINITAB tries to interpret it as a number. Since numbers do not contain colons, MINITAB will display an error message.

Store a subscript (true/false) column, based on a comparison of date values	`DateHired > TODAY() — 30`	0's for false and 1's for true, where true is any row where DateHired is later than today's date minus 30 days.

Store a subscript (true/false) column, based on a comparison of date values	This will work:
	`DateHired > DATE("3/15/99")`
	`    — 30`
		Uses the *DATE(from text)* function. This expression stores 0's for false and 1's for true, where true is any row where DateHired is later than 2/14/99. (3/15/99 minus 30 days equals 2/14/99.)
		
		Note: The date must be in double quotes and must be in a default format (see page 2-26).

	This will not work: `DateHired > (3/15/99 — 30)`	If you reference a specific date as shown here, MINITAB will interpret the slashes in the date as "divide by" signs.
	This will not work: `DateHired > ("3/15/99" — 30)`	If you reference a specific date as shown here, in double quotes, MINITAB will interpret "*3/15/99*" as a text value. Since it doesn't make sense to subtract 30 from a text value, this will not work.

Rules

- Enclose specific text values, such as "green," with double quotes. Indicate missing text values as a pair of double quotes with no space inside, for example: C1 = "".

- Indicate missing numbers or date/time values with the missing value symbol '*' (enclosed with single quotes). You do not need to enclose numbers with any characters.

- Operations are done rowwise. When MINITAB cannot calculate an expression, for example because the input is a missing value or because you try to compute the square root of a negative number, the result is set to missing. Missing is * for a numeric or date column, blank for a text column.

- MINITAB performs operations in the following order: subscripts, functions and column operations, exponentiation, "Not," multiplication and division, addition and subtraction, comparison operations, "And," and "Or."
  - Operations of equal order are performed from left to right.
  - You can override the default precedence by using parentheses. MINITAB evaluates expressions within ( ) first.

- If the last operation evaluated in an expression is a numeric operation (such as minus or *MEAN*), MINITAB stores the result as a number. If the last operation evaluated is a date/time function, such as *NOW* or *WHEN*, MINITAB stores the result as a date/time value.

  For example, the result of *TODAY()* – 30 will be a number since the last operation evaluated is minus, a numeric operation. However, the result of *DATE(TODAY()* – *30)* will be a date value, because the last operation evaluated is *DATE*, a date/time function. The order in which MINITAB performs operations is shown above.

- In MINITAB (as with most spreadsheets), if you operate on a date/time variable with a number, for example *NOW()* + 30, MINITAB assumes the number is in units of days.

- Stored constants do not recognize date/time values, only numbers. Since date/time values are stored internally as numbers, date/time values stored in a constant are the numeric equivalent of the corresponding date/time value.

Arithmetic

Absolute value   Changes all negative numbers to positive numbers. Positive numbers and zero are left unchanged.

Ceiling   Rounds numbers in this manner: The first value you enter in the box following the function (denoted as **"number"**) is the number you want rounded; the second number (**"num_digits"**) specifies how to round that number. If **num_digits** = 0, the number is rounded to the nearest integer greater than or equal to the number. If **num_digits** > 0, the number is rounded up to **num_digits** number of digits after the decimal point. If **num_digits** < 0, the number is rounded up to 1 − **num_digits** places to the left of the decimal point. For example:

```
CEILING (2.136, 0)  equals 3
CEILING (2.136, 1)  equals 2.2
CEILING (2.136, 2)  equals 2.14
CEILING (-2.136, 1) equals -2.1
CEILING (253.6, -1) equals 260
CEILING (253.6, -2) equals 300
```

Floor   Rounds numbers in this manner: The first value you enter in the box following the function (denoted as **"number"**) is the number you want rounded; the second number (**"num_digits"**) specifies how to round that number. If **num_digits** = 0, the number is rounded to the nearest integer less than or equal to the number. If **num_digits** > 0, the number is rounded down to **num_digits** number of digits after the decimal point. If **num_digits** < 0, the number is rounded down to 1 − **num_digits** places to the left of the decimal point. For example:

```
FLOOR (2.136, 0)  equals 2
FLOOR (2.136, 1)  equals 2.1
FLOOR (2.136, 2)  equals 2.13
FLOOR (-2.136, 1) equals -2.2
FLOOR (253.6, -1) equals 250
FLOOR (253.6, -2) equals 200
```

Incomplete gamma   Calculates the incomplete gamma function. The first value you enter following the function is the number you want the function taken of; the second number is the shape parameter (the upper limit of the integral).

Gamma   Calculates the gamma function.

Lngamma   Calculates the natural log of the gamma function.

Partial products   Stores the product of the first i rows of the input column in the ith row of the storage column. For example, if the first three rows of the input column contain the values 2, 5, and 3, then the first three rows of the storage column will contain 2 (equal to 2 ∗ 1), 10 (equal to 2 ∗ 5), and 30 (equal to 2 ∗ 5 ∗ 3).

Partial sums Stores the sum of the first i rows of the input column in the ith row of the storage column. For example, if the first three rows of the input column contain the values 2, 5, and 3, then the first three rows of the storage column will contain 2 (equal to 2 + 0), 7 (equal to 2 + 5), and 10 (equal to 7 + 3).

Round Rounds numbers in this manner: The first value you enter in the box following the function (denoted as "**number**") is the number you want rounded; the second number ("**num_digits**") specifies how to round that number. If **num_digits** = 0, the number is rounded to the nearest integer. If **num_digits** > 0, the number is rounded to **num_digits** number of digits after the decimal point. If **num_digits** < 0, the number is rounded to 1 − **num_digits** places to the left of the decimal point. For example:

```
ROUND (2.136, 0)  equals 2
ROUND (2.136, 1)  equals 2.1
ROUND (2.136, 2)  equals 2.14
ROUND (-2.136, 1) equals -2.14
ROUND (213.6, -1) equals 210
ROUND (213.6, -2) equals 200
```

Square root Calculates square roots. Applied to negative numbers, the result is a missing value.

Signs Converts negative numbers, zero, and positive numbers to −1, 0 and +1, respectively.

Column functions

Lag Copies the data in the input column to the storage column, moving each value down by one row and inserting the missing value symbol ∗ in the first row. (Use **Stat ➤ Time Series ➤ Lag** if you need to specify a lag other than one.)

Rank Calculates and stores the ranks of the input column. See **Manip ➤ Rank** on page 6-17 for details.

Sort Sorts the input column and stores the sorted data in the storage column. See **Manip ➤ Sort** on page 6-15 for details.

Date/Time

Current time	Returns the current time, for example, 9:26:20 AM.
Now	Returns the current date and time, for example, 3/8/99 9:24.
Today	Returns today's date, for example, 3/8/99.

Note | For the When, Date, and Time functions listed below…

If stored in a column, the result is in a date/time format. If stored in a constant, the result is the numeric representation of the date/time value. Currently, stored constants in MINITAB do not have date/time formats.

When (from text)	Returns the date and time corresponding to the argument. The argument should be a text string in a default date/time format such as "3/6/99 10:23".
When (from value)	Returns the date and time corresponding to the argument. The argument should be a column or a stored constant, but not a text string. Text columns and constants must be in a default format (see page 2-26).
Date (from text)	Returns the date portion corresponding to the argument. The argument should be a text string in a default date/time format such as "3/6/99 10:23".
Date (from value)	Returns the date portion corresponding to the argument. The argument should be a column or a stored constant, but not a text string. Text columns and constants must be in a default format (see page 2-26).
Time (from text)	Returns the time portion corresponding to the argument. The argument should be a text string in a default date/time format such as "3/6/99 10:23".
Time (from value)	Returns the time portion corresponding to the argument. The argument should be a column or a stored constant, but not a text string. Text columns and constants must be in a default format (see page 2-26).

▶ **To calculate the date from a text, numeric, or date/time column**

1 Choose **Calc ➤ Calculator**.

2 In **Store result in variable**, enter the column where you want to store the date values.

3 Enter the variable name in **Expression**. Click **OK**.

▶ Example of calculating the date from a numeric column

Suppose your worksheet contains three equivalent columns. The only difference among these columns is their type: C1 is date/time, C2 is numeric, and C3 is text. Calculating **Date(from value)** for any one of these columns, for example, *DATE(C1)*, *DATE(C2)*, or *DATE(C3)*, has the same result, as shown below:

1 Open the worksheet DATES2.MTW.

2 Choose **Calc ➤ Calculator**.

3 In **Store result in variable**, enter C4.

4 With the cursor in **Expression**, highlight **DATE (from value)** in the list of functions.

5 Click **Select** to begin building your expression with the DATE(column_or_constant) variable.

6 Double-click C2 to enter it into the expression, and click **OK**.

Data window output   The new date column appears in the worksheet as follows:

C1-D	C2	C3-T	C4-D
1/5/99 08:00	36165.3	1/5/99 8:00	1/5/99
1/6/99 09:00	36166.4	1/6/99 9:00	1/6/99
1/7/99 11:00	36167.5	1/7/99 11:00	1/7/99

Note | **Date(from text)** works the same way. For example, DATE("1/5/99 8:00") returns the date value 1/5/99.

Logarithmic functions

Log 10 Calculates logarithms to the base 10. When applied to 0 or a negative number, Log 10 stores a missing value ∗.

Antilog Calculates 10^E, where E is the input.

Natural log Calculates logarithms to the base e. When applied to 0 or a negative number, Natural log stores a missing value ∗.

Exponentiate Calculates e^E, where E is the input.

Statistics

Missing values are omitted from the calculation of the functions Sum through Normal Scores, below.

Sum   Calculates the sum.

Mean   Calculates the arithmetic mean, or average. The mean is a commonly used measure of the center of a batch of numbers.

Std. dev.   Calculates the sample standard deviation, which provides a measure of how spread out the data are. To calculate the **variance**, simply square the standard deviation value.

                     If the column contains $x_1, x_2, ..., x_n$, with mean $\bar{x}$, then the standard deviation is

$$\sqrt{\sum (x_i - \bar{x})^2 / (n-1)}$$

Minimum   Stores the smallest and the largest numbers in a column
Maximum   respectively.

Median   Stores the median of a column. The median is in the middle of the data: half the observations are less than or equal to it. Suppose the column contains n values. If n is odd, the median is the value in the middle. If n is even, the median is the average of the two middle values.

Sum of sq.   Squares each value in the column, and computes the sum of those squared values. That is, if the column contains $x_1, x_2, ..., x_n$, then sum of squares calculates $(x_1^2 + x_2^2 + ... + x_n^2)$.

Normal scores   Calculates normal scores, which can be used to produce normal probability plots and various tests. You can produce normal probability plots directly by using **Stat ➤ Basic Statistics ➤ Normality Test** or **Graph ➤ Probability Plot**. See Help for details on how MINITAB calculates normal scores.

N total   Returns the total number of observations in a column.

N nonmissing   Returns the number of nonmissing observations in a column.

N missing   Returns the number of missing observations in a column.

Trigonometry

Sine **Cosine** **Tangent**	Calculates the standard trigonometric functions. The arguments must be in radians. To convert from degrees to radians, multiply by 0.017453. The sine, cosine, or tangent of numbers very large in magnitude cannot be calculated accurately. In this case, the result is set to the missing value code * and a message is displayed. The exact magnitude depends on the computer.
Arcsine **Arccosine** **Arctangent**	Calculates the standard trigonometric functions and stores the results in radians. To convert radians to degrees, multiply by 57.297.
Degrees	Changes radians to degrees.
Radians	Changes degrees to radians.

Row statistics

Range	Calculates the difference between the largest and smallest data value.

The rest of the row statistics are the same as described in *Statistics* on page 7-11, except that the statistics are calculated on rows of data, rather than on columns.

Constants

Missing data code	Constant * (* = missing value symbol)
e (2.718...)	Constant e (e = 2.71828)
Pi (3.141...)	Constant π (π = 3.14159)

Note | MINITAB stores * in K998, e in K999, and π in K1000.

Calculating Individual Statistics for Columns and Rows

You can calculate various statistics on columns or rows. Column statistics are displayed in the Session window, and are optionally stored in a constant. Row statistics are calculated across the rows of the columns specified and stored in the corresponding rows of a new column.

You can also calculate column statistics with **Calc ➤ Calculator** (see page 7-2). The main difference is that Calculator just stores the results in the worksheet; Column Statistics displays the results in the Session window.

For definitions of the individual statistics, see *Statistics* on page 7-11.

Note | Each of these statistics can be computed with a separate session command (such as SUM and MEAN), documented in Session Command Help. If you are calculating one of these statistics in a macro, it will calculate faster with the session command MEAN than with LET.

▶ **To calculate column statistics**

1 Choose **Calc ➤ Column Statistics**.

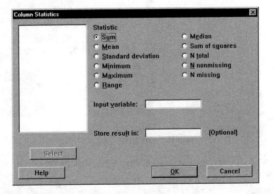

2 Under **Statistic**, choose the statistic you want to calculate.

3 In **Input variable**, enter the column of data for which you want to calculate statistics.

4 If you like, enter a constant in which to store the result in **Store result in**. Click **OK**.

Example of calculating column statistics

Suppose you want to calculate the mean of a column and store the mean in a new constant, named MeanPulse1.

1 Open the worksheet PULSE.MTW.

2 Choose **Calc ➤ Column Statistics**.

3 Under **Statistic**, choose **Mean**.

4 In **Input variable**, enter *Pulse1*. In **Store result in**, enter *MeanPulse1*. Click **OK**.

Session window output

Column Mean

```
Mean of Pulse1 = 72.870
```

To compute row statistics

1 Choose **Calc ➤ Row Statistics**.

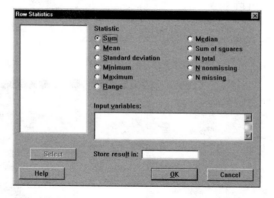

2 Under **Statistic**, choose the statistic you want to calculate.

3 In **Input variables**, enter the series of columns which contain the rows for which you want to calculate statistics.

4 In **Store result in**, enter a column in which to store the results, then click **OK**.

Example of computing row statistics

Suppose you want to store the rowwise range of C1 and C2 in a new column.

1 Choose **Calc ➤ Row Statistics**.

2 Choose **Range** from the list of statistics.

3 In **Input variables**, enter *C1 C2*. In **Store result in**, enter *RowRange*. Click **OK**.

Data window output

The new RowRange data is displayed as shown below:

C1	C2	C3
		RowRange
3	2	1
8	8	0
-1	4	5
4	-3	7
6	*	*

Standardizing Data

Standardize centers and scales columns of data. By default, the data is standardized by subtracting the mean and dividing by the standard deviation. Other standardization methods you can choose are listed on page 7-16.

▶ **To standardize your data**

1 Choose **Calc ➤ Standardize**.

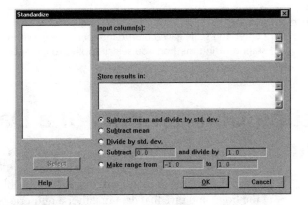

2 In **Input column(s)**, enter the columns you want to standardize.

3 In **Store results in**, enter the columns in which you want to store the standardized data.

4 If you like, choose one of the optional standardization methods described below, then click **OK**.

Standardizing methods

Subtract mean and divide by standard deviation (default method)	The result is often called a standard score or a z score. $$z = \frac{x - \bar{x}}{s}$$
Subtract mean	Subtracts the mean of the column from each value in the column.
Divide by standard deviation	Divides each value in the column by the standard deviation of the column.
Subtract *value* and divide by *value*	Subtracts then divides by the values you specify.
Make range from *value* to *value*	Transforms the data linearly so that the result has the first value you specify (−1 by default) as a minimum, and the second value you specify (+1 by default) as a maximum.

Note Using the session command CENTER, documented in Session Command Help, you can center and scale each column independently. When you use the dialog box, the standardizing method you select applies to all input columns.

Extracting Components of a Date/Time Column

You can extract one or more parts of a date/time column, such as the year, the quarter, or the hour, and save that data in either a numeric or a text column.

Choose the appropriate extract command depending on whether you want to save the extracted data in a numeric or a text column:

Calc ➤ Extract from Date/Time to Numeric saves the data in a numeric column

Calc ➤ Extract from Date/Time to Text saves the data in a text column

► **To extract one or more parts of a date/time column, saving data in a numeric column**

1 Choose **Calc ➤ Extract from Date/Time to Numeric**.

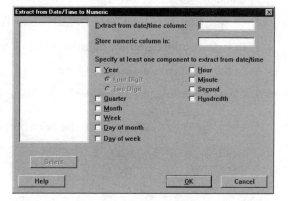

2 In **Extract from date/time column**, enter a date/time column.

3 In **Store numeric column in**, enter a storage column.

4 Check the components you want to extract, then click **OK**.

► **To extract one or more parts of a date/time column, saving data in a text column**

1 Choose **Calc ➤ Extract from Date/Time to Text**.

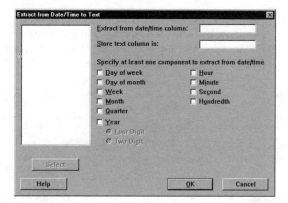

2 In **Extract from date/time column**, enter a date/time column.

3 In **Store text column in**, enter a storage column.

4 Check the components you want to extract, then click **OK**.

> ### Example of extracting parts of a date/time column

Suppose you want to create a new text column, QtrYr, from C1-D.

1 Open the worksheet DATES3.MTW.

2 Choose **Calc ➤ Extract from Date/Time to Text**.

3 In **Extract from date/time column**, enter *Date/Time*.

4 In **Store text column in**, type *QtrYr*.

5 Check **Quarter** and **Year**. Under **Year**, choose **Two Digit**. Click **OK**.

Data window output   The new QtrYr column appears in the worksheet as follows:

C1-D	C2-T
Date/Time	QtrYr
1/02/99	Q199
2/15/99	Q199
3/06/99	Q199
3/18/99	Q199
5/28/99	Q299
7/03/99	Q399

You could now use the new column QtrYr as a factor or grouping variable. You could also subset your data based on QtrYr; for example, you could copy all columns in your worksheet, using rows where QtrYr equals Q199.

Note | Formatting a date/time column, using **Editor ➤ Format Column ➤ Date/Time**, simply changes the way values display in the Data window. The values themselves are not changed. Extracting from a Date/Time column does change the values stored in the resulting text or numeric column.

8

Matrices

Matrices Overview

With MINITAB, you can create matrices and do matrix algebra and other matrix operations. Matrices are denoted by M1, M2, M3, … up to M100, or by a name you give them. You can store up to 100 matrices in the worksheet at one time. A worksheet column with n entries can be used as an n×1 matrix. A constant can be used as a 1×1 matrix. Several commands, including Regression, General Linear Model, Factor Analysis, and Cluster Analysis, can store matrices.

Matrices can only contain numeric data.

Creating a Matrix

You can create a matrix by:

- typing numbers at the keyboard
- entering values from columns or other matrices (see *Copying a Matrix* on page 8-6)
- opening a text file
- entering the same value for every cell
- setting values from a column into the diagonal of a matrix (and vice versa)

▶ **To create a matrix by typing values or entering values form a text file**

1 Choose **Calc ➤ Matrices ➤ Read**.

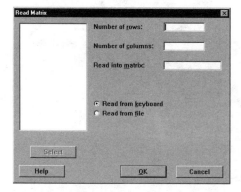

2 In **Number of rows**, enter the number of rows you want in the matrix. In **Number of columns**, enter the number of columns you want in the matrix.

3 In **Read into matrix**, enter a name or a matrix number (such as M1). Names can be up to 31 characters long. See *Naming a Matrix* on page 8-5 for other rules.

4 Do one of two things:

■ to type in data, simply click **OK**. You should now be at the DATA> prompt in the Session window where you can type in numbers.

Note If you do not see the DATA> prompt, you must enable the command language: Choose **Edit ➤ Preferences**. Click on **Session Window** to highlight it, then click **Select**. Under **Command Language**, choose **Enable**. Click **OK**.

Separate each number with a space. Each line you type corresponds to a row in the matrix. For example

Typing the numbers...	creates the matrix
DATA> 3 6 DATA> 2 9	$\begin{bmatrix} 3 & 6 \\ 2 & 9 \end{bmatrix}$

■ to enter data from a text file, choose **Read from file**. The Read Matrix From File dialog box will open.
  – In **Files of type**, choose **Text Files**.
  – In **Look in**, choose a different directory if necessary.
  – Highlight a text file, then click **OK**.

▶ **To create a matrix made up of all the same values**

1 Choose **Calc ➤ Matrices ➤ Define Constant**.

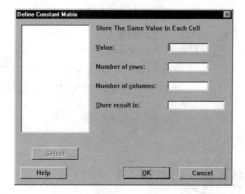

2 In **Value**, enter the number or stored constant which contains the number that you want to place in each matrix cell.

3 In **Number of rows**, enter the number of rows you want in the matrix. In **Number of columns**, enter the number of columns you want in the matrix.

4 In **Store result in**, enter a matrix name or number (such as M1). Names can be up to 31 characters long. See *Naming a Matrix* on page 8-5 for other rules. Click **OK**.

▶ **To create a matrix or column based on diagonal values**

When you create a matrix from a column of diagonal values, MINITAB places the values in the column on the diagonal, and zero's in all other cells. A square matrix is created.

When you create a column from a matrix, you must begin with a square matrix.

1   Choose **Calc ➤ Matrices ➤ Diagonal**.

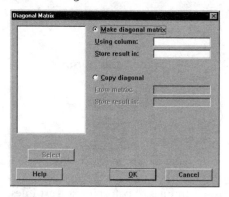

2   Do one of two things:

- to create a matrix from a column:
  - in **Using column**, enter the column to be used as the diagonal of the matrix.
  - in **Store result in**, enter a name or number for the matrix (such as M1). Names can be up to 31 characters long. See *Naming a Matrix* on page 8-5 for other rules. Click **OK**.

- to create a column from a matrix:
  - choose **Copy diagonal**.
  - in **From matrix**, enter a name or matrix number for a square matrix.
  - in **Store result in**, enter a storage column for the diagonal values, then click **OK**.

Displaying a Matrix

Matrices do not show in the Data window unless you copy them into columns. To see matrices, you need to display them in the Session window.

▶ **To see the contents of a matrix**

1 Choose **Manip ➤ Display Data**.

2 In **Columns, constants, and matrices to display**, enter one or more matrices, then click **OK**.

Tip │ The Matrices folder in the Project Manager gives the name, and the number of rows by number of columns, of matrices in the current worksheet.

Naming a Matrix

Matrix names can be up to 31 characters long. With a few exceptions, any character may be used:

- a name may not begin or end with a blank

- you can't use a single quote (') or an octothorpe (#) as part of a name

- you can't use the same name for two variables (columns, stored constants, or matrices) in the same worksheet

You can use both upper and lower case letters in a name. When you use the name in a MINITAB command, MINITAB considers upper and lower case letters equivalent. When a name is printed in the output, however, the upper and lower case letters are used.

▶ **To name or rename a matrix**

1 Open the Command Line Editor by choosing **Edit ➤ Command Line Editor**.

2 Type NAME, followed by the current name or number, followed by the equal sign, then the new name in single quotes, like this:

```
NAME M1='My Matrix'
```

3 Click **Submit Command**.

Erasing a Matrix

You can erase one or more matrices from the worksheet.

▶ **To erase matrices from the worksheet**

1 Choose **Manip ➤ Erase Variables**.

2 In **Columns, constants, and matrices to erase**, enter one or more matrices, then click **OK**.

Copying a Matrix

You can copy data from columns into a matrix, from a matrix into columns, or from one matrix to another matrix. Columns to be copied into a matrix must be the same length.

▶ **To copy to or from a matrix**

1 Choose **Calc ➤ Matrices ➤ Copy**.

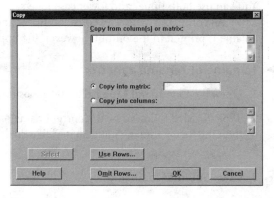

2 In **Copy from column(s) or matrix**, enter the columns or matrix you want to copy.

- In **Copy into matrix:**, enter a corresponding storage matrix name or number.

- In **Copy into columns:**, enter corresponding storage columns.

3 If you like, you can copy only rows that meet some criteria. The **Use Rows** and **Omit Rows** buttons work the same way here as they do with **Manip ➤ Copy Columns** (see *To use or omit selected rows* on page 2-13). Click **OK**.

Transposing a Matrix

You can transpose a matrix, that is, make rows into columns and columns into rows.

▶ To transpose a matrix

1 Choose **Calc ➤ Matrices ➤ Transpose**.

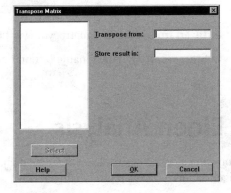

2 In **Transpose from**, enter the name or number of the matrix you want to transpose.

3 In **Store result in**, enter a matrix where you want to store the transposed data, then click **OK**.

Inverting a Matrix

You can invert a matrix, that is, compute its reciprocal.

▶ **To invert a matrix**

1 Choose **Calc ➤ Matrices ➤ Invert**.

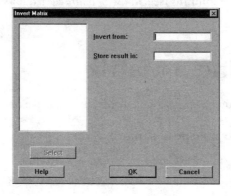

2 In **Invert from**, enter the matrix you want to invert.

3 In **Store result in**, enter a name or number for the storage matrix, then click **OK**.

Doing an Eigen Analysis

You can calculate eigenvalues (also called characteristic values, or latent roots) and eigenvectors for a symmetric matrix.

The eigenvalues will be stored in decreasing order of magnitude down a column.

▶ **To calculate eigenvalues and eigenvectors**

1 Choose **Calc ➤ Matrices ➤ Eigen Analysis**.

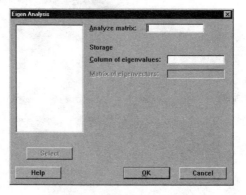

2 In **Analyze matrix**, enter a symmetric matrix to be evaluated.

3 In **Column of eigenvalues**, enter a storage column, then click **OK**.

Options

- store the eigenvectors as columns of a matrix. The first column corresponds to the first eigenvalue (largest in magnitude), the second column to the second eigenvalue, and so on.

Matrix Arithmetic

You can perform arithmetic on any combination of columns, constants, or matrices.

▶ To do matrix arithmetic

1 Choose **Calc** ➤ **Matrices** ➤ **Arithmetic**.

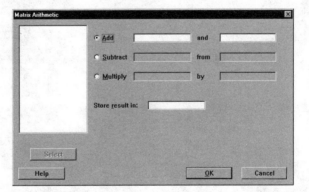

2 Choose **Add**, **Subtract**, or **Multiply**.

3 Enter two variables for the operation. These can be any combination of columns, constants, and matrices. For example, in the first **Add** box, you could enter the column C1; in the second **Add** box you could enter the matrix M1.

4 In **Store result in**, enter a storage column, constant, or matrix, whichever is appropriate. Click **OK**.

▷ **Example of matrix arithmetic**

Here are some examples of matrix arithmetic.

Note | Matrices do not show in the worksheet. To display them, choose **Manip ➤ Display Data** (see page 8-4).

	First variable	**2nd variable**	**Store result in**
Add	5	M1	M4
		$\begin{bmatrix} 1 & 2 & 3 \\ 0 & 1 & 1 \end{bmatrix}$	$\begin{bmatrix} 6 & 7 & 8 \\ 5 & 6 & 6 \end{bmatrix}$
Subtract	M2	M1	M5
	$\begin{bmatrix} 3 & 1 & 1 \\ 2 & 0 & 1 \end{bmatrix}$	$\begin{bmatrix} 1 & 2 & 3 \\ 0 & 1 & 1 \end{bmatrix}$	$\begin{bmatrix} -2 & 1 & 2 \\ -2 & 1 & 0 \end{bmatrix}$

9

Random Data and Probability Distributions

Random Data and Probability Distributions Overview

Use the commands in this chapter to obtain random samples, generate random data, and calculate probabilities for different distributions.

- **Set Base** lets you set a starting point for MINITAB's random number generator, so you can select the same random sample, or generate the same set of random data more than once—see *Setting a Starting Point for Generating or Sampling Random Data* below.

- **Random Data** can be used two ways:
  - to randomly sample rows from one or more columns in your worksheet—see *Selecting a Random Sample* on page 9-3
  - to generate random data from 19 different distributions—see *Generating Random Data* on page 9-4

- **Probability Distributions** lets you calculate the values of a probability density function (pdf), cumulative probabilities, or inverse cumulative probabilities of your data for 19 different distributions—see *Calculating Probabilities for Different Distributions* on page 9-7.

  You can also use this command to:
  - calculate a critical value for a hypothesis test, rather than looking it up in a table—see *Calculating a Critical Value for a Hypothesis Test* on page 9-11
  - calculate a p-value for a hypothesis test—see *Calculating a p-Value for a Hypothesis Test* on page 9-11.

Setting a Starting Point for Generating or Sampling Random Data

You can set a starting point for MINITAB's random number generator. This is useful when you want to select the same random sample, or generate the same set of random data more than once.

MINITAB has a long string of "random" numbers available. If MINITAB always started at the beginning of the list, you would always get the same data. To avoid this, MINITAB uses the time of day (in seconds or fractions of a second) to choose a "random" starting point in the string.

Setting a base tells the random number generator where to start. The generator will continue reading from the point where it left off unless a new base is specified. To generate the identical set of random numbers time after time, set the same base each time you select a random sample, or generate random data.

Note | If you use the same base on a different computer, you may not get the same random
         | number sequence.

▶ **To set a starting point for MINITAB's random number generator**

1 Choose **Calc ➤ Set Base**.

2 In **Set base of random data generator to**, enter a number to use as the base for the random number sequence. Click **OK**.

More | You can use the session command BASE, documented in Session Command Help, to find
         | out the current base value. Simply type BASE on the command line (without arguments).
         | MINITAB will print the base value in the Session window.

Selecting a Random Sample

You can randomly sample rows from one or more columns.

▶ **To select a random sample**

1 Choose **Calc ➤ Random Data ➤ Sample From Columns**.

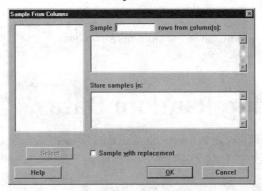

2 In **Sample**, enter the number of rows you want to sample.

3 In the box following **rows from column(s)**, enter equal-length columns from which to sample from.

4 In **Store samples in**, enter the columns in which you want to store the sample data. Click **OK**.

Options

- sample with or without replacement. By default, MINITAB samples *without replacement*, which means that the same row is not selected more than once. When you choose to sample *with replacement*, the same row can be selected more than once.

▷ Example of selecting a random sample

To select a random sample of five observations from nine rows of data, as shown:

ID	Weight		IDSample	WeightSample
1	45		2	65
2	65		9	50
3	54	→	3	54
4	67		8	41
5	65		6	88
6	88			
7	58			
8	41			
9	50			

1 Type the first two columns of data into the worksheet, naming them 'ID' and 'Weight,' as shown.

2 Choose **Calc ➤ Random Data ➤ Sample From Columns**.

3 In **Sample**, enter 5. In **rows from column(s)**, enter *ID Weight*.

4 In **Store samples in**, enter *ID Sample WeightSample*, then click **OK**.

Note | If you try this example, you will get different sampled data than shown in the table above because sampling is done randomly. Use **Calc ➤ Set Base** (page 9-2) to generate the same random sample more than once.

Generating Random Data

You can generate random data from 19 different distributions. You can use Set Base (see page 9-2) to generate the same set of data more than once.

▶ **To generate random data**

1 Choose **Calc ➤ Random Data ➤ [distribution name]**. The dialog box varies with the distribution chosen.

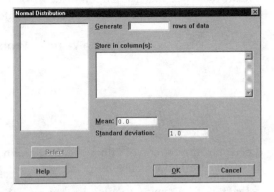

2 In **Generate__rows of data**, enter the number of rows you want to generate.

3 In **Store in column(s)**, enter the column(s) in which you want to store the data.

4 Enter the required parameters. These vary from one distribution to another. In the dialog box shown (Normal Distribution), the parameters are **Mean** and **Standard deviation**. Click **OK**.

Distributions

For the probability functions associated with each distribution, see Help.

Chi-Square Enter the degrees of freedom.

Normal Enter the mean (0 by default), and the standard deviation (1 by default).

F Enter the numerator degrees of freedom, and the denominator degrees of freedom.

T Enter the degrees of freedom.

Uniform Enter the lower endpoint (0 by default), and the upper endpoint (1 by default). MINITAB generates data from a uniform distribution that ranges from the lower endpoint to the upper endpoint.

Bernoulli Enter the probability of success. Suppose you enter a probability of success of 0.2. The new column will contain 1's (for success) with a probability of 0.2, and 0's (for failure) with a probability of 0.8.

Binomial Enter the number of trials and the probability of success.

Hypergeometric Enter the total number of items in the population, the number of successes in the population, and the number of samples.

Discrete A discrete distribution is one you define yourself. Before generating the random data, you must put the values you want included in the distribution and their corresponding probabilities into two columns in the worksheet. For example, suppose you are interested in a distribution made up of three values −1, 0, 1, with probabilities of 0.2, 0.5, and 0.3, respectively. Enter these values into the worksheet:

Value	Prob
−1	0.2
0	0.5
0	0.3

Then enter the column of values and the column of corresponding probabilities in the Discrete Distribution dialog box.

Integer Enter a minimum integer value and a maximum integer value. MINITAB generates data from a discrete uniform distribution that ranges from the minimum to the maximum integer value. Each integer in the range has equal probability.

Poisson Enter the mean, which must be greater than 0 and less than or equal to 709.

Beta Enter the first shape parameter, and the second shape parameter.

Cauchy Enter the location (0 by default), and the scale (1 by default).

Exponential Enter the mean (1 by default).

Gamma Enter the first shape parameter, and the second shape parameter.

Laplace Enter the location (0 by default), and the scale (1 by default). The Laplace distribution is also called the double exponential distribution.

Logistic Enter the location (0 by default), and the scale (1 by default).

Lognormal Enter the location (0 by default), and the scale (1 by default). A variable x has a lognormal distribution if log(x) has a normal distribution with mean equal to the value of the location, and standard deviation equal to the value of the scale.

Weibull Enter the shape parameter, and the scale parameter.

For more information on these distributions, see Help.

Calculating Probabilities for Different Distributions

You can calculate values for probability density functions, cumulative probabilities, or inverse cumulative probabilities of your data, for the distribution you choose from the menu.

■ The *probability density function* (pdf) is the curve for the distribution.

  For example, a pdf can describe the distribution of tree diameters in a young forest.

■ The *cumulative distribution function* (cdf) for any value x gives the cumulative probability associated with a probability distribution function. Specifically, a cdf gives the cumulative area under the pdf, up to the value you specify.

  For example, a cdf can tell you the proportion of trees in the young forest that are at least ten inches in diameter.

■ The *inverse cumulative probability* is the value associated with an area. It is the reverse of the cdf, which is the area associated with a value. For example, an inverse cumulative probability can tell you the width of 75% of the trees.

  Here is a visualization of these concepts:

Use **pdf** when you know x and want the corresponding y value on the curve.

Use **cdf** when you know x and want the area under the curve.

Use **inverse cdf** when you know the cumulative area under the curve and want the x value.

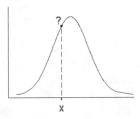 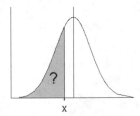 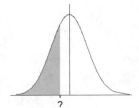

For discrete distributions (binomial, Poisson, integer, and discrete), MINITAB calculates the discrete probability function. For continuous distributions, such as the normal distribution, MINITAB calculates the continuous probability density function (often called the density function).

If you do not store the results, MINITAB displays them in the Session window. If you store the results in a column, you can see them by looking at the column in the Data window. If you store the probability in a constant, such as K2, you can see it in the Constants folder in the Project Manager window, or by printing them to the Session window using **Manip ➤ Display Data** (page 6-45).

▶ **To calculate the pdf, cdf, or inverse cdf**

1 Choose **Calc ➤ Probability Distributions ➤ distribution name**.

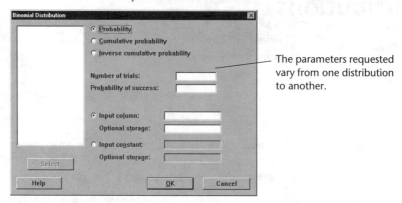

The parameters requested vary from one distribution to another.

2 Do one of the following:

- calculate the pdf—choose **Probability**

- calculate the cdf—choose **Cumulative probability**

- calculate the inverse cdf—choose **Inverse cumulative probability**

3 Enter the required parameters. These vary from one distribution to another. In the dialog box shown (Binomial Distribution), the parameters are **Number of trials** and **Probability of success**.

4 Do one of the following:

- In **Input column**, enter the column you want to evaluate. If you like, in **Optional storage**, enter a column in which to store the probabilities.

- In **Input constant**, enter the stored constant (such as K1) or number (such as 21) that you want to evaluate. If you like, in **Optional storage**, enter a constant (such as K2) in which to store the probability.

5 Click **OK**.

▷ **Example of using the probability density function (pdf)**

Suppose you bought four batteries. The package states that 95% of the batteries last at least 100 hours. If this is true, what are the chances that all four of the batteries will last at least 100 hours? That three will last that long? That none will last that long?

This is a binomial problem because two outcomes exist for each battery: the battery lasts more than 100 hours, or it does not.

1 Type the numbers 1, 2, 3, and 4 (for each of the four batteries) into a worksheet column named 'Data.'

2 Choose **Calc ➤ Probability Distributions ➤ Binomial**.

3 Choose **Probability**.

4 In **Number of trials**, enter *4*. In **Probability of success**, enter *0.95*.

5 Choose **Input column** and enter *Data*. Click **OK**.

Session window output

Probability Density Function

Binomial with n = 4 and p = 0.950000

x	P(X = x)
0.00	0.0000
1.00	0.0005
2.00	0.0135
3.00	0.1715
4.00	0.8145

Interpreting the results

The probability that all four of the batteries will last at least 100 hours is 0.8145, and the probability that only three will last that long is 0.1715. The probability that none will last that long is 0.

➤ Example of computing the cumulative probability (cdf)

Suppose you want to compute a cumulative probability for the value 27 from a normal distribution with $\mu = 28$ and $\sigma = 1$.

You are looking for the area under the curve up to 27, as shown:

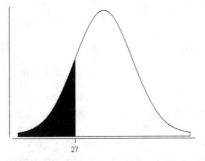

27

1 Choose **Calc ➤ Probability Distributions ➤ Normal**.

2 Choose **Cumulative probability**.

3 In **Mean**, enter *28*. In **Standard deviation**, enter *1*.

4 Choose **Input constant** and enter *27*. Click **OK**.

*Session
window
output*

Cumulative Distribution Function

Normal with mean = 28.0000 and standard deviation = 1.00000

```
        x      P( X <= x)
   27.0000        0.1587
```

Interpreting the results

The cdf for 27 is 0.1587. This value gives the area under the normal curve up to 27, shown in black.

▷ **Example of computing the inverse cumulative probability**

In the preceding example, you found the cdf for 27 (the area under the normal curve up to 27) to be 0.1587. Suppose you want to compute the inverse cumulative probability for 0.1587 from the same distribution. This value should be 27.

1 Choose **Calc ➤ Probability Distributions ➤ Normal**.

2 Choose **Inverse cumulative probability**.

3 In **Mean**, enter 28. In **Standard deviation**, enter *1*.

4 Choose **Input constant** and enter *0.1587*, then click **OK**.

*Session
window
output*

Inverse Cumulative Distribution Function

Normal with mean = 28.0000 and standard deviation = 1.00000
```
  P( X <= x)        x
     0.1587    27.0002
```

Interpreting the results

The inverse cumulative probability for 0.1587 is 27.002.

Conversely, as shown in the previous example, the cumulative probability for 27 is 0.1587. The difference of 0.0002 is due to roundoff error.

Why the inverse cumulative probability may not exist or may not be unique

For all continuous distributions handled by **Inverse cumulative probability** (inverse cdf), the inverse of the cumulative distribution function exists and is unique if $0 < p < 1$. If a density is positive over the entire real line (for example, normal), inverse cdf is not defined for either $p = 0$ or $p = 1$. If a density is positive for all values greater than some value (for example, gamma), inverse cdf is defined for $p = 0$ but not for $p = 1$. If a density is positive only on an interval (for example, beta), inverse cdf is defined for $p = 0$ and $p = 1$. Whenever inverse cdf is not defined, MINITAB returns a missing value (*) as the result.

For discrete distributions, the situation is more complicated. Suppose we compute the cdf for a binomial with n = 5 and p = 0.4. In that case, there is no value x such that the cdf is 0.5. For x = 1, the cdf is 0.3370; for x = 2, the cdf jumps up to 0.6826. If the inverse cdf is being displayed in the Session window (i.e., results are not stored), both values of x are displayed. If the inverse cdf is stored, the larger of the two values is stored.

Calculating a Critical Value for a Hypothesis Test

You can use MINITAB to calculate a critical value for a hypothesis test instead of looking in a table in a book.

▶ Example of calculating a critical value for a χ^2 test

Suppose you want to do a χ^2 test with $\alpha = 0.02$ and 12 degrees of freedom. What is the corresponding critical value? An α of 0.02 corresponds to a cumulative probability value of $1 - 0.02 = 0.98$.

1 Choose **Calc ➤ Probability Distributions ➤ Chi-Square**.

2 Choose **Inverse cumulative probability**. In **Degrees of freedom**, enter *12*.

3 Choose **Input constant** and enter *0.98*. Click **OK**.

Session window output

Inverse Cumulative Distribution Function

```
Chi-Square with 12 DF
  P( X <= x)          x
     0.9800     24.0540
```

Interpreting the results

MINITAB displays the critical value, 24.054, in the Session window. For the χ^2 test, if the test statistic is greater than the critical value, 24.054 in our case, you can conclude there is statistical evidence to reject the null hypothesis.

Calculating a p-Value for a Hypothesis Test

p-values are often used in hypothesis tests where you either accept or reject a null hypothesis. The p-value represents the probability of making a Type 1 error, or rejecting the null hypothesis when it is true. The smaller the p-value, the smaller is the probability that you would be making a mistake by rejecting the null hypothesis. A cutoff value often used is 0.05, that is, reject the null hypothesis when the p-value is less than 0.05.

MINITAB automatically displays p-values for most hypothesis tests. But you can also use MINITAB to "manually" compute a p-value.

▶ Example of calculating a p-value for an F-test

Suppose you perform a multiple regression analysis with the following degrees of freedom: df (Regression) = 3; df (Error) = 2; and the F statistic = 4.86. Now you want to calculate a p-value for the F-test.

First you calculate the cumulative distribution function (cdf). The p-value is 1 − cdf.

1 Choose **Calc ➤ Probability Distributions ➤ F**.

2 Choose **Cumulative probability**.

3 In **Numerator degrees of freedom**, enter 3. In **Denominator degrees of freedom**, enter 2.

4 Choose **Input constant** and enter 4.86.

5 In **Optional storage**, enter *K1*. Click **OK**.

K1 contains the cumulative distribution function. Now you will use the Calculator to subtract the p-value from 1.

6 Choose **Calc ➤ Calculator**.

7 In **Store result in variable**, enter *P-value*.

8 In **Expression**, enter *1−K1*. Click **OK**.

Interpreting the results

The calculated p-value, as shown in the Data window, is 0.175369. Using the 0.05 cutoff value, you would not conclude statistical significance since 0.175 is not less than 0.05.

10

Using Dynamic Data Exchange (DDE)

DDE Overview

Dynamic Data Exchange (DDE) allows you to automatically transfer data between MINITAB for Windows and other applications that support DDE. Whenever data changes in one application, it can be automatically updated in the other application.

MINITAB can send data, receive it, or send and receive at the same time. MINITAB can also send data to itself. In particular, DDE allows you to

- extract data from another program, perform statistical analyses in MINITAB, then pass the data back into a different location in the same program

- link one or more columns in MINITAB to one or more other columns in MINITAB. Among other things, this allows you to automatically recalculate a column (or columns) when data in other columns change.

- "remote control" other Windows applications by sending commands from MINITAB

- collect information from a measuring device that is connected to your computer

In MINITAB, data can only be linked to and from columns in a Data window. You cannot link to and from matrices or constants.

Each Data window contains its own set of links. Those links are saved with the Data window when you save a project, or when you save the worksheet into a separate file. If you create a link to a Data window, then change the name of the Data window, you may break the link.

Terminology: clients and servers

A DDE link consists of a client application and a server application. You create the link in the client. The link asks the server for data, then accepts data from the server whenever the data in the server change. The flow of data between two DDE applications looks as follows:

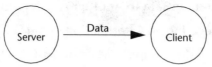

Some applications can only be DDE clients, some only servers, and some can be both. MINITAB can function as a client, a server, or both at once.

Note | The DDE dialog boxes do not generate command language in the Session window as other MINITAB dialog boxes do. If you want to perform DDE actions from the command prompt or in a macro, you can use the DDE session commands described in Session command Help.

Copying and Pasting a Link

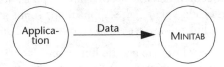

You can quickly create a DDE link that lets MINITAB receive outside data—just copy data in one application and paste the link into a MINITAB Data window. This creates a "hot link": every time the data change in the original application, the linked data will change in MINITAB.

▶ **To copy and paste a link**

1 In the other application, select the data that you want to exchange and copy it to the Clipboard.

If you cannot copy data to the Clipboard in the other application, use the method described in *Creating a Link with the Manage Links Command* below.

2 In one of MINITAB's Data windows, click in the column where you want the data to go. If you do not click on a column, MINITAB will place the linked data at the beginning of the column containing the active cell.

3 Choose **Edit ➤ Paste Link**.

If Paste Link is dimmed, the other application does not support copying and pasting of links.

After the linked data is pasted into the Data window, you can edit the link as described in *Changing a Link* on page 10-5.

DDE links are saved when you save a MINITAB project or worksheet. When you open a worksheet that contains DDE links, MINITAB attempts to reestablish the saved links.

Creating a Link with the Manage Links Command

You can establish a new DDE link that lets MINITAB receive data from another application. The Manage Links dialog box and subdialog boxes let you control various aspects of a link.

▶ **To create a link**

1 Find out the full link name for the part of application you want to link to. There are three parts of a link name: the Application, Topic, and Item. For definitions and examples of link names, see *Applications, Topics, and Items* on page 10-6.

There are several ways to get the link name:

– Copy a link to the clipboard—the link information will appear automatically in step 5 below. To copy a link, follow step 1 of *Copying and Pasting a Link* on page 10-3.

– Consult the documentation for that application.

– Copy from examples of some common links. See *Examples of link names for other applications* on page 10-7.

2 Choose which Data window should contain the link, and make that window active.

3 Choose **Edit ➤ Links ➤ Manage Links**.

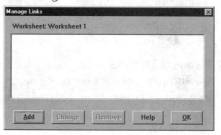

4 Click **Add**.

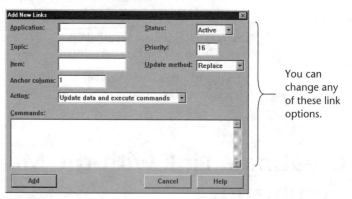

You can change any of these link options.

5 Specify an **Application**, **Topic**, and **Item**.

If you copied a link to the clipboard in step 1, these are filled in for you. You can edit them. For definitions of these terms and examples, see *Applications, Topics, and Items* on page 10-6.

6 Change any of the link options. See *Changing Link Options* on page 10-8.

7 Click **Add**. Then in the Manage Links dialog box, click **OK**.

DDE links are saved when you save a MINITAB worksheet. When you open a worksheet that contains DDE links, MINITAB attempts to reestablish the saved links.

Changing a Link

▶ **To change a link**

1 Make the desired Data window active (each Data window contains its own set of links).

2 Choose **Edit ▶ Links ▶ Manage Links**.

All available
links are shown
here. Click a
link to select it.

3 Select the desired link.

4 Click **Change**.

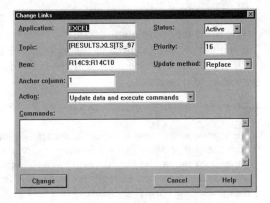

5 Change the **Application**, **Topic**, or **Item**. See *Applications, Topics, and Items* on page 10-6.

6 Change any of the link options. See *Changing Link Options* on page 10-8.

7 Click **Change**. In the Manage Links dialog box, click **OK**.

Applications, Topics, and Items

To establish a link, MINITAB (or the other application) must know the full link name. The link name has three parts: Application, Topic, and Item.

Application

Application is the name of a program that can participate in a DDE transaction. Usually, **Application** is the name of an .EXE file that starts the program, minus the .EXE extension. For example, in the case of MINITAB, MINITAB.EXE starts the program, so for the **Application** is MINITAB.

Topic

Topic is a name that depends on the type of application. In applications that use documents or data files, the topic is often the name of the file. For example, the **Topic** for a Microsoft Word document might be *mywork.doc*. The file name can also include a path, as in *c:\mywork\mywork.doc*.

If one file can contain many documents or subwindows, the **Topic** can be the name of the file in brackets, followed by the name of the document or window. For example, MINITAB projects can contain many Data windows, so a typical **Topic** would be *[minitab] worksheet 1*.

Other applications have their own names for topics.

Tip | It is a good idea to save files from other applications before establishing any links to or from them. If you establish a link before saving the file, you may need to change the link name from something like "untitled" to a file name. Likewise, before linking from MINITAB, rename a new Data window from the default of "Worksheet 1" to something meaningful, such as "First Quarter."

Item

Item is a name that depends on the type of application. In MINITAB, the item always specifies a row/column location or rectangular area in the form R4C1:R4C2. You can use all of MINITAB column 1 as an item by specifying C1. A single cell (row 4, column 1) is R4C1. Most spreadsheets use close variants of the R4C1:R3C2 format for items.

Examples of link names for other applications

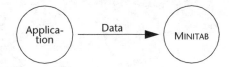

Program	Application	Topic	Item	Explanation
Lotus 1-2-3	123w	C:\123W\RESULT.WK3	A:A1..A:D50	In the file RESULT.WK3, get columns A through D, using rows 1 through 50
Microsoft Access	MSACCESS	mydata;QUERY totals	DATA	In the database named mydata, get the data from the query named "totals"
Microsoft Access	MSACCESS	mydata;TABLE Inventory	DATA	In the database named mydata, get the data from the table named "Inventory"
Microsoft Excel	excel	[RESULTS.XLS]FIRST QUARTER	R1C1:R50C4	In the workbook file RESULT.XLS, in the sheet named "First Quarter," get columns A through D, using rows 1 through 50
SPSS	SPSSWIN	!DATA	[Age Name 1 50]	Columns "Age" through "Name" using rows 1 through 50

Examples of MINITAB link names

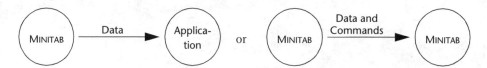

When you define MINITAB as a server from another application, specify the link name in one of the following formats. The examples assume that the project file is named "myproj.mpj," and the worksheet has the default title of "Worksheet 1":

Application	Topic	Item	Explanation
minitab	[myproj.mpj] worksheet 1	C1	retrieves all data for column 1
minitab	[myproj.mpj] worksheet 1	C1:C3	retrieves all data in columns C1–C3
minitab	[myproj.mpj] worksheet 1	R1C1	retrieves the contents of row 1, column 1
minitab	[myproj.mpj] worksheet 1	R1C1:R5C2	retrieves values from row 1 to row 5 in columns 1 and 2
minitab	system	(one MINITAB command)	executes the specified command. The command can be a macro invocation.

Note | You cannot use MINITAB column names (such as "results" or "test1") to specify the ranges. You also cannot link to matrices or constants.

Changing Link Options

▶ **To change link options**

1 Choose **Edit ➤ Links ➤ Manage Links**.

2 Click **Add** or **Change**.

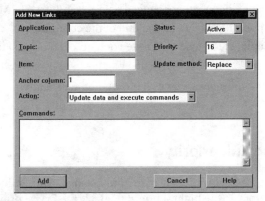

3 Specify an **Application**, **Topic**, and **Item**, described under *Applications, Topics, and Items* on page 10-6.

4 If you like, change any of the options, then click **Add** or **Change**.

5 In the Manage Links dialog box, click **OK**.

Options

- Change **Status** to resume or pause a link's activity:
  - Choose **Active** to make the link start receiving data from the other application immediately.
  - Choose **Inactive** to make the link stop receiving data until you activate. When you deactivate a link, MINITAB ignores/discards any queued transactions or incoming transactions until you reactivate the link.

More | You can also pause all DDE activity. See *Globally Stopping/Starting DDE Transactions* on page 10-14.

- Change the **Priority** of the link. See *Changing link priority* on page 10-10.

- In **Action**, choose the action that you want MINITAB to perform after each data transfer from the server application:
  - **Update data and execute commands**
  - **Update data only**
  - **Execute commands only**

  For details on executing commands, see *DDE links that execute commands* on page 10-10.

- Change the **Anchor column**. Specify the column number where you want the data to start. You only need to specify the starting column; if the **Item** references more than one column of data, other columns are inserted after the anchor column.

- Change the **Update method**. Choose one of the following to determine what happens when new or changed data is transferred to MINITAB:
  - **Append:** Add data to the end of the column(s).
  - **Replace:** Replace the entire contents of column(s) in the Data window with new data from the item you specify.
- Enter **Commands** that execute when the data are updated. See *DDE links that execute commands* on page 10-10.

Changing link priority

You can specify the priority of the link relative to other links. The priority can be any integer from 1 (the highest priority), to 32 (the lowest priority). Priority matters when you have more than one link attempting a transfer at the same time, or have several queued transactions waiting for processing. MINITAB always completes transfers on links with higher priority first, then processes data from links with lower priority. Links with the same priority are transferred on a first-in first-out basis. The default priority is 16.

▶ **To change the link priority**

1 In the Change Links or Add Links dialog box, in **Priority**, enter an integer from 1 (the highest priority), to 32 (the lowest priority).

DDE links that execute commands

You can enter commands you want MINITAB to execute every time data is transferred from the other application.

▶ **To specify commands that execute when a link updates**

1 In the Change Links or Add Links dialog box, choose an **Action** of **Update data and execute commands** or **Execute commands only**.

2 Type one or more MINITAB commands, subcommands, or %macros. Use semicolons (;) to follow a command or subcommand with another subcommand. Use periods (.) at the end of the last command or subcommand.

   Enter up to 128 characters (without line breaks). If your sequence of commands exceeds 128 characters, create a macro containing these commands (see Chapter 28, *Introducing Simple Macros*) and invoke the macro in the Commands text box. For example, entering *%mymacro* launches a macro that can contain hundreds of lines of code.

Tip | Copy and paste recently used session commands from the History folder in the Project Manager. Press [Ctrl]+[C] to copy and press [Ctrl]+[V] to paste.

Removing a Link

When a link is deleted, all existing queued requests are processed (that is, transferred into the worksheet), but no new requests are added. Requests may be queued because of an interruption or error. See *Troubleshooting DDE* on page 10-15.

▶ **To remove a link**

1 Choose **Edit ➤ Links ➤ Manage Links**.

2 Highlight the desired link.

3 Click **Remove**.

Performing a One-Time Data Transfer

A one-time data transfer, also called a "cold link," lets you bring data into MINITAB that will not be automatically updated when the original data change.

Tip | For a one-time data transfer, it is often easier to copy and paste the data normally, rather than pasting a DDE link.

▶ **To perform a one-time transfer**

1 Choose **Edit ➤ Links ➤ Get External Data**.

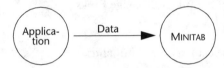

2 In **Application**, **Topic**, and **Item**, type the full DDE link name. For definitions and examples, see *Applications, Topics, and Items* on page 10-6.

3 If you wish, change the **Anchor column** and **Update method**. For details, see *Changing Link Options* on page 10-8.

Recalculating MINITAB Columns Automatically

You can set up links so that a MINITAB column automatically recalculates when the values in one or more other MINITAB columns change. The columns can be in the same Data window or in different Data windows.

▶ **To link columns**

1 In a Data window, select the server columns.

2 Chose which Data window will contain the client column and make that window active.

3 Choose **Edit ➤ Links ➤ Manage Links**.

4 Click **Add**.

5 In **Action**, select **Execute commands only**.

6 In **Commands**, type the commands to perform the recalculation. For example, if you want C2 to equal 4 times C1, you could enter the command *LET C2 = 4 * C1*.

7 Click **Add**. Then in the Manage Links dialog box, click **OK**.

▶ **Example of creating a totals column**

You can set up a column that depends on several columns, and recalculates whenever any of those columns change. For example, say you want the column C4, named "Totals", to be the sum of C1, C2, and C3. You want the total in C4 to update automatically that updates whenever C1, C2, *or* C3 change.

1 In the Data window, select C1 through C3 by dragging across the column headers.

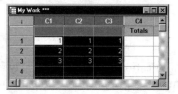

2 Choose **Edit ➤ Copy Cells**.

3 Choose **Edit ➤ Links ➤ Manage Links**.

4 Click **Add**.

5 In **Action**, select **Execute commands only**.

6 In **Commands**, type LET 'Totals' = C1 + C2 + C3.

7 Click **Add**. Then in the Manage Links dialog box, click **OK**.

The totals appear in C4. Now, every time one of the values in C1, C2, or C3 change, C4 will display a new total.

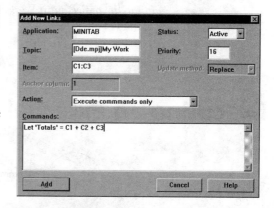

Sending Data to Another Application

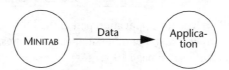

If the other application can accept DDE links, you can usually copy and paste a link from MINITAB. The application may also have DDE commands that create and modify links. To modify a link in which MINITAB is sending data to another application, use that application's DDE commands—you cannot modify the link from MINITAB.

▶ **To copy and paste a link**

1 In MINITAB, highlight cells in the Data window and choose **Edit ➤ Copy Cells**.

2 In the other application, choose the paste link command, usually **Edit ➤ Paste Link** or **Edit ➤ Paste Special**.

▶ **To create a link using the other application's DDE commands**

The application may have its own DDE commands that let you set up a link. The DDE commands may require you to use MINITAB's link name. A link name has three parts: an application, a topic, and an item. A typical MINITAB link name might be *minitab [myproject.mpj] Worksheet 1 c1.* For definitions of the parts of a link, and for examples of other legal MINITAB link names, see *Applications, Topics, and Items* on page 10-6.

Executing an External Command

Using DDE, you can execute a command in a remote application. For example, from a MINITAB session you could open a Microsoft Word file, run an Excel macro, or close WordPerfect.

▶ **To execute an external command**

1 Choose **Edit ➤ Links ➤ Execute External Command**.

2 In **Application**, type the application part of the DDE link name. For example, *excel* refers to Microsoft Excel. For other application names, see *Examples of link names for other applications* on page 10-7.

3 In **Command**, type a command in the application's command language—see that application's documentation for details. For example, if Microsoft Excel is running, and the macro sheet MACRO1.XLM is in a window, the command *[RUN("MACRO1.XLM!Record1",FALSE)]* starts the macro.

Globally Stopping/Starting DDE Transactions

You may have times when you want to suspend processing of DDE transactions. For example, you may want to analyze the data already in the worksheet without further DDE updates. Also, when many data transfers are occurring, temporarily stopping DDE transactions can improve the performance time of an analysis

Warning | While links are globally stopped, MINITAB *discards* any incoming data for client links. If you append data rather than replacing it, you can easily lose incoming data while a link is stopped.

▶ **To stop/start DDE transactions**

1 Choose **Edit ➤ Preferences**.

2 Select **DDE Links**.

3 In the MINITAB **as Client** group, do one of the following:

   ■ To stop MINITAB from responding to DDE requests, select **Ignore external data updates**

   ■ To resume, select **Process external data updates**

4 In the MINITAB **as Server** group, do one of the following:

   ■ To stop MINITAB from sending out updates, select **Ignore external requests**

   ■ To resume, select **Process external requests**

5 Click **OK** in each dialog box.

Troubleshooting DDE

Data is not updated

The following conditions cause MINITAB to stop updates and queue incoming data from DDE links:

■ Input is unresolved in the Session or Data windows, such as partially typed commands or data values.

■ Other commands or macros are executing.

■ The name of the Data window has changed, so the link is not valid.

MINITAB transfers any queued data after these conditions end.

A link for this server-topic-item already exists

Each link name (the combination of application, topic, and item names) must be unique. For example, you cannot have two links that each have the name *excel [mydata.xls] mysheet R1C1:R20C2*.

Change the new link to make it unique, or remove the original link.

There seems to be a circular reference for your DDE links

Circular links can only occur when MINITAB is simultaneously receiving and sending DDE data, and when the data being received directly or indirectly refers to the data being sent. Circular links can loop indefinitely and tie up system resources.

Sometimes a link that triggers a circular link error message is not really circular. For more information on fine-tuning DDE link timing to avoid the error message, see *To break a circular link* below.

▶ To break a circular link

1 If you know the link is circular, stop the updating by pressing [Ctrl]+[Pause] or [Ctrl]+[Break].

2 After several identical updates, MINITAB may identify the link as circular. When MINITAB encounters what looks like a circular link, MINITAB asks you if you want to ignore external requests and updates:

- Click **Yes** to stop the current DDE transaction and change your MINITAB preferences to ignore DDE updates and requests. All DDE transactions will be turned off until you change your DDE preferences to process updates and requests—see *Globally Stopping/Starting DDE Transactions* on page 10-14.

- Click **No** to stop the current DDE transaction.

3 Either remove the link (see *Removing a Link* on page 10-11) or change the anchor column to make it non-circular (see *Changing Link Options* on page 10-8).

DDE is slow

MINITAB is a robust DDE server, suitable for use over a wide range of applications. However, several factors outside MINITAB may limit DDE performance including:

- the general performance of DDE in Windows

- the memory limitations and general performance of your machine

- the number and size of other applications you have running

- the performance of DDE in other applications

MINITAB queues transfers that it can not process immediately. MINITAB then processes queued transfers in priority order as soon as possible.

If you need to improve DDE performance, consider the following:

- read and follow the suggestions in the *enhancing performance* topic in Help to increase the performance of your machine in general

- prioritize your most important DDE updates using the **Priority** field in the Manage Links dialog box (see page 10-9)

- use or upgrade to a more powerful machine to run the applications

part III

Managing the Session Window and Generating Reports

11

Using the Session Window

Using the Session Window Overview

The Session window displays the text output generated by your analyses and other work.

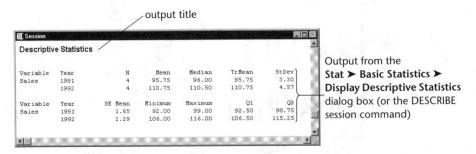

output title

Output from the
**Stat ➤ Basic Statistics ➤
Display Descriptive Statistics**
dialog box (or the DESCRIBE
session command)

Editing and formatting

You can edit and format text as you would in a word processor: add comments, cut, copy, and paste, change fonts, or find and replace numbers and text. For details, see the sections in this chapter.

Printing, saving, and generating reports

You can save and print Session window text. You also can create reports by combining Session window text and MINITAB graphs in the Project manager Report folder or in a word processor. See Chapter 12, *Saving, Printing, and Generating Reports*.

Displaying and using session commands

You can display the command language used to create the output, and type session commands in at the active MTB> prompt.

Command language is generated when you use most menus and dialog boxes (called *menu commands*), and when you type command language directly in the Command Line Editor or the Session window (called *session commands*). You can intersperse menu commands and session commands, or just use one or the other, as you prefer.

For details on turning these options on, see *Enabling and Disabling Command Language* on page 11-5. For more information on session commands, see Chapter 27, *Using Session Commands*.

Note   Whether or not commands are displayed in the Session window, the History folder always records all commands executed in your session. For more information on the History folder, see *Meet the History Folder* on page 27-5.

Selecting Text

As well as the standard ways to select text in a Windows environment (such as dragging the mouse or using ⎡Shift⎤ + a navigation key), the Session window offers three other methods that you may find useful:

To Select...	Do This...
all the contents in the Session window	Choose **Edit ➤ Select All**.
an entire line or group of lines	Drag along the left margin.
a rectangle (or column)	While holding down ⎡Alt⎤, drag the mouse to form a rectangle.

Tip | The rectangle selection option is especially useful for copying columnar output to paste into the Data window or a spreadsheet. For details, see *Copying Session Window Output into Your Worksheet* on page 11-3.

Copying Session Window Output into Your Worksheet

Sometimes you may want to store some command output in the worksheet when a command does not have an option for storage. For example, **Stat ➤ Tables ➤ Cross Tabulation** prints information in the Session window, but doesn't store results in a column, constant, or matrix.

▶ To copy to the Data window

1 Highlight the desired text in the Session window.

For example, select a rectangle of columnar output by holding down the ⎡Alt⎤ key while dragging with the mouse.

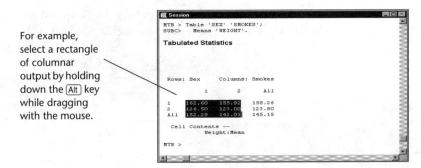

2 Choose **Edit ➤ Copy**.

3 In the Data window, place your cursor in the cell that is the top left corner of the area you want to paste to. For example, if you highlighted text in the Session window that is two columns wide and three rows long, place your cursor in a cell that has one blank column to the right and two blank rows below.

4 Choose **Edit ➤ Paste**.

5 A dialog box appears.

   ■ To paste the data across columns (one value in the first column, one value in the next column, etc.) click the **Use Spaces as Delimiters** button.

   ■ To paste all the data in one column, click the **Paste as a Single Column** button.

Making Output Editable or Read-Only

The Session window is by default set to read-only. This means that output can be copied, but it cannot be deleted or modified. If you want to add comments, cut and paste text and numbers, or use the Replace feature, you can change the Session window to Editable. You can change modes back and forth throughout a session.

▶ To change editing modes

1 Make the Session window active and choose **Editor ➤ Output Editable** to check or uncheck the menu item.

2 Check the menu item to make Session window output Editable.

3 Uncheck the menu item to make Session window output read-only.

▶ To save your preference for editable or read-only output

You can have MINITAB start each session in the mode you prefer by doing the following:

1 Choose **Edit ➤ Preferences**, click **Session Window**, then click **Select**.

2 If you want output to be read-only, check the **Output should be Read-Only** checkbox. If you want output to be Editable, uncheck it.

Enabling and Disabling Command Language

By default, the Session window shows only the output from commands. But sometimes you may want to show the command language that generated the output, or you may want to be able to type session commands directly in the Session window.

	When command language is...	
	Enabled	**Disabled** (default)
You can		
■ use menu commands	Yes	Yes
■ type commands in the Command Line Editor	Yes	Yes
■ type commands in the Session window	Yes	No
The Session window displays		
■ output from menu or session commands	Yes	Yes
■ the commands used to generate output	Yes	No
MINITAB displays error messages in	the Session window	pop-up message boxes
The History folder displays session commands	Yes	Yes

▶ **To enable or disable command language**

1 Choose **Editor ➤ Enable Commands** to check or uncheck the menu item.

2 Check the menu item to activate the MTB> command prompt in the Session window and display all subsequent commands.

3 Uncheck the menu item to disable the MTB> command prompt in the Session window and hide all subsequent commands.

▶ **To save your command language preference**

You can save your current setting so that it will be in effect the next time you use MINITAB. You can change your preference at any time.

1 Choose **Edit ➤ Preferences,** click **Session Window,** then click **Select.**

2 Under **Command Language,** click **Enable** or **Disable** as you prefer.

Using Fonts in the Session Window

Each line in the Session window has one font associated with it. Thus an entire line is always in one font.

There are three types of lines: Input/Output (I/O), Title, and Comment. You can customize the font used by each line to be any font of any size that is available on your system. For example, your Title Font could 14-point Garamond Bold and your Comment Font could be 12-point Zapf Chancery Italic.

You can also apply a font style to existing text in the Session window, regardless of its default font. For example, you could highlight several lines of regression output and apply the Comment Font. For more information, see *To apply font styles to existing text* on page 11-7.

Here are descriptions of the three font styles and when they are used by the Session window:

- **I/O Font**
  Commands you type and output generated by commands is put in the I/O font. This font is always a monospaced font, such as Courier. In monospaced fonts, all characters have the same width, so tabular and columnar output line up evenly. When you change the I/O font, the font dialog box only displays the monospaced fonts that are available on your system.

- **Title Font**
  Most commands that generate output in the Session window also generate a title for the output. MINITAB automatically puts the title in Title Font.

- **Comment Font**
  If you have set your Session window output to Editable, you can place your cursor anywhere in the Session window and type text. If you start typing on a blank line, MINITAB automatically applies the Comment Font to what you type. If you are typing on a line that already contains text, MINITAB applies the font already in use on that line. If the Session window output is set to read-only, you can still apply the Comment Font to text. For more information on output settings, see *Making Output Editable or Read-Only* on page 11-4.

▶ **To change the default font for the current session**

1 Make the Session window active and choose **Editor ➤ Select Fonts ➤** and a font style (**I/O, Title,** or **Comment**)

2 Choose any of the options in the font dialog box:

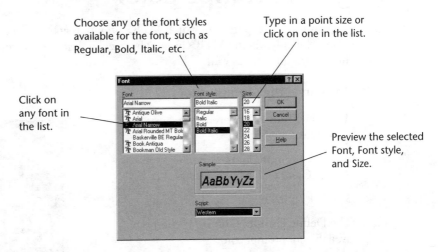

Choose any of the font styles available for the font, such as Regular, Bold, Italic, etc.

Type in a point size or click on one in the list.

Click on any font in the list.

Preview the selected Font, Font style, and Size.

When you change the default font, all the text in the Session window that has that font style is changed.

▶ **To save your font preferences**

The I/O, Title, and Comment Font settings that you select with **Editor ➤ Select Fonts** stay in effect only during the current session; when you exit and start MINITAB again, the fonts will return to their default settings. To save your current font selections for future sessions, do the following:

1 Choose **Edit ➤ Preferences**, click **Session Window**, then click **Select**.

2 Click on the **Save Current Fonts** checkbox if it is unchecked.

▶ **To apply font styles to existing text**

You can override the default font and apply the I/O, Title, or Comment Font to existing lines in the Session window. Font changes affect all the text on the line, not just any highlighted characters. You can change fonts even when the Session window is set to read-only.

1 Click in the line you want to change, or highlight a block of lines.

2 Choose **Editor ➤ Apply I/O Font**
or   **Editor ➤ Apply Title Font**
or   **Editor ➤ Apply Comment Font**

Changing the Prompt Color

An easy way to keep track of which MTB> prompt is active is to change the prompt color. Not only will the MTB> prompt be in color, but any text you type on the prompt line will be in color as well.

▶ **To change the prompt color**

1 Choose **Edit ➤ Preferences ➤ Session Window ➤ Select**.

2 Click **Prompt Color**.
   The Color dialog box appears (at right).

3 Click on the color square you want.

The **Define Custom Colors** function is not available for prompt colors.

Finding and Replacing Text and Numbers

In a typical session you may generate many pages of commands, output, and comments. The Find feature can help you quickly locate previous commands, search for particular data values in output, and even help you find out if a certain value *did not* appear in your results.

The Replace feature lets you find numbers or text and replace them with different values, either one at a time or all at once. Replace does not work, however, when the Session window output is set to read-only. See *Making Output Editable or Read-Only* on page 11-4 for more information.

▶ **To find text**

1 With the Session window active, choose **Editor ➤ Find**.

2 Type the text you want to search for in the **Find What** box.

3 Optionally, set the **Match case** or **Direction** modes (see below).

4 Click **Find Next**. If you wish to update text once you have found the text you are looking for, click the **Replace** button to bring up the Replace dialog box. Click **Close** when done.

You can search for any combination of words or numbers.

Check this box if you want to find only the text that exactly matches the upper and lowercase letters you type.

Click Replace to bring up the Replace dialog box.

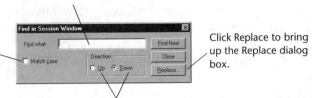

Click **Up** to search from the cursor to the beginning of the Session window.
Click **Down** to search from the cursor to the end of the Session window.

If you have sound turned on in Windows, when Find reaches the end (or the beginning, if **Direction** is set to **Up**) of the Session window without finding an occurrence of the search text, MINITAB will beep or make some other noise (depending on your Windows sound settings). See your Windows documentation for instructions on using sound.

Note | Use Ctrl + Break to interrupt a **Find** search.

▶ To find and replace text

1 With the Session window active, make the Session window editable by choosing **Editor ▸ Output Editable** if it is unchecked (if **Output Editable** is checked, you do not have to do anything).

2 Choose **Editor ▸ Replace**.

3 Type the text you want to search for in the **Find What** box.

4 Type the replacement text in the **Replace With** box.

5 Optionally, check **Match case**.

6 Click **Find Next**.

7 If text is found, click **Replace** or **Replace All**.

8 Click **Close** when done.

Type any combination of text and numbers that you want to search for, then type what you want to replace it with.

Click to find and highlight next occurrence of **Find what** text.

After **Find Next**, click to replace highlighted text.

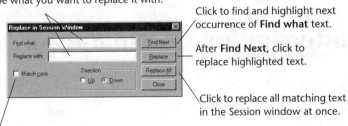

Click to replace all matching text in the Session window at once.

Say that the **Find what** string is "StDev." With **Match case** checked, MINITAB will find "StDev," but not "stdev," "stDev," or "sTdev."

When Replace reaches the end of the Session window without finding an occurrence of the search text, MINITAB will beep or make some other noise (depending on your system's sound settings). If MINITAB makes no noise, you may have sound turned off. See your system documentation for instructions on using sound.

Note | Use Ctrl+Break to interrupt a **Replace** search.

Moving to Session Window Commands

Minitab gives you several methods of navigating through your different session commands, so that you can easily jump from the results of a **Stat ➤ Regression ➤ Regression** command to the results of a **Stat ➤ Basic Statistics ➤ Display Descriptive Statistics** command.

▶ **To move to session window commands using the Project Manager**

- Right click on the command title in the Session folder in the Project Manager and choose **Go To Title**.

▶ **To move to session window commands using menu commands**

- To move *forward* to the next output section in the Session window, choose **Editor ➤ Next Command**, or click the **Next Command** toolbar button ⬇.

- To move *backward* to the previous output section, choose **Editor ➤ Previous Command,** or click the **Previous Command** toolbar button ⬆.

Tip | You can use the Next Command and Previous Command features with the Session window fonts to create placeholders in your session text. Next Command and Previous Command each search for the nearest output title (in one direction or another) and place your cursor there. If you apply the Title Font to a line of text (see *To apply font styles to existing text* on page 11-7), Next Command and Previous Command will also jump to that line.

Interrupting Commands or Macros

To interrupt the display of output from a command or the execution of a macro, type Ctrl+Break. In a macro, MINITAB finishes executing the current command, then exits the macro. Display of output is halted as soon as possible.

12

Saving, Printing, and Generating Reports

Chapter Overview

In the course of a MINITAB session, you may generate many lines of output, command language, and comments in the Session window. You can save that Session window content, print it, or use to create reports in the Project Manager ReportPad folder or in a word processor for use in print or in the Worldwide Web.

When you save your project, all the Session window contents are saved in that project file. If you like, you can also save the Session window output into its own file.

That Session window file can be saved in two formats: text or Rich Text Format (RTF). Text files, also known as ASCII files, do not contain any of the fonts that you see in the Session window, while RTF files retain the fonts. Both formats can be opened in most word processors.

You may also need to save Session window content to a file if the Session window "overflows." The Session window can contain a maximum of 15,000 lines of text by default. When the amount of text goes past this point, the Session window is said to overflow. To make room for more output, MINITAB will remove the first half of the existing text from the Session window and ask you if you want to save that text in a separate file. You can edit your preferences to change the limits of the Session window, and to change the way MINITAB handles overflow text.

This chapter ends with step-by-step instructions for printing and creating reports. You can publish a basic report simply by printing portions of the Session window. For more sophisticated reports, you will probably want to bring MINITAB output into a word processor for more extensive formatting. This is an easy process, but in our instructions you might pick up some tips on integrating text and MINITAB graphs, and on turning MINITAB items into HTML documents that can be viewed by web browsers.

Saving the Contents of the Session Window

You can save the Session window at any time. If the session has been a long one, however, the Session window may not contain the entire contents of the session, since it can only hold a maximum of 15,000 lines at one time. See *Session Window Size and Overflow* on page 12-3.

▶ **To save the Session window at any time**

1 With the Session window active, choose **File ➤ Save Session Window As**.

2 In **File name**, type a name.

3 Under **Save as type**, choose **MINITAB Session (*.txt)** or **Rich Text Format (*.rtf)**.

Tip | If you want to save only a portion of the Session window contents, highlight the text you want, then follow the steps above.

▶ **To save when closing a project**

Whenever you close a project—by opening a new or saved project, or exiting MINITAB—MINITAB will prompt you to save pieces of your project. One of those pieces is the Session window content.

1 Exit MINITAB or close a project.

2 Choose **Save Separate Pieces**.

3 When the following dialog box appears, do one of three things:

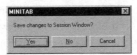

- Click **Yes** to save the contents. The **Save Window As** dialog box will appear, where you can save the text as a specific file.

- Click **No** to discard the changes.

- Click **Cancel** to return to the current project without exiting or closing.

Session Window Size and Overflow

To conserve your system's memory resources, only so much text is kept in the Session window. The default is 15,000 lines. When the Session window reaches that maximum number of lines, the contents are said to "overflow."

You can set the number of lines the Session window contains (up to the maximum of 60,000 lines). You can also choose how MINITAB should respond when the Session window overflows.

Changing the Session window text limit

If you are having performance or memory problems with your system, you may want to reduce the number of lines that the Session window can hold.

▶ **To change the text limit on the Session window**

1 Choose **Edit ➤ Preferences** and select **Session Window**.

2 In **Number of Lines**, type the desired number of lines. You can choose from 1,000 to 60,000 lines.

3 Click **OK**, then click **Save**.

How MINITAB handles overflow by default

When the window overflows, by default MINITAB will prompt you to save the Session window contents to a file or discard them.

- If you choose to save, the first half of the Session window contents are saved to a file you designate, and then removed from the Session window.

- If you choose discard, half of the contents will be removed from the Session window without being saved.

After you choose to save or discard once, MINITAB will not prompt you to choose again until you exit MINITAB and start again. If the Session window overflows again, contents will either be saved to the same session file or discarded as before.

By default, saved contents are appended to the session file.

Other ways MINITAB can handle overflow

You can edit your preferences to change how MINITAB handles Session window overflow. Instead of prompting you for a file name, MINITAB can automatically save the overflow text to a file named SESSION.TXT.

You can also choose whether MINITAB *appends* the overflow text to the session file you are saving to (whether that file is SESSION.TXT or a file name you chose when prompted), or *overwrites* the text in that session file.

Finally, you can choose for MINITAB to automatically discard the overflow text. The overflow is not saved, and you continue working with the remaining contents of the Session window.

▶ **To save automatically to SESSION.TXT**

1 Choose **Edit ➤ Preferences** and select **Session Window**.

2 Under **On Session Window Overflow**, choose **Save to file: session.txt**.

The file SESSION.TXT will be saved in your main MINITAB directory (for example, C:\MTBWIN). You will not be prompted for a file name on exit or when overflow occurs. MINITAB then saves the contents to this same file, every session.

3 Click **OK**, then click **Save**.

▶ **To change your preference for overwriting or appending to session files**

1 Choose **Edit ➤ Preferences** and select **Session Window**.

2 Under **When Saving on Overflow**, choose one of these options:

■ **Overwrite file contents**
MINITAB will erase the old contents of the file and replace them with the new text.

■ **Append to file contents**
MINITAB will add the new text to the end of the file. Note that if you choose this option in combination with **Save to file: session.txt**, over time you may create a very large session file.

3 Click **OK**, then click **Save**.

▶ **To discard automatically**

1 Choose **Edit ➤ Preferences** and select **Session Window**.

2 Under **On Session Window Overflow**, choose **Discard contents**.

3 Click **OK**, then click **Save**.

Printing the Contents of the Session Window

▶ **To print the entire window**

1 Make the window active.

2 Choose **File ➤ Print Session Window** and click **OK**.

▶ **To print individual command output**

1 Select one or more command output titles from the Session folder in the Project Manager.

2 Right-click on the selected titles with the mouse.

3 Select **Print**.

▶ **To print blocks of text**

1 Select text in the Session window.

2 Choose **File ➤ Print Session Window**.

3 Make sure **Print range** is set to **Selection**, then click **OK**.

Creating Reports in the ReportPad Folder

You can quickly create reports of your data in the Project Manager ReportPad folder using **Append to Report**. Use the ReportPad folder to store graphs, Session window output, and text (such as user comments and notes). All output in the ReportPad folder is fully editable, and you can save the contents of the ReportPad folder as an RTF (Rich Text Format) file that can be displayed in other applications. You can edit and print the reports directly from the ReportPad folder, or open and edit them in a word processing program for enhanced formatting options.

▶ **To append graphs and Session window output to the ReportPad folder**

1 Do one of the following:

■ Right-click on the Graph window or Session window section you want to append to the ReportPad contents, or

■ In the Session or Graphs folder, highlight the graphs or Session window output titles you want to append to the ReportPad contents.

2 Choose **Append to Report**.

▶ **To save a report file to use in another application**

1 Right click on the Report folder.

2 Choose **Save Report As**.

3 In **File name**, type a name.

4 Click **Save**.

Creating Reports in a Word Processor

When it is time to present the results of your analyses, you may want to create a report in a word processor, such as WordPerfect or Microsoft Word. Word processors allow you more flexibility and formatting options than MINITAB's Session window or ReportPad folder.

You can copy and paste Session window output or graphs into a word processor or, if you have already created a report in the ReportPad folder, you can copy or move the entire contents of the ReportPad folder to a word processor with one command.

▶ **To copy the contents of the ReportPad folder to a word processor**

1 Make sure the word processor application and MINITAB are running.

2 Right-click on the ReportPad folder.

3 Choose **Copy to Word Processor**.

Note The **Move to Word Processor** command moves the contents of the ReportPad folder to a word processor, and empties the ReportPad folder.

▶ To create a report using copy and paste

1 Make sure the word processor application and MINITAB are running.

2 In the Session window, select the text you want. See *Selecting Text* on page 11-3.

3 Copy the text using **Edit ➤ Copy**.

4 In the word processor, choose the paste command (usually **Edit ➤ Paste**).

The fonts will appear in the word processor just as they do in the Session window.

5 Copy and paste any graphs by following these three steps:

- With the Graph window active, choose **Editor ➤ View**.

- Choose **Edit ➤ Copy Graph**.

- In the word processor, choose the paste command (usually **Edit ➤ Paste**).

Depending on the word processor you are using, the graph will be pasted as an OLE object, a metafile drawing, or a bitmap. For details, see *Copying and Pasting Graphs* on page 26-6.

▶ To create a report with text and graph files

1 In the Session window, select the text you want. See *Selecting Text* on page 11-3.

2 Save the selection as a Rich Text Format (RTF) file. See *To save the Session window at any time* on page 12-2.

3 Save any graphs in the file format that is understood by your application.

- With the Graph window active, choose **File ➤ Save Graph As**.

- Under **Save as type**, choose an appropriate file type.

  Most Windows word processors can import Windows bitmap (BMP) files. Macintosh word processors can import Tagged Image Format (TIFF or TIF) files.

- In **File name**, enter a name. Click **Save**.

4 In the word processor, import the text and graphics files. See your application's documentation for details.

Tip | Use your word processor's tables feature to place text and graphs side-by-side. Create a table with one row and two columns. Place the Session window text in the one column and the graph in other. Or, create more complex tables, placing text and graphs wherever you like.

Creating Reports for the Worldwide Web

You can place your MINITAB text and graphs in an HTML file that can be viewed on the Internet with a web browser. HTML stands for HyperText Markup Language. HTML files are plain text files that contain *tags* that tell a browser how to format and display the text between the tags. The text can be words and numbers, or the name of a graphics file that the browser should display.

The steps below outline how to create a simple HTML file, or web page. Of course, there are many more elements you could add to the page. We cannot give you instructions on how to use HTML tags, connect to the internet, create a web site, or upload HTML files to a web server.

▶ **To create an HTML document**

1   Save the desired Session window contents as plain text (not RTF). See *To save the Session window at any time* on page 12-2.

2   Save any graphs you want in a JPEG or PNG format.

   ■ With the Graph window active, choose **File ➤ Save Graph As**.

   ■ Under **Save as type**, choose a JPEG or PNG file type.

       Almost all web browsers understand Joint Photographic Experts Group (JPEG or JPG) files. As of this writing, most browsers do not understand Portable Network Graphics (PNG, pronounced "ping") files, though PNG files have been approved as a standard for graphics files. You will probably get crisper graphs and smaller file sizes using PNG rather than JPEG.

   ■ In **File name**, enter a name. Click **Save**.

3   In a word processor or text editor (like Notepad), open the Session window text file.

4   At the top of the file, before Session window content begins, insert these three lines:
```
<HTML>
<Body>
<PRE>
```

5   At the bottom of the file, after Session window content ends, add these three lines:
```
</PRE>
</Body>
</HTML>
```

6   If have a graph, place your cursor in the body of the Session window content where you want the graph to appear, and insert the following line:
```
<img src="myfile.jpg">
```

    Substitute your file name for "myfile.jpg." Insert as many graphs as you have graph files.

7   Save the text file with any name you like, using the extension HTM or HTML.

8 Place the text file and any graphics files on your web server. See your system administrator for details.

More	The <PRE> and </PRE> tags make all the text between them appear in browsers in a monospaced font. Since MINITAB output is space-delimited, you need the PRE tags to allow columns of numbers line up correctly.

part IV

Graphing Data

13

Graphics Overview

Chapter Overview

This chapter describes the concepts and terminology you should know to make effective use of MINITAB's graphs. You probably do not need to read this information when you first use graphs. You may, however, want to refer back to the sections in this chapter upon reading about graphics features that use these concepts.

There are four different types of graphs:

- **Core graphs**—versatile graphs with many options that allow you to create everything from basic scatter plots to complex multiple-graph layouts

- **3D graphs**—Scatter plots, wireframe plots, and surface plots based on three variables

- **Specialty graphs**—graphs that combine elements of core graphs, so you can create sophisticated graphs with a few mouse clicks

- **Character graphs**—"typewriter" style graphs that appear as text in the Session window

Most of these graphs appear on the **Graph** menu.

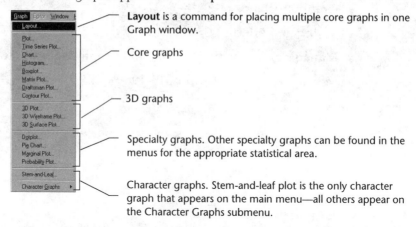

Layout is a command for placing multiple core graphs in one Graph window.

Core graphs

3D graphs

Specialty graphs. Other specialty graphs can be found in the menus for the appropriate statistical area.

Character graphs. Stem-and-leaf plot is the only character graph that appears on the main menu—all others appear on the Character Graphs submenu.

Except for character graphs, which appear in the Session window, all these graphs appear in Graph windows. In a Graph window you can:

- Edit the graph—modify and add text, shapes, and other graph elements with point-and-click tools

- Brush the graph—highlight data points to identify corresponding observations in the Data window

- Print and save the graph

Core Graphs

In their simplest forms, core graphs comprise some of the most commonly used graphs, including scatter plots, bar charts, and time series plots. But core graphs also have a large number of options that allow you to create a virtually unlimited variety of two-dimensional graphs, and even graphs composed of multiple smaller graphs.

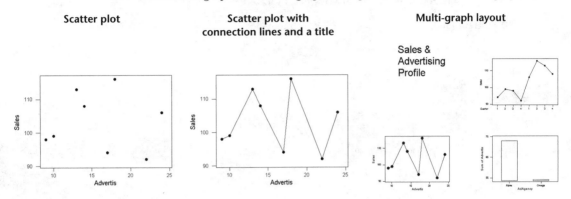

Each core graph has its own unique set of options. In addition, all of the graph commands have graphics options that are described in the following chapters:

Chapter and title	Shows you how to...
14 *Core Graphs*	create each core graph and use the options that are *unique* to that graph (options that are shared by more than one graph are described in the chapters below).
15 *Core Graphs: Displaying Data*	use symbols, connection lines, bars, and other data display elements to represent data points.
16 *Core Graphs: Groups and Multiple Graphs*	show multiple relationships between variables and subgroups within variables. The relationships can be displayed on one graph, on multiple graphs in different Graph windows, on multiple graphs overlaid in the same Graph window, or on multiple graphs placed in different areas of one Graph window.
17 *Core Graphs: Annotating*	add text and graphical objects to graphs, such as titles, footnotes, lines, and polygons.
18 *Core Graphs: Customizing the Frame*	customize the axes, ticks, and other frame elements that surround a graph.
19 *Core Graphs: Controlling Regions*	change the properties of the four different regions that make up a Graph window, including sizing, background colors and fill patterns.

3D Graphs

While two-dimensional graphs describe data for two variables—x and y—three-dimensional graphs display data for three variables: x, y, and z.

MINITAB provides, appropriately enough, three 3D graphs: 3D Scatter Plot, 3D Wireframe Plot, and 3D Surface Plot.

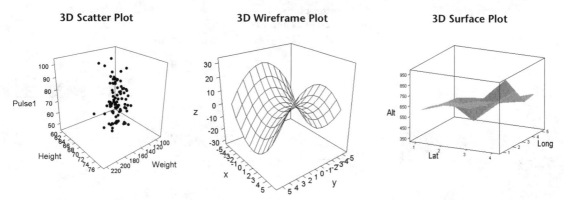

3D graphs and their graphics options are described in the following chapters:

Chapter and title	Shows you how to...
20 *3D Graphs*	create 3D scatter, wireframe, and surface plots, then change the appearance of symbols and projection lines (on the scatter plot) and surfaces (on the wireframe and surface plots).
21 *3D Graphs: Viewing Tools*	control how the graph is viewed in three-dimensional space. You can set the relative positions of the viewer and the graph, the height and width of the viewing field, and the method of projecting the object onto the space (orthographic or perspective projection).
22 *3D Graphs: Lighting and Rendering Tools*	set the position, color, and brightness of lights, as well as the method MINITAB uses to render surfaces and lights. The rendering method affects the speed and accuracy with which a graph is displayed.

Specialty Graphs

Using the core graph commands, you could create an incredible variety of two-dimensional graphs. The drawback is that for a complex graph, you might have to follow a large number of steps. With specialty graphs, the work is already done for you. The specialty graph commands let you specify just a few options to create useful, complex graphs.

The marginal plot, for example, makes it easy to create a scatter plot that has histograms for each variable placed in the margins.

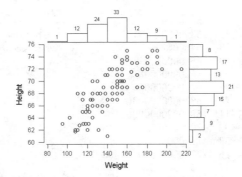

Specialty graphs and their graphics options are described in the following chapters:

Chapter and title	Show(s) you how to…
23 *Specialty Graphs*	create specialty graphs that are useful across many statistical disciplines. These are the graphs that appear in the **Graph** menu.
Various chapters	create specialty graphs that are specific to a statistical area. These graphs may appear in the menus for the statistical area, or as graph options in the dialog boxes for analysis commands.

Character Graphs

Character graphs are graphs made up of text characters that display in the Session window. Character graphs can be useful when you want to display results in a text-only form, such as an e-mail message. For example, here is a typical stem-and-leaf plot:

Session window output

Character Stem-and-Leaf Display

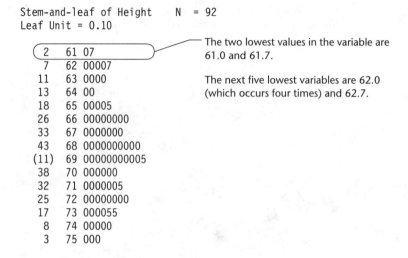

```
Stem-and-leaf of Height    N  = 92
Leaf Unit = 0.10

    2    61  07
    7    62  00007
   11    63  0000
   13    64  00
   18    65  00005
   26    66  00000000
   33    67  0000000
   43    68  0000000000
  (11)   69  00000000005
   38    70  000000
   32    71  0000005
   25    72  00000000
   17    73  000055
    8    74  00000
    3    75  000
```

The two lowest values in the variable are 61.0 and 61.7.

The next five lowest variables are 62.0 (which occurs four times) and 62.7.

While character graphs have their uses, most of the time you will want to use the other types of graphs (that is, graphs that appear in Graph windows), for two reasons:

- With the exception of the stem-and-leaf plot, each character graph has a more powerful core graph counterpart

- Character graphs can not be edited, brushed, or saved in a graphics file

Chapter and title	Show(s) you how to...
23 *Specialty Graphs*	create a stem-and-leaf plot. This is the only character graph that appears on the main menu.
In Help, the topic *Using Character Graphs*	create other character graphs.

Note | In the documentation, the terms "graphs" and "graphics" generally refer to graphs that display in Graph windows.

Graph Editing

After you produce a graph in a Graph window, you can edit it. Graph editing is useful for putting text, lines, marker symbols, and polygons anywhere on an existing graph. You can also edit and change the attributes of objects generated with the existing graph. The graph editing tools, shown below, are often easier to use than the graph's options dialog boxes.

Use the **Tool palette** to create text, rectangles, ovals, markers, and polygons.

Use the **Attribute palette** to change the color, size, and type of objects on the graph.

Note | The changes you make with graph editing tools apply only to that particular Graph window, and do not affect the settings in the dialog box that created the graph. For example, say that you create a plot with the Plot dialog box, then use the graph editing features to change all the plot's symbols from black to red. When you open the Plot dialog box again, the symbol attributes will still be set to black; when you click **OK**, a second Graph window will appear that contains a plot with black symbols.

Chapter and title	Shows you how to...
24 *Editing Graphs*	add text and objects, then move, manipulate, and change the appearance of new and existing objects.

Graph Brushing

Graphs allow you to visually see the relationships between points. However, after you make a graph, you often want to learn more about a point, or a group of points. Brushing allows you to highlight points on a graph and see the corresponding observations (rows) in the Brushing palette and in the Data window.

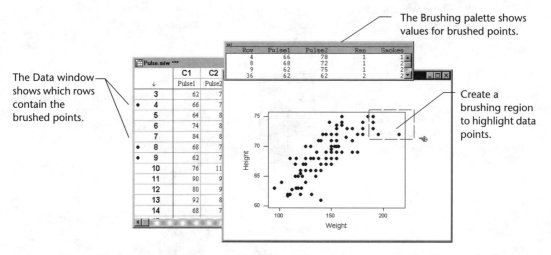

The Brushing palette shows values for brushed points.

The Data window shows which rows contain the brushed points.

Create a brushing region to highlight data points.

Brushing is especially good for showing the characteristics of outliers and telling whether points that lie in a brushing region share other characteristics.

Chapter and title	Shows you how to...
25 *Brushing Graphs*	brush one or more graphs, control the Brushing palette, and add indicator variables.

Saving and Printing Graphs

Once you create a graph, you can save it, copy and paste it to another application, and print it. A saved graph can be viewed and edited again later in MINITAB, or used in another application.

Chapter and title	Shows you how to...
26 *Saving and Printing Graphs*	save graphs in a variety of graph formats, open graphs in MINITAB, print them, and control Graph window titles and positions.

Managing, Arranging, and Naming Graph Windows

You can use the Graphs folder in the Project Manager to manage multiple Graph windows.

By highlighting the graphs from the list in the Graphs folder and right-clicking with the mouse, you can:

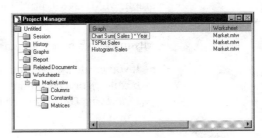

- **Save**, **Copy**, or **Print** one or more graphs
- **Tile** multiple graphs across the MINITAB screen for easy viewing and comparison
- **Rename** individual graphs
- Append graphs to the ReportPad folder

▶ **To select multiple graphs**

- Select contiguous graphs by clicking and dragging
- Add or subtract discontiguous graphs by using ⌈Ctrl⌋+click

▶ **To tile multiple graphs**

1 Highlight one or more graphs in the Graphs folder.

2 Right-click on the highlighted graphs.

3 Choose **Tile**.

4 Optionally, choose **Tile With Worksheet** to tile the worksheet along with the selected graphs.

▶ **To name a Graph window**

1 Select a graph in the Graphs folder.

2 Do either of the following:

- right-click and click **Rename** or
- click again on the selected graph

3 Type a name, up to 31 characters.

Graph window names do not print, nor are they retained when you save a graph as a separate file (MGF, JPEG, etc.). To give a graph a title that does save and print with the graph, use the graph editing tools (see Chapter 24, *Editing Graphs*).

Missing Values and Graphs

In all types of graphs, missing values are omitted from the graph. After generating the graph, MINITAB will print a note in the Session window that tells the number of missing values that were omitted.

Missing values have additional effects in three cases:

- If you create a core graph that uses category variables (such as the x variable in boxplots), or a core graph that displays data differently for each group (see *Displaying Data for Each Group* on page 16-5), the missing values form a separate group.

  For example, say you want to create a graph of student pulse rates, with a separate boxplot for each sex. Pulse1 is the y variable, and Sex is the category variable that contains the sex of each participant (1 = male, 2 = female, and * = missing). When Sex contains a few missing values, the resulting graph looks like this:

Boxplot showing missing values as a group

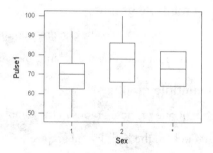

- With time series plots, MINITAB skips each interval that has a missing value, but connects the points before and after the missing value.

- With character graphs, if you use a column that contains missing values as an argument for a subcommand, MINITAB generates an error message and does not produce a graph until you supply a valid subcommand and argument.

14

Core Graphs

Core Graphs Overview

You can use the core graph commands to quickly create graphs of various types: scatter plots, time series plots, charts, and more. But what sets core graphs apart from other types of MINITAB graphs is the ability to create multiple graphs at once (in different Graph windows or the same window) and to completely customize the appearance of each graph. These two abilities, collectively called *graphics options*, allow you to create a virtually unlimited variety of two-dimensional graphs.

As well as the graphics options that they share with each other, most core graphs also have options that are unique to that graph.

In this chapter, you will learn how to create basic graphs and use the options that are unique to each core graph. For each core graph, you will also see a brief description of the graphics options that are available to that graph.

Common Core Graph Graphics Options

Most graphics options are shared by all of the core graphs, and are described within their own chapters. For a definitive list of which options are available to which graph, see the description of each graph in this chapter, or look up the graphics option in the following chapters:

Chapter and title	Shows you how to...
15 *Core Graphs: Displaying Data*	use symbols, connection lines, bars, and other data display elements to represent data points.
16 *Core Graphs: Groups and Multiple Graphs*	show multiple relationships between variables and subgroups within variables. The relationships can be displayed on one graph, on multiple graphs in different Graph windows, on multiple graphs overlaid in the same Graph window, or on multiple graphs placed in different areas of one Graph window.
17 *Core Graphs: Annotating*	add text and graphical objects to graphs, such as titles, footnotes, lines, and polygons.
18 *Core Graphs: Customizing the Frame*	customize the axes, ticks, and other frame elements that surround a graph.
19 *Core Graphs: Controlling Regions*	change the properties of the four different regions that make up a Graph window, including sizing, background colors, and fill patterns.

You access most of the graphics options from the main dialog box of each core graph. All core graphs have a similar dialog box structure. For an overview of this structure, see *Accessing graphics options from core graph dialog boxes* on page 14-6.

Displaying the data

You can alter the way your data appear on the graph. You can choose one or more data display elements, then change the attributes for each element. Chapter 15, *Core Graphs: Displaying Data*, discusses these options in detail, but here is an overview of the data display elements that are available.

Element	Definition	Example	Attributes
Symbols	Dots, circles, squares, etc., that appear for each point on the graph		type, color, and size of symbols
Connection lines	Lines that connect points		■ type, color, size of lines ■ straight or steplike lines
Projection lines	Lines that extend from each point to an axis or base point		■ line type, color, and size ■ base location for each projection ■ direction of the projection (to the x- or y-axis)
Areas	Filled areas under points		■ type and color of fills ■ type, color, and size of edge lines ■ base location for each point ■ extension of areas in the x- or y-direction ■ straight or steplike edge lines

Element	Definition	Example	Attributes
Bars	Bars that represent categories (charts and histograms only)		■ type and color of fills ■ type, color, and size of edge lines ■ base location for each point ■ extension of bars in the x- or y-direction
LOWESS lines	Smoothed points connected with lines LOWESS stands for LOcally-WEighted Scatter plot Smoother.		■ type, color, and size of lines ■ degree of smoothness as determined by the f value ■ amount of influence of outliers on the smoothed values

Groups and multiple graphs

Most often you will generate one graph at a time. However, the core graph commands also allow you to create many graphs at once, or elegantly display multiple relationships on one page. For details, see Chapter 16, *Core Graphs: Groups and Multiple Graphs*. You can:

■ display data elements differently for each group, or for each point, in a graph.

■ generate multiple graphs, each in its own Graph window, from one dialog box. Graphs can have different scales, or have the same scale.

■ overlay several graphs, or create a layout of several graphs, on one page—the graph types can be different.

Annotating the graph

You can add text and graphical objects to your graph. See Chapter 17, *Core Graphs: Annotating*. You can:

■ create titles and footnotes

■ add data labels

■ place text anywhere on the graph

■ draw symbols, lines, or polygons anywhere on the graph

Customizing the graph frame

You can customize the axes, ticks, and other elements that border the data, as well as the elements that span the borders of a graph, such as reference lines and grid lines. See Chapter 18, *Core Graphs: Customizing the Frame.*

You can

- redefine the minimum and maximum values of the scales
- customize the axis line appearance, length, and labels
- customize tick line appearance, location, and labels
- add grid lines
- add reference lines and labels to the graph
- suppress all the frame elements at once

Controlling regions

Each graph window contains one *page*, or *page region.* Each page can contain three other types of regions: *figure* regions (one for each graph on the page); *data* regions (one inside each figure region); and, if you use groups or multiple graphs on one page, a *legend* region.

The **page region** contains all three graphs.

Each graph is enclosed by a **figure region**, shown here with dashed lines.

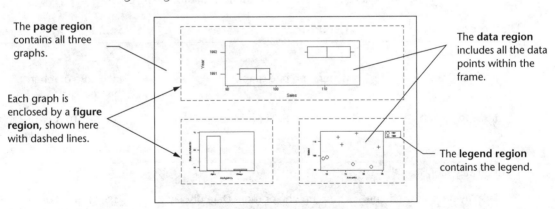

The **data region** includes all the data points within the frame.

The **legend region** contains the legend.

For details, see Chapter 19, *Core Graphs: Controlling Regions.*

You can

- change the location, size, and appearance of each region
- customize the appearance of text within the legend region
- specify the aspect ratio, or shape, of a page region

Accessing graphics options from core graph dialog boxes

You access most of these options from the main dialog box of each core graph. All core graphs use a similar dialog box structure. For example, here is the main dialog box for plots (**Graph ➤ Plot**):

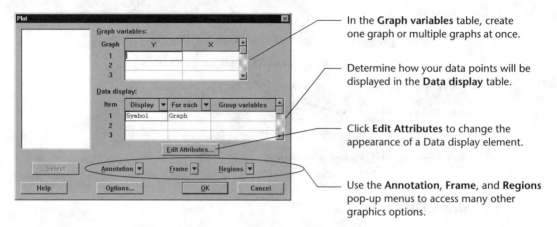

In the **Graph variables** table, create one graph or multiple graphs at once.

Determine how your data points will be displayed in the **Data display** table.

Click **Edit Attributes** to change the appearance of a Data display element.

Use the **Annotation**, **Frame**, and **Regions** pop-up menus to access many other graphics options.

This chapter will not go into detail on how to use these dialog box items, though you will see some of the items used in simple core graphs, examples, and tips. For full details, see the dialog item chapter locations in the following chart:

Dialog box item	Used for...	See...
Graph variables table:		
Row for Graph 1	generating one graph	each core graph in this chapter
Rows for Graph 2–100	generating multiple graphs	Chapter 16, *Core Graphs: Groups and Multiple Graphs*
Data display table:		
Display drop-down menu	choosing one or more Data display elements	Chapter 15, *Core Graphs: Displaying Data*
For each ➤ Graph	controlling how the corresponding data display element will appear on multiple graphs	Chapter 16, *Core Graphs: Groups and Multiple Graphs*
For each ➤ Group	making the corresponding data display element appear differently for each group in a grouping variable	Chapter 16, *Core Graphs: Groups and Multiple Graphs*

Dialog box item	Used for...	See...
For each ➤ Point	making symbols or projection lines appear differently for each data point in the graph	Chapter 16, *Core Graphs: Groups and Multiple Graphs*
Grouping variables	specifying which column holds the grouping variable—used only when **For each** is set to **Group**	Chapter 16, *Core Graphs: Groups and Multiple Graphs*
Edit Attributes button	changing the attributes of the currently selected item in the Data display table	Chapter 15, *Core Graphs: Displaying Data*
Annotation pop-up menu	adding text and graphical objects to the graph	Chapter 17, *Core Graphs: Annotating*
Frame pop-up menu	■ customizing the axes, ticks, and other frame elements that surround a graph	Chapter 18, *Core Graphs: Customizing the Frame*
	■ overlaying multiple graphs on the same page	Chapter 16, *Core Graphs: Groups and Multiple Graphs*
Regions pop-up menu	■ controlling the appearance of areas of a graph	Chapter 19, *Core Graphs: Controlling Regions*
	■ setting the size and position of the Figure region for placing multiple graphs on one page	Chapter 16, *Core Graphs: Groups and Multiple Graphs*

Plots

A plot displays points at paired coordinates from two variables: one variable provides the coordinates for the vertical y-axis, and one variable provides the coordinates for the horizontal x-axis. The default form of a plot is a scatter plot, which displays symbols for those data points.

Default plot: a scatter plot

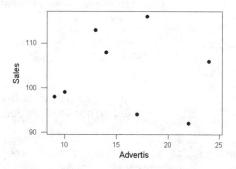

If you change the data display elements of a plot from the default symbols, you can create area plots, line plots, and smoothed line plots. You can also create combination plots that use multiple data display elements, such as symbols and lines together:

Area plot   **Line plot**   **Combination scatter/line plot**

      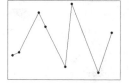

Data

Provide one column for the y-axis, and one column for the x-axis. Columns can be numeric or date/time, but must be of equal length. MINITAB automatically omits missing values from graphs. If you want to generate multiple graphs at once, you need a y-axis column and an x-axis column for each graph.

Note When used in the **Plot** command, date/time variables reflect the actual times measurements were taken, and thus can be used to plot unequally-spaced time series. When used in the **Time Series Plot** command, however, date/time variables can be used only as stamps for equally-spaced time series.

Note As with most graphs, the tick labels for date/time variables appear on the plot in the same format as they appear in the date/time column in the Data window.

▶ **To create a plot**

1 Choose **Graph ➤ Plot**.

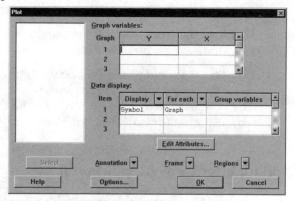

2 Enter a column in row 1 of **Y** and a column in row 1 of **X**.

3 If you like, use any of the options below, then click **OK**.

Options

Plot dialog box

The Plot dialog box includes the typical core graph dialog box controls. You can create multiple graphs and control a wide variety of graphics options. The following table outlines each of the dialog box features and indicates which chapter covers the feature in more detail:

Data display	Groups and multiple graphs	Annotation	Frame	Regions
Symbols	Display data for each group	Titles	Axes	Figure
Connection lines	Multiple graphs at once	Footnotes	Ticks	Data
Projection lines	Same scales across graphs	Text	Grids	Legend
Areas	Overlaying graphs	Lines	Reference lines	Aspect ratio of a page
LOWESS lines	Laying out graphs on the same page	Polygons	Change the scale	
		Markers	Suppressing frame elements	
		Data labels		
Chapter 15	Chapter 16	Chapter 17	Chapter 18	Chapter 19

Options subdialog box

- **Add Jitter**. Add "jitter" to the display of data points so that you can see overlapping points. See *Adding jitter to overlapping points* below.

- **Transform the x- or y-axis**. You can perform a log scale transformation. See Help in your MINITAB application for details.

- **Transpose the x- and y-axes**. Transposing the axes switches the x-axis with the y-axis, so that the x-axis is vertical and the y-axis is horizontal. Transposing does not change the type or name of the axis: the x-axis remains the x-axis whether it is horizontal or vertical, just as the y-axis remains the y-axis whether it is horizontal or vertical.

Adding jitter to overlapping points

You can add jitter to randomly offset points, according to the values in the offset distance fields, so that you can see overlapping points.

The average offset distance can be set for the x- and y-directions by entering values ranging from 0 to 1. The default value is 0.025. A larger value gives a larger average offset distance. This is an average; the actual distance is pseudo-randomly generated for each plot. The values are fractions of the range of data in each direction. Values are usually quite small to minimize distortion. You can stretch points out in just one direction by setting one direction to 0 and the other direction to a larger value.

▶ To add jitter

1 From the main graph dialog box, click **Options**.

2 Check **Add Jitter to Direction**.

3 Optionally, change the average offset distance (the default value of 0.025 will otherwise take precedence). In **X** and/or **Y**, enter a number ranging from 0 to 1.

4 Click **OK** in each dialog box.

Plot without jitter

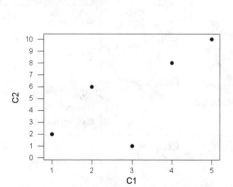

Plot with jitter

you can now see that there are three *2s* and two *4s*

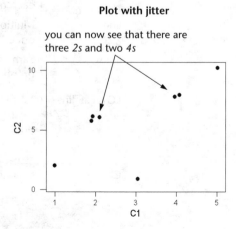

Tip	Since jittering relies on a random function, jittered plots do not look the same each time you generate them. You can generate a plot several times to see which plot shows your data points most clearly. To produce identical graphs, set the base of the MINITAB random number generator by choosing **Calc ➤ Set Base** and typing an integer, such as *123*.

Time Series Plots

Time series plots display measurement data on the y-axis versus time data on the x-axis. By default, points on the graph are displayed as symbols connected by lines. The x-axis time scales can be labeled in a variety of ways:

- *index* units, integers that represent generic units of time (each observation is labeled with a consecutive integer, as in 1, 2, 3)

- *date/time stamp*, taking values from an assigned date/time column

- *calendar* units (days, months, quarters, or years—up to three in combination)

- *clock* units (days, hours, minutes, or seconds—up to three in combination)

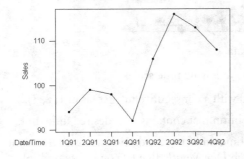

**Time Series Plot:
X-axis with a date/time stamp column**

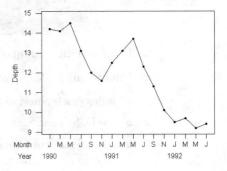

**Time Series Plot:
X-axis with two Calendar units, Month and Year**

MINITAB assumes that the y-axis data occurred in the order that the values appear in the column, in equally-spaced time intervals. If the data did not occur that way, you may want to use the Plot command (page 14-7) to plot the y-axis data versus a date/time column on the x-axis.

Data

For a single time series plot, you need one column of numeric data for the y-axis. MINITAB assumes that the data in the column occurred in the order that the values appear in the column, with equally-spaced time intervals. If you want to use the stamp option, you also need one column of date/time data.

If you want to generate multiple graphs at once, provide one column of numeric data for each graph. If you use the stamp option, all graphs use the same date/time column.

If data are missing for either single time series plots or multiple time series plots, no symbols will be plotted at the corresponding time unit.

▶ **To create a time series plot**

1 Choose **Graph ➤ Time Series Plot** or **Stat ➤ Time Series ➤ Time Series Plot**.

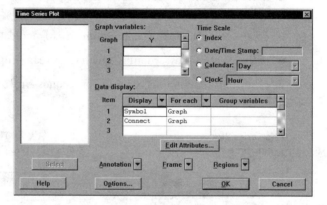

2 In **Y**, enter the column of numeric data.

3 Under **Time Scale**, choose one of the following time scales:

- **Index** (each observation is labeled with a consecutive integer, as in 1, 2, 3).

- For **Date/Time Stamp**, enter a column that contains your desired time unit.

- For **Calendar** or **Clock**, choose a time unit from the drop-down list. The lists also contain combinations of units, such *Day Month*, that let you create multiple rows of axis labels.

4 Choose any of the graphics options outlined in *Options* on page 14-13, and click **OK**.

▷ **Example of a time series plot using a date/time stamp column**

In the MARKETD.MTW worksheet, the variable *Date* is a date/time column that has the format qQyy, as in 4Q92 to stand for the fourth quarter of 1992. This same format will be used as the tick labels on the graph.

1 Open the worksheet MARKETD.MTW.

2 Choose **Graph ➤ Time Series Plot**.

3 In **Y**, enter *Sales*.

4 Under **Time Scale**, choose **Date/Time Stamp** and enter *Date*. Click **OK**.

Graph window output

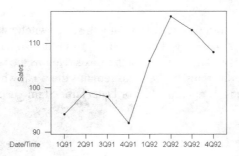

Options

Time Series Plot dialog box

The Time Series Plot dialog box includes the typical core graph dialog box controls. You can create multiple graphs and control a wide variety of graphics options. The following table outlines each of the dialog box features and indicates which chapter covers the feature in detail:

Data display	Annotation	Frame	Regions	Groups and multiple graphs
Symbols	Titles	Axes[a]	Figure	Display data for each group
Connection lines	Footnotes	Ticks[a]	Data	
	Text	Grids[a]	Legend	Multiple graphs at once
Projection lines	Lines	Reference lines	Aspect ratio of a page	Same scales across graphs
Areas	Polygons	Change the scale		Overlaying graphs
LOWESS lines	Markers			Laying out graphs on the same page
	Data labels	Suppressing frame elements		
Chapter 15	Chapter 17	Chapter 18	Chapter 19	Chapter 16

a. Axes, ticks, and grids have special properties when used with time series plots that have multiple time unit scales on the x-axis. In each item description in Chapter 18, see the section on using the item with time series plots.

Options subdialog box

- **Customize the time scale.** You can set several fields in the subdialog box which affect factors such as start time, time intervals, range displayed or time units. See *Customizing the time scale* on page 14-14.

- **Transform the x- or y-axis.** You can perform a log scale transformation. See Help in your MINITAB application for details.

- **Transpose the x- and y-axes.** Transposing the axes switches the x-axes with the y-axes, so that the x-axes is vertical and the y-axes is horizontal. Transposing does not change the type or name of the axis: the x-axis remains the x-axis whether it is horizontal or vertical, just as the y-axis remains the y-axis whether it is horizontal or vertical. Transpose is not available for Date/Time Stamp using Time Series Plots.

Customizing the time scale

If you choose an index, calendar, or clock time scale in the main dialog box, you can click **Options** to customize the time scale units. Each time unit has a range and a default start value. However, the following options are available:

- limit the time unit's *range*, such as displaying only the hours between 8am and 5pm

- determine intervals within a range, such as displaying every other month

- start with a particular date or time, such as starting with June data

- choose multiple calendar or clock units, yet display just the axis label rows you want

Time scale defaults

Time scale	Time unit	Range	Default start value
Index	Generic	All integers	1
Calendar	Day	1 to a maximum of 31, depending on the month	1
	Month	1 to 12	1
	Quarter	1 to 4	1
	Year	Positive integers	1900
Clock	Second	0 to 59	0
	Minute	0 to 59	0
	Hour	0 to 23	0

Note | The Month and Year units account for different length months and leap years.

▶ **To specify ranges or intervals**

1 In the Time Series Plot main dialog box, choose a time scale of **Index**, **Calendar**, or **Clock**.

2 Click **Options** for a subdialog box that contains features for the scale you chose.

3 Under **Assignment of Time to Data**, click in the **Cycle through values** box for the time unit you want to affect.

4 Type a range and the intervals within that range that you want to display.

   ■ Specify a range by typing two numbers separated by a colon. For example, *1:12* means display the units 1 through 12.

   ■ Specify an interval by typing a slash (the division character) and a number. For example, 1:12/2 means show every other unit in a range: 1 3 5 7… or January, March, May, July…

5 Click **OK**.

▶ **To specify start time**

1 In the Time Series Plot main dialog box, choose a time scale of **Index**, **Calendar**, or **Clock**.

2 Click **Options**. A time-scale-specific subdialog box appears.

3 Under **Start times**, click in row 1 under the time unit you want to affect. Type the starting value. See the table on page 14-14 for the range of legal values, and for the default start times.

4 Fill in start values for any other cells in row 1.

   If you set a start time for one unit in a row, you must specify start times for all other units in the row. The start times table only contains multiple columns if you specified in the main dialog box a Calendar or Clock scale with multiple time units (for example, the Calendar scale that includes Day, Month, and Year).

5 If, in the main Time Series Plot dialog box, you specified several time series plots, you can specify a separate set of start times for each plot. In row 2 give all the start values for the second graph, in row 3 give all the start values for the third graph, and so on.

6 Click **OK**.

> ### Example of graphing bimonthly data with custom start times

The following graph shows how the depth of a reservoir fluctuates over time. Measurements were collected on a bimonthly basis (in months 1, 3, 5, 7, 9, and 11) starting in January of 1990. The month names on the graph are abbreviated: "J" = January, "M" = March, etc.

1 Open the worksheet EXH_GRPH.MTW.

2 Choose **Graph ➤ Time Series Plot**.

3 In **Y**, enter *Depth*.

4 Under **Time Scale**, choose **Calendar**, then choose **Month Year**.

5 Click **Options**. In the **Start time** table, under **Month**, type *1*. Under **Year**, type *1990*.

6 Under **Assignment of Time to Data**, type *1:12/2* in **Month**. Click **OK** in each dialog box.

Graph window output

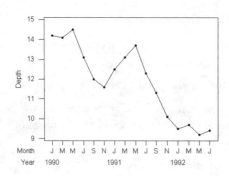

More | For an example of a time series plot that displays data collected four times in one minute, see *Example of hiding axis label rows* on page 14-17.

▶ To hide the display of time scales on the x-axis

When you choose a time scale with multiple time units—for example, a Clock time scale of *Day Hour Minute*—the graph displays a row of axis labels for each unit. You may want to hide some axis label rows to make a cluttered graph look cleaner.

1 In the Time series plot main dialog box, choose **Calendar** or **Clock** and pick an entry from the list that has multiple time units.

2 Click **Options**. Under **Assignment of Time to Data**, uncheck **Show** for each time unit you want to hide.

▷ Example of hiding axis label rows

You can turn the cluttered graph on the left into the clean graph on the right by only displaying the Day axis.

1 Open the worksheet EXH_GRPH.MTW.

2 Choose **Graph ➤ Time Series Plot**.

3 In **Y**, type *Temp*.

4 Click **Clock** and choose **Day Hour Minute**.

5 Click **Options**. Under **Assignment of Time to Data**, in **Minute**, type *0:59/30*.

   This tells MINITAB that the measurements occurred every 30 minutes.

6 Do one of the following:

   ■ To create the graph on the left, click **OK** in each dialog box.

   ■ To create the graph on the right, uncheck **Show** for **Hour** and **Minute**, then click **OK** in each dialog box.

Default axis label rows

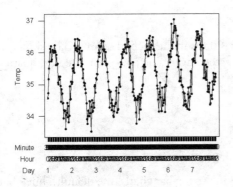

Hidden axis label rows

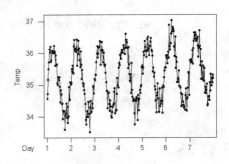

▷ Example of overlaying multiple time series plots

You can overlay several time series plots, to better see how groups are related. Say you want to show the relationship over time between the dollars generated by sales (Sales) and the dollars spent on advertising (Advertis). You can make Advertis lag Sales by a quarter by changing the start times of the variables.

1 Open the worksheet MARKET.MTW.

2 Choose **Graph ➤ Time Series Plot**.

3 Under **Y**, enter *Sales* in row 1 and enter *Advertis* in row 2. Under **Time Scale**, choose **Calendar**, then choose **Quarter Year**.

4 Click **Options**. Under **Start time**, in the **Quarter** column, type *1* in row 1 and type
    2 in row 2. In the **Year** column, type *1991* in rows 1 and 2. Click **OK**.

5 Choose **Annotation ➤ Title**. In **Title**, type *Do Sales Lag Advertising?* Click **OK**.

6 Choose **Frame ➤ Multiple Graphs**. Click **Overlay graphs on the same page**. Click
    OK in each dialog box.

*Graph
window
output*

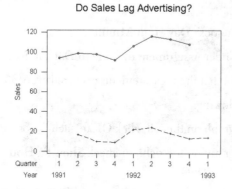

Interpreting the results

The dashed line for advertising expenses starts in the second quarter. The similarity
between the patterns suggests that increased advertising pays off in the next quarter
with increased sales.

Charts

You can produce many kinds of charts, including bar charts (the default), line charts,
symbol charts, area charts, and projection (spike) charts. All of these charts can take
two forms:

■ **Chart of counts** shows the count of each unique observation in a single column.

■ **Chart of a function by group** uses one column of measurement data for the y-axis,
    and a second column as a category, or grouping variable, that appears on the x-axis.
    By default, one bar displays for each group, and the height of each bar is set by the
    sum function—the height of each bar is the sum of observations for that group.

A chart of counts
Each time a defect was found in a product, the ID number (1, 3, 5, or 7) for the plant where the product was manufactured was entered in the column Plant. This graph shows the total number of defects found in each plant.

A chart of a function by group
The column Sales contains the sales revenue over two years, and Year contains the year in which the sales occurred, 1991 or 1992.

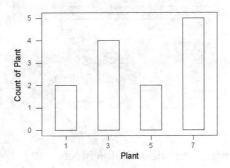

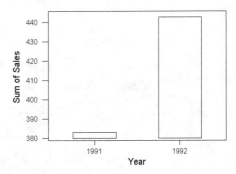

As well as the all the graphics options that come with core graphs, charts have options for changing the function of the y-axis (for example, from sums to means), grouping categories with clustering and stacking, controlling the order of categories in the x-axis, and more.

More   Histograms and pie charts are similar to charts. See *Histograms* on page 14-28. See *Pie Charts* on page 23-5.

Data

- For a chart of counts, you need one column of categorical data for the x-axis.

- For a chart of sums (or some other function) by group, you need one column of measurement data for the y-axis, and one column of categorical data for the x-axis.

- For either type of chart, if you use groups within the categorical variable (clustering or stacking), you need additional columns of categorical data.

Categorical data can be numeric, text, or date/time. Measurement (or continuous) data, must be numeric.

▶ **To create a chart**

1 Choose **Graph ➤ Chart**.

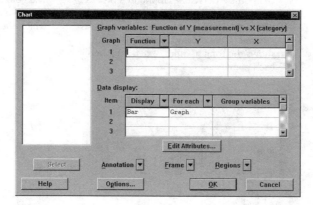

2 To create

- a chart of counts, enter a categorical column in **X**.

- a chart of sums (or some other function), enter a column of measurement data in **Y** and a column of categorical data in **X**.

3 If you like, use any of the options below, and click **OK**.

Options

Chart dialog box

The Chart dialog box includes the typical core graph dialog box controls. You can create multiple graphs and control a wide variety of graphics options. The following table outlines each of the dialog box features and indicates which chapter covers the feature in more detail:

Data display	Annotation	Frame	Regions	Groups and multiple graphs
Symbols	Titles	Axes	Figure	Display data for each group
Connection lines	Footnotes	Ticks	Data	
	Text	Grids	Legend	Multiple graphs at once
Projection lines	Lines	Reference lines	Aspect ratio of a page	Same scales across graphs
	Polygons			
Areas	Markers	Change the scale		Overlaying graphs
Bars	Data labels	Suppressing frame elements		Laying out graphs on the same page
Chapter 15	Chapter 17	Chapter 18	Chapter 19	Chapter 16

Tip Often, when you cluster or stack groups, you will want to display each bar in the cluster or each block in the stack with a different color or fill. To do that, use that same grouping variable in the data display table that you used as the clustering or stacking variable.

Note With charts, the data display grouping variable can only be one of the variables already specified as a cluster, stack, or x-axis variable.

In addition to the typical core graph features, you can change the function for the y-axis variable from sums to means, medians, or other functions. See *Changing the function for y-axis variables* on page 14-22. You can also set the starting point for the y-axis. See *Setting the chart's y-axis to start at zero* on page 14-22.

Options subdialog box

- **Group categories** within the x-variable with clustering and stacking. See *Grouping within categories by clustering and stacking* on page 14-24.

- **Control the order** of categories in the x-axis. You can choose between an increasing or decreasing Y axes. See *Ordering category groups based on y-values* on page 14-25.

- **Accumulate Y across X** to display the data as a cumulative frequency scale. Therefore, each bar represents the sum of the preceding categories and the current category. See *Accumulate Y across X (cumulative frequency scale)* on page 14-26.

- **Total Y to 100%** within each category to display the data as a percentage scale, comparing the categories with each other. See *Totalling Y to 100% within each X category (percent scales)* on page 14-27.

- **Transpose the x- and y-axes** to switch the x-axis with the y-axis, so that the x-axis is vertical and the y-axis is horizontal. See *Transposing X and Y* on page 14-28.

Setting the chart's y-axis to start at zero

By default, MINITAB tries to emphasize the variation in the data, and so often does not place the chart's y-scale minimum at 0. You can force the y-scale to start at any value you wish, including 0. MINITAB automatically sets the y-scale minimum to zero when:

- the Chart function is Count, N, or Nmiss
- you have both positive and negative data, and the Chart function is Sum, Mean, Median, Minimum, or Maximum

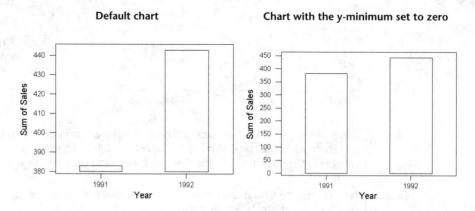

▶ To set the y-axis minimum to zero

1 From the Chart main dialog box, choose **Frame ➤ Min and Max**.

2 Check **Y minimum** and type *0* in the box. Click **OK** in each dialog box.

Changing the function for y-axis variables

If you specify a y-variable in the Chart main dialog box, the y-axis values on the graph are a function of that y-variable. The default function is a sum of the observations for each group. You can specify any of the following functions:

Chart function	Y-Axis displays
Sum (default)	sum of values
Count	number of values (frequency)
N	number of non-missing values
Nmiss	number of missing values
Mean	mean of values

Chart function	Y-Axis displays
Median	median of values
Minimum	the smallest value
Maximum	the largest value
Stdev	standard deviation of values
Ssq	sum of squares of values

▶ **To change the function for the y-axis**

1 In the Chart main dialog box, in the **Graph variables** table, click in row 1 of the **Function** column.

2 Choose an item from the **Function** drop-down list.

Note If you are specifying multiple graphs in the graph variables table, you can select a different function for each graph.

▷ **Example of a chart of means**

In the following chart, the height of a bar is the mean of the sales for that year.

1 Open the worksheet MARKET.MTW.

2 Choose **Graph ➤ Chart**.

3 Choose **Function ➤ Mean**.

4 In **Y**, enter *Sales*. In **X**, enter *Year*. Click **OK**.

Graph window output

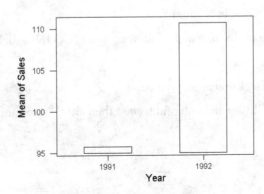

Grouping within categories by clustering and stacking

Clustering and stacking let you show subgroups within the groups on the x-axis. Clustering shows each subgroup as a separate bar. Stacking shows subgroups as blocks stacked on top of each other. You can use cluster and stack together, with blocks displaying in each cluster.

▶ **To cluster or stack**

1 In the Chart main dialog box, click **Options**.

2 Do one or both of the following:

   ■ Check **Cluster** and enter a column that contains the subgroups.

     If you want to adjust the distance between bars in the cluster, enter a value in **Offset** that is greater than or equal to 0 (bars display on top of each other) and less than 1.

   ■ Check **Stack** and enter a column that contains the subgroups.

▶ **Example of clustering and stacking**

The graphs below show sums of sales categorized by years, then further subdivided into quarters. In the first graph, sums of sales by quarter are clustered within each year. In the second graph, sums of sales by quarter are stacked within each year. The third graph shows two clusters, one for each ad agency, with quarters stacked within each cluster.

1 Open the worksheet MARKET.MTW.

2 Choose **Graph ➤ Chart**.

3 In **Y**, enter *Sales*. In **X**, enter *Year*.

4 Click **Options**. Do one of the following and click **OK** in each dialog box:

   ■ Check **Cluster** and enter *Quarter*.

   ■ Check **Stack** and enter *Quarter*.

   ■ Check **Cluster** and enter *AdAgency*, then check **Stack** and enter *Quarter*.

Clustered by quarter   **Stacked by quarter**   **Clustered by ad agency
and stacked by quarter**

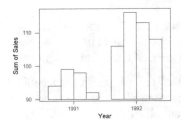 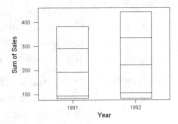 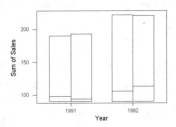

Ordering category groups based on y-values

You can present the groups in the chart in increasing order (from smallest to largest) or decreasing order (from largest to smallest) based on the y-axis values.

Chart with increasing order   **Chart with decreasing order**

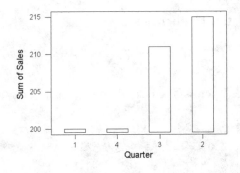 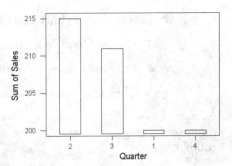

Changing the order of categories does not affect the ordering within clusters, stacks, or cluster/stack combinations—instead, the options move entire clusters, stacks, or cluster/stack combinations into order by the sum of the values in each x-axis column.

Note | When you reorder categories in combination with other options that affect the display of categories, MINITAB processes the options in this order: (1) display categories in increasing or decreasing order, (2) accumulate Y across X, and (3) total Y to 100% within each X category.

Note | You can only use the category ordering options, while overlaying multiple charts in the same graph window, when all charts use the same categorical (x) variable. For details, see *Overlaying charts and boxplots* on page 16-19.

Accumulate Y across X (cumulative frequency scale)

If you create a chart using both an x- and y-axis, you can use a cumulative frequency scale on the y-axis. Thus the height of the third bar, for example, is the sum of the observations in the first three categories.

If you use the cumulative scale with clustering and/or stacking, the same bars are cumulative across cluster or stack groupings. Therefore, the y-value of the second bar in a cluster will add to the y-value of the second bar in the next cluster, and so on.

For the cumulative scale to work properly, all cluster/stack groups (that is, all possible bar positions) must have at least one non-missing observation. You may wish to add appropriate dummy observations (with values of, for example, 0) for each cluster/stack group so all cluster/stack groups have at least one non-missing observation.

Note | When you use the cumulative frequency scale in combination with other options that affect the display of categories, MINITAB processes the options in this order: (1) display categories in increasing or decreasing order, (2) accumulate Y across X, and (3) total Y to 100% within each X category.

▶ To use a cumulative frequency scale

1 In the Chart main dialog box, click **Options**.

2 Check **Accumulate Y across X**.

▶ Example of a chart with a cumulative frequency scale

1 Choose **Graph ➤ Chart**.

2 In **Y**, enter *Sales*. In **X**, enter *Quarter*.

3 Click **Options**. Check **Accumulate Y across X**. Click **OK** in each dialog box.

Graph window output

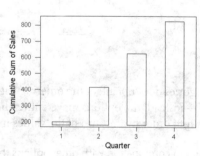

Totalling Y to 100% within each X category (percent scales)

You can use a percent scale on the y-axis, which is useful when you are clustering or stacking. The parts of each cluster or each stack (that is, each category) add up to 100%. When you use stack and cluster options together, the parts of each cluster/stack combination add up to 100%.

Note | When you use the percent scale in combination with other options that affect the display of categories, MINITAB processes the options in this order: (1) display categories in increasing or decreasing order, (2) accumulate Y across X, and (3) total Y to 100% within each X category.

▶ **To use a percent scale**

1 In the Chart main dialog box, click **Options**.

2 Check **Total Y to 100% within each X category**.

▷ **Example of percent scales with clustering and stacking**

1 Choose **Graph ➤ Chart**.

2 In **Y**, enter *Sales*. In **X**, enter *Year*.

3 Click **Options**.

4 Check **Total Y to 100% within each X category**.

5 Do one of the following and click **OK** in each dialog box.

■ To cluster, check **Cluster** and enter *Quarter*.

■ To stack, check **Stack** and enter *Quarter*.

Percent scale with clustering   **Percent scale with stacking**

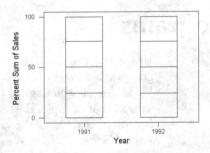

Transposing X and Y

You can switch, or *transpose*, the position of the x- and y-axes. Transposing the axes switches the x-axis with the y-axis, so that the x-axis is vertical and the y-axis is horizontal.

Transposing does not change the type or name of the axis: the x-axis remains the x-axis whether it is horizontal or vertical, just as the y-axis remains the y-axis whether it is horizontal or vertical. Keep this in mind when you use graphics options—such as the data display, annotation, or frame items—that require you to specify locations or directions in terms of the axis.

A chart with default x- and y-axis

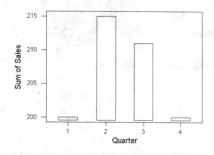

Same chart with transposed x- and y-axes

Note | The transposing X and Y option is available for all core graphs except matrix plots and draftsman plots.

Histograms

Histograms, like charts, show bars for each group in an x-axis variable. But while the groups in a chart correspond to the discrete categories of the x-axis variable (Flaw1, Flaw2, etc.), the groups in a histogram are *intervals* of continuous data in an x-axis variable. For example, all the values between 0.5 and 1.5 might be grouped in an interval labeled "1," all the values between 1.5 and 2.5 might be grouped in an interval labeled "2," etc.

Histograms separate the data into appropriate intervals (sometimes called bins) on the x-axis. For each interval, MINITAB draws a bar whose height, by default, is the number of observations, called the *frequency*, that fall in that interval.

For example, the Capital column contains the capital expenses (in thousands of dollars) for each quarter over two years. A histogram of that column would look like this:

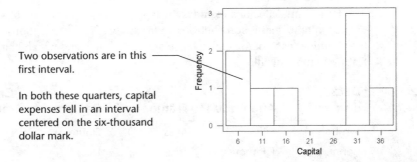

Two observations are in this first interval.

In both these quarters, capital expenses fell in an interval centered on the six-thousand dollar mark.

You can change the way intervals are calculated or specify which intervals you want to display. You can also change the scale of the y-axis from a frequency scale to a percent or cumulative scale.

Note | Observations that fall on interval boundaries are placed into the interval to the right, with one exception: observations on the boundary of the interval that is farthest to the right are placed in that last interval.

Data

You must have one column of numeric or date/time data for the x-axis. Missing data are automatically omitted from interval calculations.

▶ To create a histogram

1 Choose **Graph ➤ Histogram**.

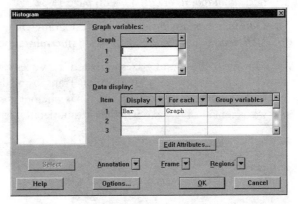

2 In **X**, enter the column containing the continuous data.

3 If you like, use any of the options on the next page, and click **OK**.

Options

Histogram dialog box

The Histogram dialog box includes the typical core graph dialog box controls. You can create multiple graphs and control a wide variety of graphics options. The following table outlines each of the dialog box features and indicates which chapter covers the feature in more detail:

Data display	Annotation	Frame	Regions	Groups and multiple graphs
Symbols	Titles	Axes	Figure	Display data for each group
Connection lines	Footnotes	Ticks	Data	Multiple graphs at once
Projection lines	Text	Grids	Legend	Same scales across graphs
Areas	Lines	Reference lines	Aspect ratio of a page	Overlaying graphs
Bars	Polygons	Change the scale		Laying out graphs on the same page
	Markers	Suppressing frame elements		
	Data labels			
Chapter 15	Chapter 17	Chapter 18	Chapter 19	Chapter 16

Options subdialog box

- **Change the scale** of the y-axis from frequencies to percentages or densities—see *Changing y-axis scales* on page 14-31.

- **Set ticks** to appear in the middle of each interval or at the boundaries—see *Placing ticks at midpoints or cutpoints* on page 14-32.

- **Define how many intervals** your histogram will contain, and define the size—see *Defining the number and position of intervals* on page 14-32.

- **Transpose the x- and y-axes** to switch the x-axes with the y-axes, so that the x-axes is vertical and the y-axes is horizontal. Transposing does not change the type or name of the axis: the x-axis remains the x-axis whether it is horizontal or vertical, just as the y-axis remains the y-axis whether it is horizontal or vertical.

More | You can create a histogram that is overlaid with a normal curve—see page 14-34.

Changing y-axis scales

You can use six types of scales on the y-axis, as shown below.

Scale	Height of each bar equals...	Example
Frequency (default)	the number of observations that fall in that interval.	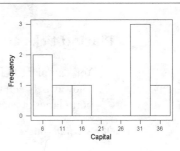
Percent	the percentage of the total number of observations that fall in that interval.	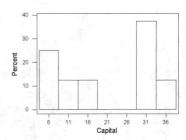
Density	a function of the area of that interval. The total area of all bars is one. The area of one bar is the proportion of the observations in that interval. Thus, the height of a bar is: $$\frac{\text{number of observations in interval}}{(\text{number of observations in all intervals}) * (\text{width of interval})}$$ A density scale is useful for viewing probability density functions.	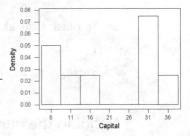
Cumulative Frequency Cumulative Percent or Cumulative Density	the frequency, percentage, or density of that interval plus all previous intervals. For example, in the cumulative frequency histogram at right, the third bar is the sum of the number of observations in the first three intervals.	

▶ **To change the y-scale**

1 In the Histogram main dialog box, click **Options**.

2 Under **Type of Histogram**, choose the scale you want: **Frequency**, **Percent**, **Density**, **Cumulative Frequency**, **Cumulative Percent**, or **Cumulative Density**.

Placing ticks at midpoints or cutpoints

You can place ticks at the midpoints or cutpoints of each interval. Midpoints are the midway between the boundaries of each interval. Cutpoints are the left and right boundaries of each interval.

Default histogram—ticks at midpoints   **Histogram with ticks at cutpoints**

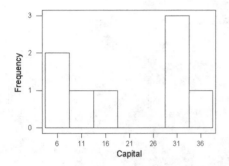   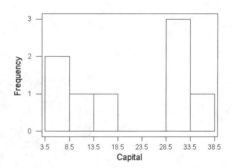

▶ **To place ticks at midpoints or cutpoints**

1 From the Histogram main dialog box, click **Options**.

2 Under **Type of intervals**, choose **MidPoint** or **CutPoint**. Click **OK**.

Defining the number and position of intervals

You can control the number of intervals, the positions of individual ticks, and the boundaries of each interval.

▶ **To define the number and position of intervals**

1 From the main Histogram dialog box, click **Options**.

2 Under **Type of histogram**, choose **MidPoints** or **CutPoints**. See *Placing ticks at midpoints or cutpoints* above.

3 Under **Definition of intervals**, choose one of the three options: **Automatic**, **Number of intervals**, or **Midpoint/cutpoint positions**.

4 If you chose **Number of intervals**, or **Midpoint/cutpoint positions**, enter values as needed (see table below for details). Click **OK** in each dialog box.

Option	You specify…	MINITAB finds…
Automatic	nothing	the number of intervals, the boundaries of those intervals, and and the tick positions that make sense for the data
Number of intervals	how many intervals you want (from 2 to 100)[a]	the best boundaries and tick positions for those intervals
Set midpoint/ cutpoint positions (when midpoints is selected)	the position of each midpoint tick. The values must be equally spaced, as in 5 10 15 20…	the boundaries that fit those midpoints
Set midpoint/ cutpoint positions (when cutpoints is selected)	the position of each cutpoint tick. The first value you type is the left boundary of the first interval, the second value is the boundary between the first and second interval, the third value is the boundary between the second and third interval, etc. The values do not have to be equally spaced, as in 2 5 8 9…	nothing—the number of intervals, their boundaries, and the tick positions have been set by you

a. When you set the number of intervals, MINITAB will not display the first and/or last intervals if they do not contain any observations. This can result in a histogram with one or two fewer intervals than you specified.

▷ Example of setting cutpoint positions

A histogram of capital expenses with ticks at cutpoints shows the first tick at 3.5 and the last tick at 38.5. You decide that the histogram would look nicer with a range of 5 to 40, with intervals every five values.

1 Open the worksheet MARKET.MTW.

2 Choose **Graph ➤ Histogram**.

3 In **X**, enter *Capital*.

4 Click **Options**. Choose **CutPoint**.

5 Do one of the following:

- To create the histogram on the left (with ticks at default cutpoints), click **OK** in each dialog box.

- To create the histogram on the right, (with specified cutpoints), choose **Midpoint/cutpoint positions** and type *5:40/5*. Click **OK** in each dialog box.

Histogram with ticks at default cutpoints

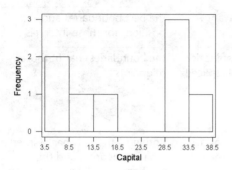

Histogram with ticks at specified cutpoints

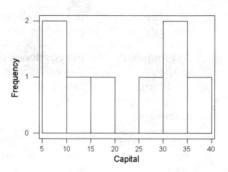

Creating a histogram with a normal curve

You may find it helpful to see how the bars in your histogram match a normal curve. For example, here is how a histogram of capital expenses would look with an overlaid normal curve:

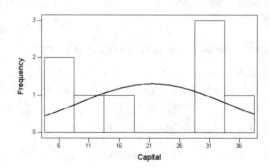

Histogram of Capital, with Normal Curve

▶ **To quickly create a histogram with a normal curve**

1 Choose Stat ➤ Basic Statistics ➤ Display Descriptive Statistics.

2 In **Variables**, enter a column containing numeric data.

3 Click **Graphs**. Choose **Histogram of data, with normal curve**. Click **OK** in each dialog box.

Boxplots

Boxplots, also called box-and-whisker plots, are particularly useful for showing the distributional characteristics of data. By default, a boxplot consists of a box, whiskers, and outliers.

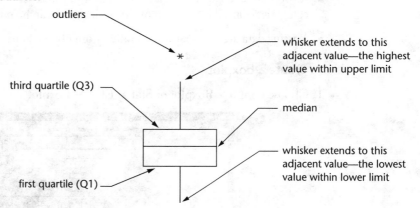

A line is drawn across the box at the median. Outliers are points outside of the lower and upper limits that are plotted with asterisks (∗). By default, the bottom of the box is at the first quartile (Q_1), and the top is at the third quartile (Q_3) value. The whiskers are the lines that extend from the top and bottom of the box to the adjacent values. The adjacent values are the lowest and highest observations that are still inside the region defined by the following limits:

Lower Limit: $Q_1 - 1.5 (Q_3 - Q_1)$
Upper Limit: $Q_3 + 1.5 (Q_3 - Q_1)$

Note   The character graph version of Boxplot (documented in Help) uses different calculations for the placement of boxes, whiskers, and outliers.

In MINITAB you can create a single boxplot, or a graph that contains one boxplot for data within each category of a grouping variable. For example, the column Pulse2 contains measurements of students' pulses after an experiment. The column Sex contains the sex of each person: 1 = male and 2 = female.

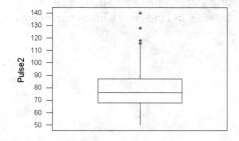

Boxplot of the variable Pulse2

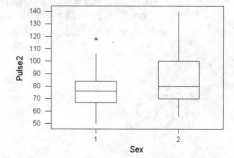

Boxplots of Pulse2, one for males and one for females

Data

- For a single boxplot, you must have one numeric column of measurement (continuous) data for the y-axis variable.

- If you want to create boxplots for each group, you must also have a column of categorical data. The column of categorical data can be numeric, text, or date/time.

- Missing data are automatically omitted from observations.

▶ To create a boxplot

1 Choose **Graph ➤ Boxplot** or **Stat ➤ EDA ➤ Boxplot**.

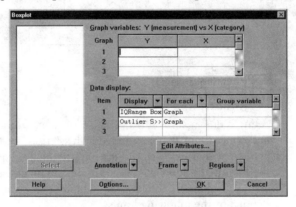

2 In **Y**, enter the column containing the measurement data.

3 To create boxplots for each group in a grouping variable, enter a column in **X**.

4 If you like, use any of the options below. Click **OK**.

Options

Boxplot dialog box

The Boxplot dialog box includes the typical core graph dialog box controls. You can create multiple graphs and control a wide variety of graphics options. The following table outlines each of the typical dialog box features and indicates which chapter covers the feature in more detail:

Data display	Annotation	Frame	Regions	Groups and multiple graphs
Boxes	Titles	Axes	Figure	Display data for each group
Symbols	Footnotes	Ticks	Data	
Connection lines	Text	Grids	Legend	Multiple graphs at once
	Lines	Reference lines	Aspect ratio of a page	Same scales across graphs
	Polygons	Change the scale		Overlaying graphs
	Markers			Laying out graphs on the same page
	Data labels	Suppressing frame elements		
This chapter	Chapter 17	Chapter 18	Chapter 19	Chapter 16

In addition to the features listed above, the main Boxplot dialog box also houses features which provide more control over each of the graph elements. You can:

■ Choose one of three box types: one that shows the interquartile range (IQRange Box), one that shows the confidence intervals for the median (CI Box), and one that shows the entire range of values (Range Box). See *Choosing a box type* on page 14-38.

■ Change the attributes of the boxes, including fill types and colors, edge line types, colors, sizes, and box width. You can even make the width of boxes proportional to sample size, or turn the whiskers on and off. See *Choosing a box type* on page 14-38.

■ Display symbols for individual points, medians, or outliers, and change the attributes of those symbols. See *Displaying symbols and connection lines* on page 14-41.

■ Connect medians with lines, and change the attributes of those lines. See *Displaying symbols and connection lines* on page 14-41.

Options subdialog box

Transpose is the only option available in the Options subdialog box for Boxplots. Transpose the x- and y-axes to switch the x-axes with the y-axes, so that the x-axes is vertical and the y-axes is horizontal. Transposing does not change the type or name of the axis: the x-axis remains the x-axis whether it is horizontal or vertical, just as the y-axis remains the y-axis whether it is horizontal or vertical.

Choosing a box type

You can use three box types, by themselves or in combination. Each box is a Data display element with attributes that you can modify.

Element	Definition	Example	Attributes
Interquartile (IQ) Range Box	Shows the interquartile range, with the box bottom at the 25th percentile and box top at the 75th percentile		■ Fill patterns and colors ■ Edge line types and colors ■ Box widths—can widen automatically, to a set value, or to a proportion of the box's sample size ■ Whiskers—show or hide them
Confidence Interval (CI) Box	Shows a 95% confidence interval for the median		■ All of the attributes for IQ Range boxes ■ Confidence interval—change from 95% to another value
Range Box	Shows a box that extends from the minimum to the maximum values		■ All of the attributes for IQ Range boxes except whiskers

▶ **To choose a box type**

1 In the Boxplot main dialog box, click in a row of the **Data display** table.

2 Under **Display**, choose **IQRange**, **CI Box**, or **Range Box**. Under **For each**, choose **Graph**.

3 If you want to display more than one type of box, click in another row of the **Data display** table, and repeat step 2. The boxes will display in row order, with the row 1 box in back.

4 If you want to change the attributes of the box, click in the row of the box you want to affect, and click **Edit Attributes**. Change the attributes and click **OK**.

For details on how to change the attributes, click the **Help** button.

▷ **Example of modifying the attributes of boxes**

The following graphs show a series of modifications to a boxplot.

This first graph shows the default interquartile (IQ) range boxes for the pulse rates of two groups, males and females.

1 Open the worksheet PULSE.MTW.

2 Choose **Graph ➤ Boxplot**.

3 In **Y**, enter *Pulse2*. In **X**, enter *Sex*. Click **OK**.

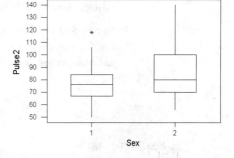

This second graph makes the width of the IQ range boxes proportional to each box's sample size.

4 Choose **Graph ➤ Boxplot**. The Boxplot dialog box contains the previous settings.

5 Click **Edit Attributes**. Check **Box width proportional to sample size**. Click **OK** in each dialog box.

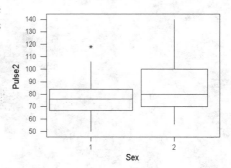

This third graph adds a confidence interval (CI) box. To make the CI box stand out, its fill is changed to solid black.

6 Choose **Graph ➤ Boxplot**.

7 In row 3 of the **Data display** table, choose **Display ➤ CI Box** and **For each ➤ Graph**.

8 Click **Edit Attributes**. Choose **Fill Type ➤ Solid**, then choose **Back Color ➤ Black**. Click **OK** in each dialog box.

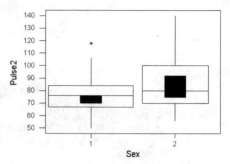

The fourth and final graph makes the CI boxes display differently depending on the group.

9 Choose **Graph ➤ Boxplot**.

10 In row 3 of the **Data display** table, choose **For each ➤ Group**. In **Group variable**, enter *Sex*. Click **OK**.

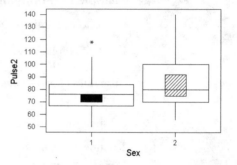

Displaying symbols and connection lines

You can clarify the position of data points on your boxplot by using symbols and connection lines. Boxplots use four special data display elements, each of which has attributes that you can change.

Element	Definition	Example	Attributes
Median symbols	A symbol at the median		■ symbol type, color, and size For details, see *Symbols* on page 15-5.
Outlier symbols	A symbol (asterisk, by default) for each outlier		■ symbol type, color, and size For details, see *Symbols* on page 15-5.
Individual symbols	A symbol (filled circle, by default) for each observation		■ symbol type, color, and size For details, see *Symbols* on page 15-5.
Median connection lines	Lines that connect the medians of multiple boxplots (visible only when boxplots use a categorical x-variable)		■ line type, color, and size ■ straight or step-like lines For details, see *Connection Lines* on page 15-7.

Matrix Plots

A matrix plot is a two-dimensional matrix of individual plots (see *Plots* on page 14-7). Matrix plots are good for, among other things, seeing the two-variable relationships among a number of variables all at once. This can help you save time because you can often identify the meaningful relationships with a single graph. You plot up to 20 variables at once.

For example, here is a matrix plot of three variables that are measurements of human participants in an experiment: Height (in inches), Weight (in pounds), and Pulse1 (pulse rate, in beats per second).

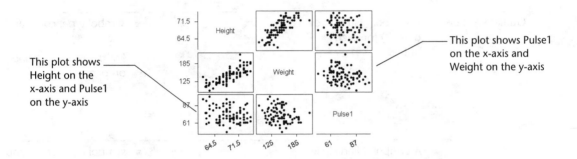

This plot shows Height on the x-axis and Pulse1 on the y-axis

This plot shows Pulse1 on the x-axis and Weight on the y-axis

More | A Draftsman plot, also called a casement display, is similar to a matrix plot. See *Draftsman Plots* on page 14-46.

Data

You need at least two and no more than 20 numeric or date/time columns. Observations in date/time columns will display as their underlying numeric values, not as formatted dates or times. For example, 1/1/97 will display as 35431. Missing values in any column will be omitted from the graph.

▶ **To create a matrix plot**

1 Choose **Graph ➤ Matrix Plot**.

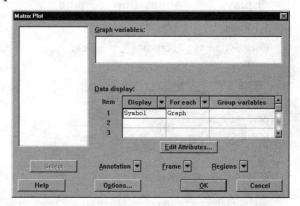

2 In **Graph variables**, enter from two to 20 columns. The columns will be graphed in the order you enter them; for example, entering *Height Weight Pulse1* creates the matrix plot shown on page 14-42.

3 If you like, use any of the options listed below, and click **OK**.

Note | The same y-scale is used for all plots in a given row, and the same x-scale is used for all plots in a given column. When you have ten or less plots in a row or column, the default ticks are at the first and third quartiles. When you have more than ten plots in a row or column, no ticks or external axis labels display.

Options

Matrix Plot dialog box

The Matrix Plot dialog box includes the typical core graph dialog box controls. You can create multiple graphs and control a wide variety of graphics options. The following table outlines the Matrix Plot dialog box features and indicates which chapter covers the feature in more detail:

Data display	Annotation	Frame	Regions	Groups and multiple graphs
Symbols	Titles	Axes[b]	Figure	Display data for each group
Connection lines	Footnotes	Ticks[bc]	Data	
	Text	Grids[b]	Legend	Laying out graphs on the same page
Projection lines	Lines	Reference lines[b]	Aspect ratio of a page	
	Polygons			
Areas	Markers	Suppressing frame elements[b]		
LOWESS lines[a]	Data labels			
Chapter 15	Chapter 17	Chapter 18	Chapter 19	Chapter 16

a. In matrix plots, you cannot store fits and residuals with LOWESS lines.

b. In matrix plots, you can only address the entire graph (for axes) or all graphs at once (for ticks, grids, reference lines, minimums, and maximums). The frame options you choose apply to all graphs in the matrix plot.

c. By default, tick labels on the x-axes of matrix plots are at a 30-degree angle. Tick labels on the bottom x-axis of matrix plots are placed differently than tick labels on the top x-axis of matrix plots: top tick labels place text to the upper right of the reference point; bottom tick labels place text to the lower left of the reference point.

Options subdialog box

- Display all of the matrix, or just a portion of it. See *Displaying a full or partial matrix* on page 14-45.

- Place variable labels along the diagonal of the matrix, or at the boundaries. See *Placing variable labels* on page 14-46.

- Add "jitter" to arrange the display of data points so that you can see overlapping points. See *Adding jitter to overlapping points* on page 14-10.

Tip | You can put more than one matrix plot in a single Graph window by specifying **Graph ➤ Layout**, specifying several matrix plots (along with other graphs) in separate commands, then specifying **Graph ➤ End Layout**.

Displaying a full or partial matrix

By default, MINITAB displays the full matrix of plots, but you can choose to display just the lower left or upper right triangle of the matrix.

Full matrix (the default)

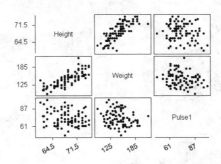

Lower left matrix   **Upper right matrix**

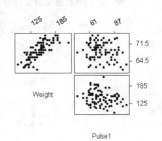

Note | When you display just the upper right triangle of a matrix, the default sides for tick and axis lines and labels shift to the upper and right sides, respectively.

▶ **To display a full or partial matrix**

1 In the Matrix Plot main dialog box, click **Options**.

2 Under **Matrix Display**, choose **Full**, **Lower left**, or **Upper right**. Click **OK**.

Placing variable labels

You can place the variable labels along the empty diagonal of the matrix (the default), or at the boundary of the matrix.

Diagonal variable labels (the default)   **Boundary variable labels**

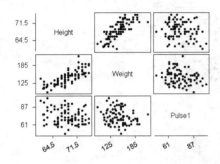 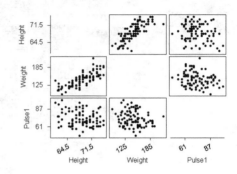

▶ **To place variable labels**

1 In the Matrix Plot main dialog box, click **Options**.

2 Under **Variable Label Placement**, choose **Diagonal** or **Boundary**. Click **OK**.

Draftsman Plots

A draftsman plot, also called a casement display, is a two-dimensional matrix of separate plots. Like matrix plots, draftsman plots are good for seeing the two-variable relationships between a number of variables all at once. This can help you save time because you can often identify the meaningful relationships with a single graph and then quickly explore them. You can plot up to 20 y-axis variables versus 20 x-axis variables at once. For example, the following draftsman plot displays two variables on the y-axis versus three variables on the x-axis.

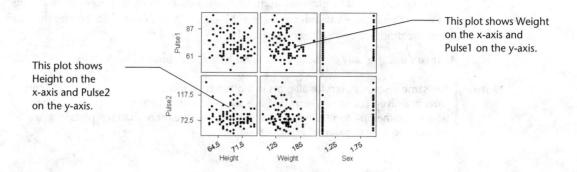

This plot shows Weight on the x-axis and Pulse1 on the y-axis.

This plot shows Height on the x-axis and Pulse2 on the y-axis.

More | A Draftsman plot, also called a casement display, is similar to a matrix plot. See *Matrix Plots* on page 14-42.

Data

You need at least three columns of data: one column for the y-axis and two for the x-axis, or vice versa. The columns can be numeric or date/time. You can have no more than 20 columns for each axis.

Observations in date/time columns will display as their underlying numeric values, not as formatted dates or times. For example, 1/1/97 will display as 35431. Missing values in any column will be omitted from the graph.

▶ **To create a draftsman plot**

1 Choose **Graph ➤ Draftsman Plot**.

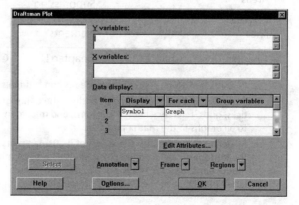

2 In **Y variables**, enter from 1 to 20 columns.

3 In **X variables**, enter from 1 to 20 columns. You must have a total of at least three variables.

The columns will be graphed in the order you enter them. For example, entering *Pulse1 Pulse2* in **Y variables** and *Height Weight Sex* in **X variables** creates the x-axis on the draftsman plot shown on page 14-47.

4 If you like, use any of the options listed below, and click **OK**.

Note | The same y-scale is used for all plots in a given row, and the same x-scale is used for all plots in a given column. When you have ten or less plots in a row or column, the default ticks are at the first and third quartiles. When you have more than ten plots in a row or column, no ticks or external axis labels display.

Options

Draftsman plot dialog box

The Draftsman Plot dialog box includes the typical core graph dialog box controls. You can create multiple graphs and control a wide variety of graphics options. The following table outlines the Draftsman Plot dialog box features and indicates which chapter covers the feature in more detail:

Data display	Annotation	Frame	Regions	Groups and multiple graphs
Symbols	Titles	Axes[b]	Figure	Display data for each group
Connection lines	Footnotes	Ticks[bc]	Data	
	Text	Grids[b]	Legend	Laying out graphs on the same page
Projection lines	Lines	Reference lines[b]	Aspect ratio of a page	
Areas	Polygons	Suppressing frame elements[b]		
LOWESS lines[a]	Markers			
	Data labels			
Chapter 15	Chapter 17	Chapter 18	Chapter 19	Chapter 16

a. In draftsman plots, you cannot store fits and residuals with LOWESS lines.

b. In draftsman plots, you can only address the entire graph (for axes) or all graphs at once (for ticks, grids, reference lines, minimums, and maximums). The frame options you choose apply to all graphs in the matrix plot.

c. By default, tick labels on the x-axes of draftsman plots are at a 30-degree angle. Tick labels on the bottom x-axis of matrix plots are placed differently than tick labels on the top x-axis of matrix plots: top tick labels place text to the upper right of the reference point; bottom tick labels place text to the lower left of the reference point.

Options subdialog box

■ Add "jitter" to arrange the display of data points so that you can see overlapping points. See *Adding jitter to overlapping points* on page 14-10.

Contour Plots

A contour plot is a two-dimensional graph of three measurement variables: x, y, and z. You can think of the z-variable as extending in/out of the graph plane. The contour lines represent the magnitude of the z-variable. In the graph, contours made up of equal z-values display as lines (or as areas between the lines) in the x-y plane.

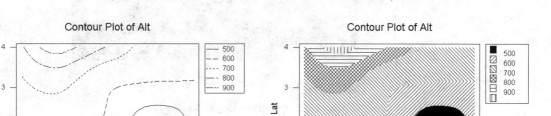

If two or more points have the same x- and y-values, MINITAB uses the median of all the z-values for those points as the new z-value.

More | This is a general purpose contour plot, for any x, y, and z data. The response surface contour plot for Designed Experiments (**Stat ➤ DOE ➤ RS Plots**) is specifically designed to produce contour plots for functions supported by MINITAB's Response Surface commands.

Data

You need three numeric columns of equal length, each containing at least three non-missing values. Missing values are omitted from the graph.

▶ To create a contour plot

1 Choose **Graph ➤ Contour Plot**.

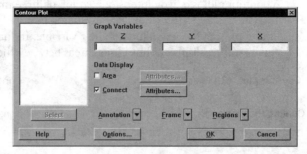

2 Enter a column for **Z**, a column for **Y**, and a column for **Y**.

3 If you like, use any of the options below and click **OK**.

Options

Contour plot dialog box

The Contour Plot dialog box includes the typical core graph dialog box controls. You can create multiple graphs and control a wide variety of graphics options. The following table outlines the Contour Plot dialog box features and indicates which chapter covers the feature in more detail:

Data display	Annotation	Frame	Regions	Groups and multiple graphs
Connection lines[a]	Titles	Axes	Figure	Laying out graphs on the same page
Areas[ab]	Footnotes	Ticks	Data	
	Text	Grids	Legend	
	Lines	Reference lines	Aspect ratio of a page	
	Polygons	Suppressing frame elements		
	Markers			
This chapter	Chapter 17	Chapter 18	Chapter 19	Chapter 16

a. Contour plots do not support grouping variables with connection lines or areas since the contours are actually groups themselves.

b. Contour plots do not support area edge lines. Use connection lines with areas to accomplish this.

You can also access controls for displaying the contour plot with connection lines, areas, or both from within the main Contour Plot dialog box. See *Using connection lines and areas with contour plots* on page 14-53.

Options subdialog box

- **Control the number and position** of contour levels (See *Controlling the number and position of contour levels* below).

- **Change the mesh** (grid of points) of the graph: increase the resolution to get a higher level of detail, or lower the resolution to speed up drawing of the graph. See *Changing the mesh* on page 14-52.

- **Enter a z-value** to be used for the four corners of the grid, that is, the background level (see Help for details).

- **Transpose the x- and y-axes** to switch the x-axes with the y-axes, so that the x-axes is vertical and the y-axes is horizontal. Transposing does not change the type or name of the axis: the x-axis remains the x-axis whether it is horizontal or vertical, just as the y-axis remains the y-axis whether it is horizontal or vertical.

Controlling the number and position of contour levels

By default, MINITAB will automatically determine how many contour levels to use for your data, as well as the z-variable values that correspond to those levels. MINITAB tries to find logical positions for contour levels, but you can override the default if you wish. You can specify:

- the number of contour levels you want (from 2 to 15), letting MINITAB calculate the position of those levels.

- the z-variable values where you want each contour level to be set, which implicitly determines the number of contour levels in the graph (i.e., if you specify four values, four contour levels will be created). You can specify from 2 to 15 data values. The data values that you specify are in terms of your z-variable. For example, if the values in your z-variable range from 0 to 12, you might specify values of 2, 6, 8, and 10.

Note | When you use areas with a contour plot, the number of areas created equals the number of levels plus one.

▶ To specify the number and position of contour levels

1 In the Contour Plot main dialog box, click **Options**.

2 Under **Contour Levels**, do one of the following:

- To let MINITAB decide the number of contour levels (from four to seven) and their positions, choose **Automatic**.

- To set the number of contour levels, choose **Number**, then type a number from 2 to 15.

- To specify z-variable values of the contour levels, choose **Values**, then enter from 2 to 15 values in increasing order. You can also put the contour level values in a column in your worksheet and enter the column here.

Changing the mesh

By default, MINITAB creates a mesh, or grid, with 15 points in the X direction and 15 points in the Y direction. You can change the default mesh to:

- improve the resolution of contour levels—a mesh with more points results in a higher resolution

- improve the speed of drawing the graph—a mesh with fewer points results in faster drawing speed

▶ **To improve the resolution of contour levels**

You can improve the resolution of contour levels, especially when you have many contour levels, by defining a finer grid. MINITAB interpolates a z-value for each point on the grid and displays only these interpolated z-values on the graph.

1 In the Contour Plot main dialog box, click **Options**.

2 Choose **Interpolate data over a specified mesh**.

3 Under **X-Mesh Positions**, do one of the following:

- To increase the resolution while letting MINITAB choose the positions of points, choose **Number** and enter a value higher than 15.

- To increase the resolution while specifying the positions of points yourself, choose **Values** and enter between 2 and 101 data values in increasing order (or, enter the data values in a column and specify the column here).

4 Repeat step 2 for **Y-Mesh Positions**.

▶ **To improve the speed of drawing the contour plot**

If you have many data points, you can do either of the following to improve drawing speed:

- Choose **Use data defined over a regular mesh**—that way, MINITAB will check for a regular mesh, and if it finds one, will display the graph without taking the time to calculate a z-value at each mesh point. If the mesh is not regular, MINITAB still produces a correct contour plot with a 15 × 15 mesh, and calculates z-values on the mesh by interpolation.

- Choose **Interpolate data over a specified mesh**, then specify a low number of x- and y-mesh positions, such as 10 and 10.

Using connection lines and areas with contour plots

Contour plots can be displayed with connection lines, areas, or both. By default, MINITAB creates each connection line with a unique line type (such as solid, dashed, or dotted). If you have selected to display areas, by default each area also has a unique area type (a fill pattern such as solid, empty, or hatched). Lines and areas have these attributes:

Data display element	Attributes
Connection lines	Line type, color, and size
Areas	Fill type and color

You can change the attributes of each connection line or area. The number of lines or areas depends on the number of contour levels in the graph:

- the number of connection lines created is equal to the number of contour levels

- the number of areas created is equal to the number of contour levels plus one

How many levels are in a contour plot? That depends on whether you created a default plot or manually set the number of levels (see *Controlling the number and position of contour levels* on page 14-51). By default, MINITAB automatically creates four to seven levels, depending on your data. To see how many levels would be used for your data, you can generate the graph and look at the graph legend. If you specify more attributes than there are levels, the attributes will be ignored.

Note | Unlike the other core graphs, there is no place in the contour plot's main dialog box to specify a grouping variable for each data display element. This is because the connect lines or areas are groups by themselves—the grouping variable is the z-variable.

Attribute codes

With contour plots you specify attribute settings differently than you do in other core graphs. Instead of picking line types, area colors, and other settings from drop-down lists, you type attribute codes, specifying as many codes as you need to affect all the possible areas or lines.

Why use codes? Because the number of contour levels in a contour plot is undetermined until the plot is created, the attribute subdialog box cannot present the definitive number of attribute choices.

Below are the code numbers for the attributes you can affect.

Line types:

Code	Line type	Name	Code	Line type	Name
0		None	4	— · — · — ·	Dash 1-Dot
1	————————	Solid	5	— ·· — ·· — ··	Dash 2-Dot
2	— — — — —	Dash	6	————————	Dash 3-Dot
3	· · · · · · · · · · · ·	Dot	7	— — —	Long Dash

Fill types:

Code	Fill type	Name	Code	Fill type	Name
0		None	5		Horizontal line
1		Solid (background is white)	6		Vertical line
2		Right slant	7		Cross line
3		Left slant	8		Dots
4		Cross slant	9		Squares

Colors for lines and areas:

Code	Color	Code	Color	Code	Color
0	White				
1	Black	6	Magenta	11	Dark Cyan
2	Red	7	Yellow	12	Dark Magenta
3	Green	8	Dark Red	13	Dark Yellow
4	Blue	9	Dark Green	14	Dark Gray
5	Cyan	10	Dark Blue	15	Light Gray

▶ **To change the attributes of connection lines and areas**

1 Check the element you want (**Connect** for connection lines and **Area** for areas) and click **Attributes**.

2 Do one or more of the following:

- For connection lines, click in **Line type**, **Line color**, or **Line size** and enter a code for each level you want to affect.

- For areas, click in **Fill type** or **Fill color**, and enter a code for each level you want to effect.

You can type code numbers, specify a stored constant (such as K1 or K2) that contains the code, or specify a column (such as C1 or C2) that contains one or more codes. For example, if the constant K1 contains the number 3, when you enter K1 in **Line type**, you will get a dotted line.

Note | If you do not enter enough settings to give each line or area a unique attribute, MINITAB cycles through the list until all lines or areas are assigned an attribute. For example, if you assign the line color codes 1 (black) and 2 (red), the first line will be black, the second line will be red, the third line will be black, etc.

▷ **Example of a contour plot with colored areas**

Say you want to create a color-coded contour plot of some longitude, latitude, and altitude data. In the example below, first you will set the number of contour levels to five—this way, you will know exactly how many fill colors to specify. Then you will set the fill type for all areas to solid (fill type code of "1"). Last, you'll specify five colors using the color codes: light gray (15), red (2), green (3), blue (4), and cyan (5).

1 Open the worksheet EXH_GRPH.MTW.

2 Choose **Graph ▸ Contour Plot**.

3 Enter *Alt* in **Z**, *Lat* in **Y**, and *Long* in **X**.

4 Uncheck **Connect**.

5 Check **Area** and click **Attributes**.

6 In **Fill type**, type *1*.

7 In **Fill color**, type *15   2   3   4   5*.

8 Click **OK** in each dialog box.

*Graph
window
output*

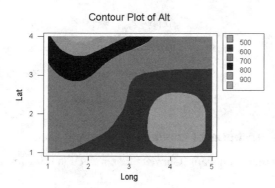

15

Core Graphs: Displaying Data

Displaying Data Overview

One of the distinguishing features of core graphs is the rich variety of ways you can display the data in your graph. For each core graph, you can represent the data with one or more *data display elements*, such as symbols, lines that connect data points, and areas. Each data display element has several *attributes*, such as size, color, and fill pattern. You can change each of these attributes to achieve a wide range of effects.

You can also apply the attributes selectively. Most of the time, you will want to apply the attributes to all the points in a graph at once (for example, turning all the symbols blue). But you can also apply different attributes to each group of points (turning all the symbols for 1991 blue and all the symbols for 1992 red), or apply different attributes to each point in the graph (giving each symbol a different color). Below is a table of data display elements and their attributes.

Element	Definition	Example	Attributes
Symbols	Dots, circles, squares, etc., that appear for each point on the graph		■ type, color, and size of symbols
Connection lines	Lines that connect points		■ type, color, and size of lines ■ straight or step-like lines ■ connection order (Plots only)
Projection lines	Lines that extend from each point down to the x or y-axis		■ type, color, and size of lines ■ base location for the projection ■ direction of the projection (to the x- or y-axis)

Element	Definition	Example	Attributes
Areas	Filled areas under points		■ type and color of fills ■ type, color, and size of edge lines ■ base location ■ extension of areas in the x- or y-direction ■ straight or stepped edge lines
Bars	Bars that represent categories (charts and histograms only)		■ type and color of fills ■ type, color, and size of edge lines ■ base location for each group ■ extension of areas in the x- or y-direction
LOWESS lines	Smoothed points connected with lines. LOWESS stands for LOcally-Weighted Scatter plot Smoother.		■ type, color, and size of lines ■ degree of smoothness as determined by the f value ■ amount of influence of outliers on the smoothed values

Data display elements available to each core graph

Each data display element described in this chapter is shared by two or more core graphs. Data display elements that are unique to one core graph are described with that graph. For example, median boxes are used only by boxplots, and are described with the other boxplot options in Chapter 14, *Core Graphs*.

Some of the data display elements described in this chapter can also be used by 3D graphs, specialty graphs, and control charts. For those graphs, however, the elements are activated differently, and not all of the attributes described in this chapter will apply. For information on using data display elements with those types of graphs, see the chapters that describe those graphs.

The following table shows which data display elements can be used with each core graph.

Data display elements	Plots	Charts	Histograms	Boxplots	Time series plots	Matrix plots	Draftsman plots	Contour plots
Symbols	●	●	●		●	●	●	
Connection lines	●	●	●		●	●	●	●[a]
Projection lines	●	●	●		●	●	●	
Area	●	●	●		●	●	●	●[a]
Bars		●	●					
LOWESS lines	●		●		●	●	●	

a. Contour plots implement connection lines and areas slightly differently than other core graphs. Those options are described under *Using connection lines and areas with contour plots* on page 14-53.

▶ **To design a core graph**

1 Choose a core graph from the Graph menu.

   Core graphs are plots, charts, histograms, boxplots, time series plots, matrix plots, draftsman plots, and contour plots. A dialog box will appear for each of the core graphs which will have a Graph variables table and a Data display elements table.

2 In the **Graph variables** table, enter the variables you want to graph.

3 Choose a data display element from the **Display** drop-down menu in the **Data display** table.

   You can enter an element in an empty or non-empty cell; the item you choose will overwrite existing contents. Each core graph has one or more data display elements chosen by default.

4 In the same row of the **Data display** table, click in a cell in the **For each** column and choose an item from the drop-down list.

   ■ **For each ➤ Graph** applies the same attributes to every point in the graph.

   ■ **For each ➤ Group** applies different attributes to each group in a grouping variable. In other words, you can edit the attributes for each group.

If you chose **For each ➤ Group**, click in the **Group variables** cell and enter a column. For more information on displaying data for each group, see *Displaying Data for Each Group* on page 16-5.

■ **For each ➤ Point** applies different attributes to each data point. This option is not available for all data display elements.

5 Click on **Edit Attributes** to change the element attributes. The Edit Attributes subdialog box will display all the attributes that you can change for that element. For more information on the Edit Attributes subdialog box, see the attributes editing guidance for each of the following element sections. Click **OK**.

Symbols

Symbols can be used to display data points for the following core graphs: plots, charts, histograms, time series plots, matrix plots, and draftsman plots. You can display each data point as a symbol. You can also change the type, color, and size of the symbols. The following graph uses symbols to display the data points.

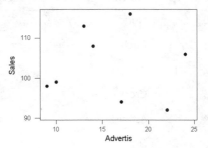

Using symbols

▶ To display data with symbols

1 In a core graph main dialog box, click in a row in the **Data display** table.

2 Choose **Display ➤ Symbol** in the **Data display** table.

3 Choose **For each ➤ Graph** in the **Data display** table.

This will apply the same attributes to every symbol in the graph—all symbols will be the same type, color, and size. You can also choose to display different attributes for each group in a grouping variable, or for each point—see *Displaying Data for Each Group* on page 16-5 and *Displaying Data for Each Point* on page 16-11.

4 You can also view the symbol attributes by clicking on **Edit Attributes**.

▶ To edit the symbol attributes

1 Click **Edit Attributes** in the core graph main dialog box. The following **Symbol** subdialog box will appear.

2 Do one or more of the following, then click **OK**.

- In **Type**, choose a symbol type name from the drop-down list, or enter a type code (see below).

- In **Color**, choose a color name from the drop-down list, or enter a color code (see *Lists of Symbols, Colors, Lines, and Fills* on page 15-26).

- In **Size**, choose a size from the drop-down list, or enter a value. The value can be any positive real number. Larger numbers give larger symbol sizes.

Symbol types

Code	Type	Name	Code	Type	Name
0		None			
1	○	Circle	16	◆	Solid Diamond
2	+	Plus	17	◇	Dot Diamond
3	×	Cross	18	⊕	Plus Diamond
4	✳	Asterisk	19	△	Triangle
5	·	Dot	20	▲	Solid Triangle
6	●	Solid Circle	21	△	Dot Triangle
7	⊙	Dot Circle	22	▷	Triangle Right
8	⊕	Plus Circle	23	▶	Solid Triangle Right
9	⊗	Cross Circle	24	▷	Dot Triangle Right
10	◎	Circle Circle	25	◁	Triangle Left
11	□	Square	26	◀	Solid Triangle Left
12	■	Solid Square	27	◁	Dot Triangle Left
13	⊡	Dot Square	28	▽	Triangle Down
14	⊠	Cross Square	29	▼	Solid Triangle Down
15	◇	Diamond	30	▽	Dot Triangle Down

▷ **Example of changing default symbols to crosses**

1 Open the worksheet MARKET.MTW.

2 Choose **Graph ➤ Plot**.

3 In **Y**, enter *Sales*. In **X**, enter *Advertis*.

Notice that by default, Symbol is already chosen as a data display element.

4 Click **Edit Attributes**.

5 Choose **Type ➤ Cross**. Click **OK** in each dialog box.

Graph window output

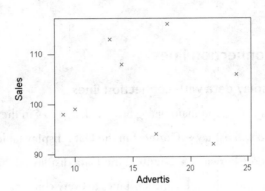

Connection Lines

Connection lines can be used to display data for the following core graphs: plots, charts, histograms, time series plots, matrix plots, draftsman plots, and contour plots. Connection lines connect the points on a graph with lines. You can change the type, color, and width of the lines. You can also decide whether the lines should be straight or stepped, and the order at which the points are connected (Plot only). The following graph uses connection lines to display the data points.

Note | Contour plots implement connection lines and areas slightly differently than other core graphs. Those options are described under *Using connection lines and areas with contour plots* on page 14-53.

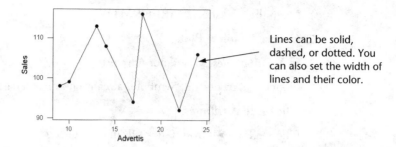

Lines can be solid, dashed, or dotted. You can also set the width of lines and their color.

Using connection lines

▶ To display data with connection lines

1 In a core graph main dialog box, click in a row in the **Data display** table.

2 Choose **Display ➤ Connect** in the **Data display** table.

3 Choose **For each ➤ Graph** in the **Data display** table.

This will apply the same attributes to every connection line in the graph—all lines will be the same type, color, and size. You can also choose to display different attributes for each group in a grouping variable—see *Displaying Data for Each Group* on page 16-5.

4 You can also view the line attributes by clicking on **Edit Attributes**.

▶ To edit the connection line attributes

1 Click **Edit Attributes** in the core graph main dialog box. The following **Connect** subdialog box will appear.

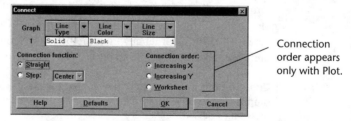

Connection order appears only with Plot.

2 Do one or more of the following, then click **OK**:

- In **Line Type**, choose a line type name from the drop-down list, or enter a type code (see *Line and edge types* on page 15-27).

- In **Line Color**, choose a color name from the drop-down list, or enter a color code (see *Colors* on page 15-27).

- In **Line Size**, choose a size from the drop-down list, or enter a value. The value can be any positive real number. Larger numbers give wider lines.

- Under **Connection function**, choose straight or stepped lines. If you choose stepped lines, you can also set the position of points in relation to the steps. For details, see *Stepped Connection Lines and Areas* on page 15-22.

- (Plots Only) Under **Connection order**, choose **Increasing X**, **Increasing Y**, or **Worksheet** order. **Increasing X**, the default, connects points horizontally from the smallest x-axis value to the largest. **Increasing Y** connects points vertically from the smallest y-axis value to the largest. **Worksheet**, which cannot be used with step-like lines set to center, connects points in the order they occur in the worksheet.

Projection Lines

Projection lines can be used to display data for the following core graphs: plots, charts, histograms, time series plots, matrix plots, and draftsman plots. A projection line joins each point to a base with a line. You can change the type, color, and width of the lines. You can also decide the base location for each projection, and the direction of the projection toward either of the axes. The following graph below plots Sales versus Index, using the default projection line type, a solid line.

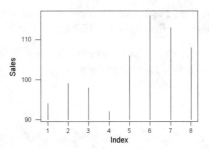

Using projection lines

▶ **To display data with projection lines**

1   In a core graph main dialog box, click in a row in the **Data display** table.

2   Choose **Display ➤ Project** in the **Data display** table.

3   Choose **For each ➤ Graph** in the **Data display** table.

This will apply the same attributes to every projection line in the graph—all lines will be the same type, color, and size. You can also choose to display different attributes for each group in a grouping variable or for each data point—see *Displaying Data for Each Group* on page 16-5 and *Displaying Data for Each Point* on page 16-11.

4 You can also view the line attributes by clicking on **Edit Attributes**.

▶ **To edit the projection line attributes**

1 Click **Edit Attributes** in the core graph main dialog box. The following **Project** subdialog box will appear.

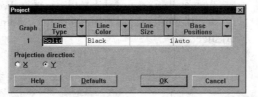

2 Do one or more of the following, then click **OK**.

- In **Line Type**, choose a line type name from the drop-down list, or enter a type code (see *Line and edge types* on page 15-27).

- In **Line Color**, choose a color name from the drop-down list, or enter a color code (see *Colors* on page 15-27).

- In **Line Size**, choose a size from the drop-down list, or enter a value. The value can be any positive real number. Larger numbers give wider lines.

- In **Base Positions**, enter a data value. For details, see *Base of Projection Lines, Areas, or Bars* on page 15-23.

- Under **Projection direction**, choose **X** or **Y**. For details, see *Direction for Projection Lines and Areas* on page 15-24.

Areas

Areas can be used to display data for the following core graphs: plots, charts, histograms, time series plots, matrix plots, draftsman plots, and contour plots. They can only be used on graphs with 900 or less points. Areas connect the points on a graph with lines, then fill the area beneath the lines with patterns and colors. The area attributes which you can set are:

- the type and color of fill
- the type, color, and width of the edge lines
- the base location for each point
- the projection of areas toward either of the axes
- the smoothness of the lines edges—straight or stepped

The following area graph below plots Sales versus Index, using the default line type and the cross slant pattern fill.

Note | Contour plots implement connection lines and areas slightly differently than other core graphs. Those options are described under *Using connection lines and areas with contour plots* on page 14-53.

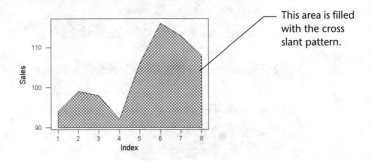

This area is filled with the cross slant pattern.

Using areas

▶ To display data with areas

1 In a core graph main dialog box, click in a row in the **Data display** table.

2 Choose **Display ➤ Area** in the **Data display** table.

3 Choose **For each ➤ Graph** in the **Data display** table.

   This will apply the same attributes to every area in the graph—all areas will have the same fill pattern, color, etc. You can also choose to display different attributes for each group in a grouping variable—see *Displaying Data for Each Group* on page 16-5.

4 You can also view the area's attributes by clicking on **Edit Attributes**.

▶ **To edit the area attributes**

1 Click **Edit Attributes** in the main core graph dialog box. The following **Area** subdialog box will appear.

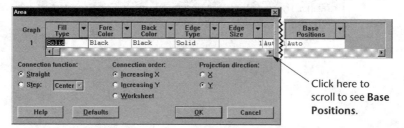

Click here to scroll to see **Base Positions**.

2 Do one or more of the following, then click **OK**.

- In **Fill Type**, choose a fill pattern name from the drop-down list, or enter a type code. For a list of available types, see *Fill types* on page 15-28.

- In **Fore Color**, choose a color name from the drop-down list, or enter a color code. Fore color controls the color of the edge lines and pattern lines. For example, if you choose a **Fill Type** of horizontal lines, and a **Fore Color** of red, the area will be outlined in red, and the area would be filled with red horizontal lines on a background of white (the default). For a list of available colors, see *Colors* on page 15-27.

- In **Back Color**, choose a color name from the drop-down list, or enter a color code. Back Color controls the background color of the pattern. For example, if you choose a **Fill Type** of horizontal line, and a **Back Color** of green, you would see black lines (the default) against a green background. For a list of available colors, see *Colors* on page 15-27.

- In **Edge Type**, choose an edge type name from the drop-down list, or enter a type code. For a list of edge types, see *Line and edge types* on page 15-27.

- In **Edge Size**, choose a size from the drop-down list, or enter a value. The value can be any positive real number. Larger numbers give wider lines.

- In **Base Positions**, enter a data value. For details, see *Base of Projection Lines, Areas, or Bars* on page 15-23.

- Under **Connection function**, choose straight or stepped edge lines. If you choose stepped lines, you can also set the position of points in relation to the steps. For details, see *Stepped Connection Lines and Areas* on page 15-22.

- (Plot only) Under **Connection order**, choose **Increasing X**, **Increasing Y**, or **Worksheet** order. **Increasing X**, the default, connects points horizontally from the smallest x-axis value to the largest. **Increasing Y** connects points vertically from the smallest y-axis value to the largest. **Worksheet**, which cannot be used with step-like lines set to center, connects points in the order they occur in the worksheet.

■ Under **Projection direction**, choose **X** or **Y**. For details, see *Direction for Projection Lines and Areas* on page 15-24.

Bars

Bars can be used to display data for the Chart and Histogram core graphs. Bars are rectangles that join each point to a base. You can set the type and color of the fills, as well as the type, color, and size of edge lines. You can also set the width and base location for each of the bars.

The first example that follows is a bar chart. The height of each bar is the sum of Sales for the corresponding year. The bars are separated from each other by default.

The second example is a histogram of Sales. In the second example, the height of a bar is the number of observations in the corresponding interval, and the bars are not separated.

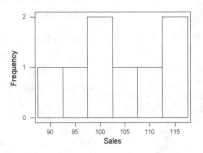

Using bars

▶ **To display data with bars**

1 In a core graph main dialog box, click in a row in the **Data display** table.

2 Choose **Display ➤ Bar** in the **Data display** table.

3 Choose **For each ➤ Graph** in the **Data display** table.

This will apply the same attributes to every bar in the graph—all bars will have the same fill pattern, color, etc. You can also choose to display different attributes for each group in a grouping variable—see *Displaying Data for Each Group* on page 16-5.

4 You can view any of the area attributes by clicking on **Edit Attributes**.

▶ **To edit the bar attributes**

1 Click **Edit Attributes** in the main core graph dialog box. The following **Bar** subdialog box will appear.

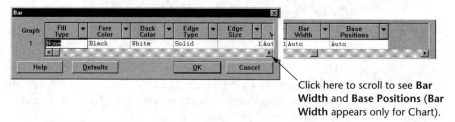

Click here to scroll to see **Bar Width** and **Base Positions** (**Bar Width** appears only for Chart).

2 Do one or more of the following, then click **OK**.

- In **Fill Type**, choose a fill pattern name from the drop-down list, or enter a type code. For a list of available types, see *Fill types* on page 15-28.

- In **Fore Color**, choose a color name from the drop-down list, or enter a color code. Fore color controls the color of the edge lines and pattern lines. For example, if you choose a Fill Type of horizontal lines, and a Fore Color of red, the bar will be outlined in red, and the bar would be filled with red horizontal lines on a background of white (the default). For a list of available colors, see *Colors* on page 15-27.

- In **Back Color**, choose a color name from the drop-down list, or enter a color code. Back Color controls the background color of the pattern. For example, if you choose a Fill Type of horizontal line, and a Back Color of green, you would see black lines (the default) against a green background. For a list of available colors, see *Colors* on page 15-27.

- In **Edge Type**, choose an edge type name from the drop-down list, or enter a type code. For a list of edge types, see *Line and edge types* on page 15-27.

- In **Edge Size**, choose a size from the drop-down list, or enter a value. The value can be any positive real number. Larger numbers give wider lines.

- (Charts only) In **Bar Width**, enter a number to specify the width of the boxes. The number can be any real number from 0 to 1, with 0 being a line and 1 the largest possible width, enclosing the full extent of the data. The default is .5, which makes each box take half the maximum width. The default is different when you use the chart's cluster option—see the note below.

- In **Base Positions**, enter a data value. For details, see *Base of Projection Lines, Areas, or Bars* on page 15-23.

- Under **Projection direction**, choose **X** or **Y**. For details, see *Direction for Projection Lines and Areas* on page 15-24.

Note | When you use the cluster option with charts, the default width of each bar in a cluster is 1/(number of bars in each cluster + 1). For example, with clusters that contain four bars, the width of each bar is 1/(4 + 1) or 0.2.

▷ **Example of setting bars to solid colors**

In order to change bars to solid colors, you set the fill type to solid, then set the back color to the color you want. In this chart, you will set the bars to solid black.

1 Open the worksheet MARKET.MTW.

2 Choose **Graph ➤ Chart**.

3 In **Y**, enter *Sales*. In **X**, enter *Year*.

4 Click **Edit Attributes**.

5 Choose **Fill Type ➤ Solid**.

6 Choose **Back Color ➤ Black**. Click **OK** in each dialog box.

Graph window output

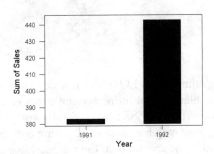

LOWESS Lines

LOWESS stands for LOcally-WEighted Scatter plot Smoother. The LOWESS routine takes the points from the graph, calculates a smoothed line relationship between them, then displays only the smoothed line. The method used for calculating the line is described in *LOWESS Calculation Method* on page 15-18.

You can use LOWESS lines with the following core graphs: plots, histograms, time series plots, matrix plots, and draftsman plots. The line attributes you can set are:

■ the type, color, and size (width) of lines

■ the degree of smoothness as determined by the *f* value

■ the degree of influence of outliers on the smoothed values

■ columns to store fits and residuals

Compare the following two graphs: a connection line graph and a LOWESS graph.
The LOWESS line graph can sometimes be more representative of the data.

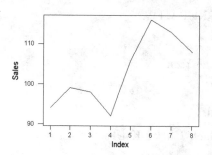

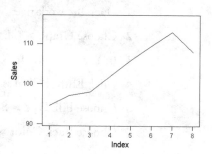

Among other uses, a LOWESS line can help you to explore the relationship between
two variables without fitting a specific model (such as a straight line or predefined
distribution). LOWESS lines generally work best with relationships described by gently
sloping lines with few areas of changing curvature. A good fit should show a generally
horizontal line around 0 on the y-axis.

Tip	Occasionally, a LOWESS line may stretch outside of the data region and be clipped. To view the entire line, change the maximum or minimum of the data range (see *Changing the Scale with Minimum and Maximum Values* on page 18-26) or turn off clipping in the data region (see *To turn data region clipping on and off* on page 19-20).

Using LOWESS lines

▶ To display data with LOWESS lines

1 In a core graph main dialog box, click in a row in the **Data display** table.

2 Choose **Display ➤ Lowess** in the **Data display** table.

3 Choose **For each ➤ Graph** in the **Data display** table.

   This will apply the same attributes to every LOWESS line in the graph—all lines
   will have the same line type, color, etc. You can also choose to display different
   attributes for each group in a grouping variable—see *Displaying Data for Each
   Group* on page 16-5.

4 You can view any of the line attributes by clicking on **Edit Attributes**.

▶ **To edit the LOWESS line attributes**

1 Click **Edit Attributes** in the main core graph dialog box. The following **Lowess** subdialog box will appear.

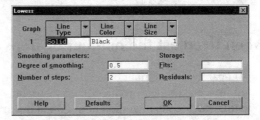

2 Do one or more of the following, then click **OK**.

- In **Line Type**, choose a line type name from the drop-down list, or enter a type code (see *Line and edge types* on page 15-27).

- In **Line Color**, choose a color name from the drop-down list, or enter a color code (see *Colors* on page 15-27).

- In **Line Size**, choose a size from the drop-down list, or enter a value. The value can be any positive real number. Larger numbers give wider lines.

- In **Degree of smoothing**, enter a value from 0 to 1. This value is the fraction (f) of the total number of points to use when calculating the smoothed (or fitted) values from a given point. The default is 0.5. For details, see *When to adjust the degree of smoothing* on page 15-17.

- In **Number of steps**, enter a number from 1 to 10 to specify the number of iterations of smoothing (robust steps) used to limit the influence of outliers on the smoothed y-values. The default is 2. For details, see *When to adjust the number of steps* on page 15-18.

- (Not available for matrix plots or draftsman plots) Under **Storage**, you can choose to store statistics in worksheet columns. If you specified more than one graph in the **Graph variables** table of the main graph dialog box, specify more than one column for each item:
  - In **Fits**, enter the column(s) where you want to store the new y-values that make up the smoothed line(s). These values are often referred to as fitted values, fits, or $\hat{Y}$'s.
  - In **Residuals**, enter the column(s) where you want to store residual values for the curve(s). The residuals are the original y-values minus the fitted values. For the ith observation, the residual is $Yi - \hat{Y}i$.

When to adjust the degree of smoothing

LOWESS lines generally work best when the fraction (f) of points is large enough to give a smooth fit without distorting the underlying relationship between the variables.

You may want to adjust the default value of f (0.5) when this is not the case. Cleveland [2] suggests that the best combination is as follows: Make f as large as possible, but maintain unrelatedness in a separate LOWESS plot of the y-value residuals versus the x-values from the graph, as shown in *LOWESS Calculation Method* below.

When to adjust the number of steps

You can set the number of iterations of smoothing (robust steps) to use to limit the influence of outliers on the smoothed y-values. Each step reduces the weights given to outliers in the next iteration of weighted linear regression based upon the size of residuals in the previous LOWESS step. For more details, refer to step 4 of the *LOWESS Calculation Method* on page 15-19. When you set the number of steps to 0, step 4 of the LOWESS method is eliminated entirely. Cleveland [2] suggests that two robust steps adequately smooth outlier effects for most data.

LOWESS Calculation Method

The LOWESS routine calculates a new smoothed y-value for an (x, y) point by doing the following:

1 The routine selects a 0.5 fraction, (f), of all points, using the points closest in x-value on either side of the point. The selected points are called the $f \cdot n$ points. The selection often results in more points selected from one side of the x-value than the other. The example below shows the fraction of points selected for a given point:

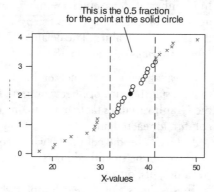

2 The routine calculates weights using the distance between each point in the selected fraction and the point to be smoothed as follows:

$$\text{weight for a point} = \left[1 - \left(\frac{\text{distance from the selected point}}{\text{max. distance between selected point and the } (f \cdot n) \text{ points}} \right)^3 \right]^3$$

This equation produces weights for the fraction that have a relationship like the following:

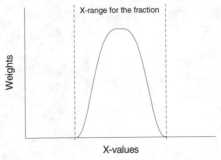

3 The routine performs a weighted linear regression on all points in the selected fraction of the data using the weights from step 2 to produce an initial smoothed value.

4 Finally, the routine limits the influence of outliers on the results by using two further iterations of step 3 (called robust steps) with new weights calculated as follows:

$$\text{weight} = \left[1 - \left(\frac{|\text{residual for the point from previous step}|}{6 \cdot \text{median of all }|\text{residuals}|\text{ from previous step}}\right)^2\right]^2$$

▶ Example of checking the LOWESS fit with residual plots

Say that you want to see how well the default LOWESS f-value of 0.5 fits your data. In the following example, you will first create a plot that uses the default f-value setting and store the residuals in a column in the worksheet. You will then plot the residuals versus the original x-values. Next you will create a new plot of the original variables using a different f-value, store the new residuals, and plot the new residuals versus the original x-values.

Step1: Create the plot with default f-value settings

1 Open PULSE.MTW.

2 Choose **Graph ➤ Plot**.

3 In **Y**, enter *Pulse1*. In **X**, enter *Pulse2*.

4 In the **Data display** table, choose **Display ➤ Lowess**.

   Notice that this replaces the symbol data display element.

5 Click **Edit Attributes**.

6 In **Residuals**, type *Resi1*. Click **OK** in each dialog box.

Data window output   Residuals appear in the column named Resi1.

Graph window output

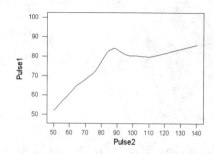

Step 2: Plot the residuals

Next you will plot the y-value residuals against the independent (x-axis) variable.

1 Choose **Graph ➤ Plot**.

Notice that the dialog box contains the last-used settings.

2 In **Y**, enter *Resi1*.

3 Click **Edit Attributes**.

4 In **Residuals**, delete *Resi1*. Click **OK** in each dialog box.

If you did not delete *Resi1*, you would overwrite the data in that column with the residuals for this new plot.

Graph window output

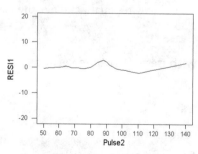

A good fit should show a generally horizontal line around 0 on the y-axis. The graph above shows some trend, indicating a need to adjust the f-value.

Step 3: Adjust the f-value and store new residuals

1 Choose **Graph ➤ Plot**.

2 In **Y**, enter *Pulse1*.

3 Click **Edit Attributes**.

4 In **Degree of smoothing**, type *0.3*.

5 In **Residuals**, type *Resi2*. Click **OK** in each dialog box.

Data window output   Residuals appear in the column named Resi2.

Graph window output

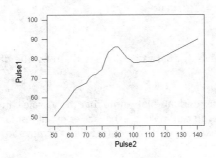

Step 4: Plot the new residuals

Finally, you will plot the new residuals, using the default degree of smoothing of 0.5.

1 Choose **Graph ➤ Plot**.

2 In **Y**, enter *Resi2*.

3 Click **Edit Attributes**.

4 In **Degree of smoothing**, type *0.5*.

5 In **Residuals**, delete *Resi2*. Click **OK** in each dialog box.

The new plot of residuals appears below right. For comparison, we also show the plot of the first residuals from page 15-20.

Graph window output

Plot of residuals for f value of 0.5.

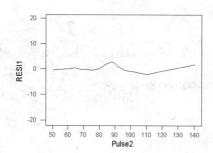

Plot of residuals for f value of 0.3

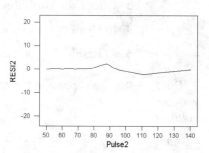

The second plot of residuals, for data smoothed with an f value of 0.3, shows a flatter relationship.

Note | When generating multiple residuals plots, note that the y-scale can change. To make comparisons more clear, you can make the axis scales on all residual plots equivalent by setting minimum and maximum data ranges (see *Changing the Scale with Minimum and Maximum Values* on page 18-26).

References for LOWESS

[1] W.S. Cleveland (1979). "Robust locally weighted regression and smoothing scatterplots." *Journal of the American Statistical Association*, 74, 829–836.

[2] W.S. Cleveland (1985). *The Elements of Graphing Data*. Wadsworth Advanced Books and Software. Monterey, CA.

Stepped Connection Lines and Areas

You can specify to connect points with straight lines, or lines that follow a step pattern. For stepped lines, the data point can be in the center of the step, to the left of the step, or to the right. In the examples below, the solid circles were added for clarity using the Symbol data display element.

Note | Contour plots do not use stepped lines.

Straight lines

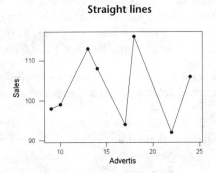

Stepped lines with points at the center of steps

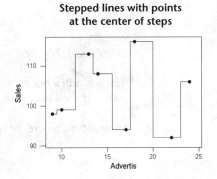

Stepped lines with points to the left of steps

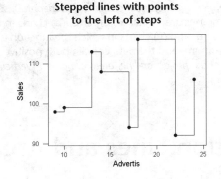

Stepped lines with points to the right of steps

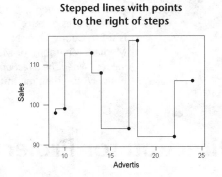

Base of Projection Lines, Areas, or Bars

In most cases, the base of each projection line, area, or bar starts by default at the minimum data value in the graph and extends to the current data point (the exceptions to this rule are noted below). You can change the base from the default to any data value. For example, the following plots display projection lines and areas that have a base of 100:

Projection lines with base of 100

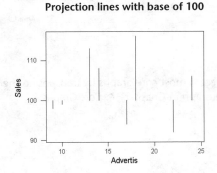

Areas with base of 100

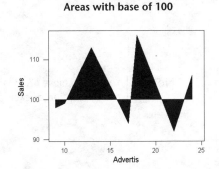

Usually you will specify just one value for the base; that value then becomes the base for all points on the graph. You may also specify a different base for each group in a grouping variable, or (for projection lines) for each point—see *Displaying Data for Each Group* on page 16-5 and *Displaying Data for Each Point* on page 16-11.

Tip | You can add a horizontal or vertical base line by adding a reference line that has the same data value as your base. See *Reference Lines and Labels* on page 18-22.

When setting a base for bars, if you set the base to a value lower than the data minimum, the bar is cut off at the data minimum. To show the entire bar, change the data minimum—see *Changing the Scale with Minimum and Maximum Values* on page 18-26.

Note | *When the direction of the projection line, area, or bar is X (horizontal)*, some graphs have default bases of zero. The graphs are: (a) all histograms; (b) charts in which the function is set to Count, N, or NMissing; and (c) charts in which the function is set to Sum, Mean, Median, Minimum, or Maximum, and the data contain both positive and negative values. *When the direction of the projection line, area, or bar is Y (vertical)*, the default base is always the data minimum.

Direction for Projection Lines and Areas

Projection lines can project along the y-axis (vertically) or the x-axis (horizontally) direction. For example, here are plots with projection lines and areas in the x direction.

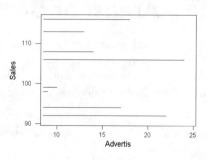

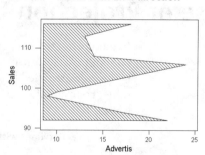

Note | You can achieve a similar affect in most core graphs by transposing the x- and y-axes. See the description of each core graph in Chapter 14, *Core Graphs*.

➤ **Example of using two projection lines with different directions**

In the following plot, you will add one projection line that uses the default attributes (a solid line projecting in the y direction) and another projection line that is dashed and projection in the x direction.

1 Open the worksheet MARKET.MTW.

2 Choose **Graph ➤ Plot**.

3 In **Y**, enter *Sales*. In **X**, enter *Advertis*.

4 In row 1 of the **Data display** table, choose **Display ➤ Project**.

5 In row 2 of the **Data display** table, choose **Display ➤ Project** and **For each ➤ Graph**.

6 Click **Edit Attributes**.

7 Under **Line Type**, choose **Dash**.

8 Under **Projection direction**, choose **X**. Click **OK** in each dialog box.

Graph window output

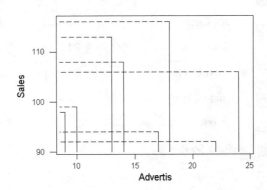

Lists of Symbols, Colors, Lines, and Fills

Symbol types

Code	Type	Name		Code	Type	Name
0		None		16	◆	Solid Diamond
1	○	Circle		17	◇	Dot Diamond
2	+	Plus		18	⊕	Plus Diamond
3	×	Cross		19	△	Triangle
4	✳	Asterisk		20	▲	Solid Triangle
5	·	Dot		21	△	Dot Triangle
6	●	Solid Circle		22	▷	Triangle Right
7	⊙	Dot Circle		23	▶	Solid Triangle Right
8	⊕	Plus Circle		24	▷	Dot Triangle Right
9	⊗	Cross Circle		25	◁	Triangle Left
10	◎	Circle Circle		26	◀	Solid Triangle Left
11	□	Square		27	◁	Dot Triangle Left
12	■	Solid Square		28	▽	Triangle Down
13	▫	Dot Square		29	▼	Solid Triangle Down
14	⊠	Cross Square		30	▽	Dot Triangle Down
15	◇	Diamond				

Colors

Applies to:

- Symbols
- Connection lines
- Projection lines

- Areas (fore and back colors)
- Bars (fore and back colors)
- LOWESS lines

Code	Color	Code	Color	Code	Color
0	White				
1	Black	6	Magenta	11	Dark Cyan
2	Red	7	Yellow	12	Dark Magenta
3	Green	8	Dark Red	13	Dark Yellow
4	Blue	9	Dark Green	14	Dark Gray
5	Cyan	10	Dark Blue	15	Light Gray

Line and edge types

Applies to:

- Connection lines
- Projection lines
- Area edges

- Bar edges
- LOWESS lines

Code	Line type	Name	Code	Line type	Name
0		None	4	— — — —	Dash 1-Dot
1	————	Solid	5	— - — - — - -	Dash 2-Dot
2	— — — — —	Dash	6	——————	Dash 3-Dot
3	- - - - - - - -	Dot	7	— — —	Long Dash

Fill types

Applies to:

- Area fills
- Bar fills

Code	Fill type	Name	Code	Fill type	Name
0		None	5		Horizontal line
1		Solid (background is white)	6		Vertical line
2		Right slant	7		Cross line
3		Left slant	8		Dots
4		Cross slant	9		Squares

16

Core Graphs: Groups and Multiple Graphs

Groups and Multiple Graphs Overview

Many of the graphs that you will create do not require groups or multiple graphs; the graphs will simply show the intersection of points for two variables. For example, in a graph of quarterly sales, with quarters on the x-axis and sales totals on the y-axis, there will be one point that represents the sales for the first quarter, one point for sales in the second quarter, and so on.

But, sometimes you will want to create graphs that compare data from two or more groups. For example, you might want to compare the quarterly sales for 1991 versus the quarterly sales for 1992. You could show this comparison using one of four methods:

Display data for each group in one graph

Create one graph that shows a solid line for 1991 sales and a dashed line for 1992 sales. MINITAB automatically creates different data display attributes for each group (solid lines and dashed lines), then creates a legend to identify those groups.

Quarterly Sales 1991-1992

Create several graphs at once

In the same dialog box, specify one set of variables to show 1991 sales and one set of variables for 1992 sales. When you click **OK**, each graph appears in a Graph window.

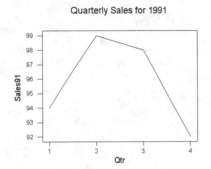

Overlay graphs

In the same dialog box, specify one set of variables to show 1991 sales and one set of variables for 1992 sales, then specify to overlay the two graphs. MINITAB automatically creates different data display attributes for each graph (solid lines for the 1991 graph and dashed lines for the 1992 graph). The resulting graph would be similar to the graph for displaying data for each group, with the exception that no legend appears.

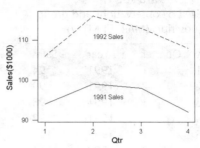

Create a multi-graph layout

Create one graph for 1991 sales and one graph for 1992 sales, then position the graphs so that they appear in the same Graph window. This is especially handy for placing different types of graphs in the same Graph window, such as placing charts beneath the plots of quarterly sales.

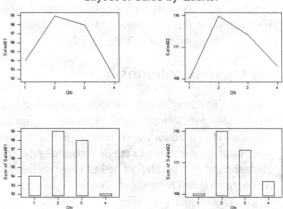

Organizing Your Data

The method you use depends not only on how you want to communicate the relationship between those groups and variables, but also on how your data set are organized in the worksheet. In the overview, for example, the graphs all used the same data, but they are organized in two different ways. Here are two ways that information could be organized into a data set:

Data set 1: Organized by observations and group subscripts (MARKET.MTW)				Data set 2: Organized by groups in separate columns			
Row	Quarter	Year	Sales	Row	Qtr	Sales91	Sales92
1	1	1991	94	1	1	94	106
2	2	1991	99	2	2	99	116
3	3	1991	98	3	3	98	113
4	4	1991	92	4	4	92	108
5	1	1992	106				
6	2	1992	116				
7	3	1992	113				
8	4	1992	108				

Using group subscripts

You can enter all the data in one column and set up a second column of subscripts to identify the group. Data set 1 uses several columns from the worksheet MARKET.MTW. The quarterly sales totals are in the column Sales; the columns Quarter and Year are *subscript* columns that identify when each value occurred. The first method in the Groups and Multiple Graphs Overview section used this data set.

Using separate columns

You can also enter the data for each group in separate columns. The second data set has the sales for 1991 and 1992 in separate columns. This gives us just four rows and eliminates the need for the column Year. Splitting a variable into two separate variables is useful if you are going to create separate graphs for each group, or if you are going to analyze a group separately. The last three methods outlined in the Groups and Multiple Graphs Overview section used the second data set.

Stacking to organize your data

You can use both organizational styles, depending on your needs. You can use the **Manip ➤ Stack** and **Manip ➤ Unstack Columns** commands to convert one form to the other. If all the columns have unique names (notice that Quarter is changed to Qtr, above), the two sets of variables can be in the same worksheet. If variables have the same names, you can store them in different worksheets, with both worksheets open in your project.

➤ Example of unstacking (splitting) Sales into Sales_1991 and Sales_1992

1 Choose **Manip ➤ Unstack Columns**.

2 In **Unstack the data in**, enter *Sales*.

3 In **Using subscripts in**, enter *Year*.

4 Under **Store the unstacked data**, choose **After last column in use**. Check **Name the columns containing the unstacked data**. Click **OK**.

   MINITAB places the Sales values with the lowest Year number (1991) into the first column after the last column in use, and assigns that column the name *Sales_1991*. Then it places Sales values for the next lowest Year number (1992) in the next available column, and assigns the name *Sales_1992*.

More | You could also turn the second data set into the first by stacking the columns. For more information, see *Stacking Columns* on page 6-28.

Displaying Data for Each Group

With core graphs, you can make the data display elements—such as symbols, connection lines, and areas—display differently for each group of a grouping variable.

For example, say that you have sales data for two years. The Sales column contains the sales figures, and the Year column contains the year that each sales value occurred in: 1991 or 1992. If you create a scatter plot of Sales by Quarter and specify Year as a grouping variable, the symbols for values that occurred in 1991 will appear differently than symbols for values that occurred in 1992.

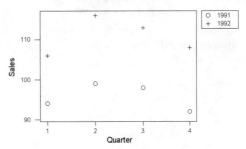

Note Contour plots do not use any of the grouping features described in this section. Each contour level is already a group that is displayed by a line or area that has its own data display attributes. See *Using connection lines and areas with contour plots* on page 14-53.

Groups are defined by the distinct values of a variable. A grouping variable can be any text, numeric, or date/time column in a worksheet. In the table below, we have defined groups in two different ways.

Grouping by Year   **Grouping by AdAgency**

Row	Year		Row	AdAgency	
1	1991	Group 1	1	Omega	Group 2
2	1991		2	Omega	
3	1991		3	Alpha	Group 1
4	1991	Group 2	4	Alpha	
5	1992		5	Alpha	
6	1992		6	Alpha	Group 2
7	1992		7	Omega	
8	1992		8	Omega	

- In numeric grouping variables, groups are assigned in increasing order. For example, in Year, 1991 is group 1, 1992 is group 2.

- In date/time grouping variables, groups are also assigned in increasing order. For example, 1/01/97 (not shown) is group 1; 2/01/97 is group 2.

- In text grouping variables, groups are assigned in alphabetical order. For example, in AdAgency, Alpha is group 1, and Omega is group 2.

More You can change the default order in which text groups are assigned using the Value Order command. See *Ordering Text Categories* on page 6-19

Grouping changes the graph only in how the data display elements are displayed. Furthermore, a grouping variable only affects the data display element that it is assigned to—if symbols are being grouped by Year, connection lines will appear unchanged. You can assign different grouping variables to different data display elements. For example, symbols can be grouped by Year, and connection lines can be grouped by AdAgency.

▶ **To display data for a group**

1 In the core graph main dialog box, click in a row of the **Data display** table.

2 Under **Display**, choose a data display element.

3 Under **For each**, choose **Group**.

4 Under **Group variables**, enter a column.

5 If you like, change the attributes of the groups (see *Assigning attributes to groups* on page 16-8).

For an example of a graph that uses multiple grouping variables, see *Example of editing the attributes of multi-variable groups* on page 16-10.

Groups within groups: using multiple grouping variables

Groups can also be composed of unique combinations of values across two or three variables. For example, you could specify both Year and AdAgency (in that order) as grouping variables; the groups would be assigned as follows:

Grouping by Year and AdAgency

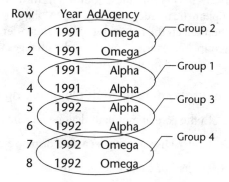

| Note | All core graphs can use from one to three grouping variables, with two exceptions: boxplots can use only one grouping variable; contour plots cannot use any grouping variables. |

Groups are assigned in the order that the grouping variables are specified in the dialog box. In the example above, MINITAB first divides the rows by Year, 1991 and 1992. MINITAB then divides those two groups by the name of the ad agency. For example, 1991 is divided into "1991 Alpha" and "1991 Omega."

If you change the order in which grouping variables are specified, you change the grouping order. Compare the group order of these three-variable groups:

Grouping
by Year, AdAgency, and Quarter

Row	Year	AdAgency	Quarter	**Group #**
1	1991	Omega	1	**3**
2	1991	Omega	2	**4**
3	1991	Alpha	3	**1**
4	1991	Alpha	4	**2**
5	1992	Alpha	1	**5**
6	1992	Alpha	2	**6**
7	1992	Omega	3	**7**
8	1992	Omega	4	**8**

Grouping
by Quarter, Year, and AdAgency

Year	AdAgency	Quarter	**Group #**
1991	Omega	1	**1**
1991	Omega	2	**3**
1991	Alpha	3	**5**
1991	Alpha	4	**7**
1992	Alpha	1	**2**
1992	Alpha	2	**4**
1992	Omega	3	**6**
1992	Omega	4	**8**

Notice how MINITAB orders the groups. When grouping by Year, AdAgency, and Quarter (above left), MINITAB first selects rows with the lowest value in Year, 1991 (rows 1–4). From those four rows, MINITAB selects rows that have the earliest alphabetical order in AdAgency, Alpha (rows 3 and 4). From those two rows, MINITAB then selects the row with the lowest quarter, 3 (row 3), which makes that row 3 the first group. You can see how the order changes when MINITAB selects first by Quarter, then by Year, and finally by AdAgency.

▶ **To display data by multiple grouping variables**

1 In the core graph main dialog box, click in a row of the **Data display** table.

2 Under **Display**, choose a data display element.

3 Under **For each**, choose **Group**.

4 Under **Group variables**, enter two or three columns.

5 If you like, change the attributes of the groups (see below).

For an example of a graph that uses multiple grouping variables, see *Example of editing the attributes of multi-variable groups* on page 16-10.

Assigning attributes to groups

MINITAB automatically assigns different data display attributes to each group. If you use grouping variables with the symbol data display element, MINITAB will use a different symbol type for each group. By default, a circle will be provided for Alpha data points and a plus will be provided for Omega data points. You can accept the default attributes, or specify different attributes for each group.

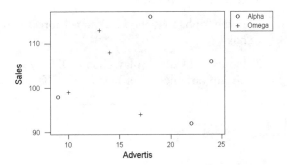

Note | If you specify more than one graph in the **Graph variables** table, then use grouping variables with data display elements, attributes are assigned to the groups and not to the graphs. For an example, see *Example of editing attributes for groups with multiple overlayed graphs* on page 16-18.

▶ **To edit the attributes of groups**

1 Click in the row of the **Data display** table that contains the grouped data display element.

2 Click **Edit Attributes**.

MINITAB displays one row of attributes for each group. For example, the attributes dialog box for a symbol grouped by Year looks like this:

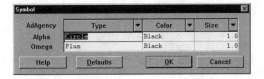

3 Change any of the attributes for that data display element. For a description of each data display element and its attributes, see Chapter 15, *Core Graphs: Displaying Data*.

▶ **Example of editing the attributes of two groups**

The following graph uses two data display elements, each with its own grouping variable. The connection line will have different line types for each year, and the symbol will have a different type for each ad agency.

1 Open the worksheet MARKET.MTW.

2 Choose **Graph ➤ Plot**.

3 In **Y**, enter *Sales*. In **X**, enter *Index*.

4 In the **Data display** table, choose **For each ➤ Group**. In **Group variables**, enter *AdAgency*.

5 Click **Edit Attributes**.

6 In the **Alpha** row, choose **Type ➤ More Types ➤ Square**. Click **OK** in each dialog box.

7 In row 2 of **Data display**, choose **Display ➤ Connect**, and **For each ➤ Group**. In **Group variables**, enter *Year*. Click **OK**.

Graph window output

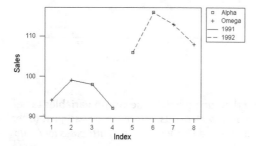

Example of editing the attributes of multi-variable groups

This plot has four groups, defined by Year and AdAgency, with custom-picked symbol types for each group. The legend is moved to the top of the graph (for details on controlling legends, see *Legend Regions* on page 19-20).

1 Open the worksheet MARKET.MTW.

2 Choose **Graph ➤ Plot**.

3 In **Y**, enter *Sales*. In **X**, enter *Advertis*.

4 Under **Data display**, choose **For each ➤ Group**. In **Group variables**, enter *Year AdAgency*.

5 Click **Edit Attributes**.

6 Choose a symbol type for each group:

   - In the **1991 Omega** row, choose **Type ➤ Solid Circle**.

   - In the **1991 Alpha** row, choose **Type ➤ More Types ➤ Solid Square**. Click **OK**.

   - In the **1992 Omega** row, choose **Type ➤ Circle**.

   - In the **1992 Alpha** row, choose **Type ➤ More Types ➤ Square**. Click **OK** in each dialog box.

7 Choose **Regions ➤ Legend**.

8 Set the position of the legend region:

   - In **X minimum**, type *0.4*.

   - In **X maximum**, type *0.65*.

- In **Y minimum**, type *0.81*.
- In **Y maximum**, type *0.99*.

9 Click **OK** in each dialog box.

*Graph
window
output*

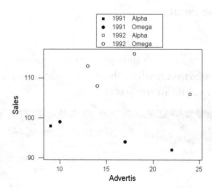

Displaying Data for Each Point

The symbol and projection line data display elements can represent a single data point. By default, MINITAB assigns the same attributes to each data point. You can choose to display data for each point, then assign specific attributes to specific points.

Note | This option is only available for two core graphs, plots and time series plots, and only when those graphs use the data display elements of symbols or projection lines.

For example, here is a graph with each symbol set to a different type:

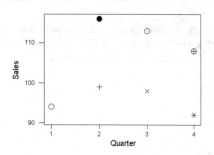

▶ **To display data for each point**

1 In the core graph main dialog box, click in a row of the **Data display** table.

2 Under **Display**, choose **Symbol** or **Project**.

3 Under **For each**, choose **Point**.

4 Click **Edit Attributes**.

MINITAB will display a row for each data point. For example, here is the Edit Attributes dialog box for Symbol, when there are eight data points (eight values in the x-variable and eight values in the y-variable):

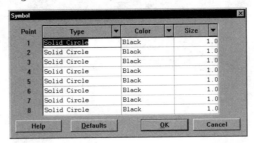

5 Change the attributes for the points you want to appear differently, then click **OK**.

Creating Several Graphs at Once

In the core graph dialog boxes, you can specify sets of variables for several graphs, click **OK**, and generate all the graphs at once. Each graph, by default, appears in its own Graph window. This can save you a lot of time if you need to create many graphs of the same type. You can also specify that the graphs use the same scales for X or Y axes, thus creating multiple graphs that are easy to compare to each other.

Note | This option is not available for matrix plots, draftsman plots, or contour plots.

More | If you want multiple graphs to appear in the same Graph window, you can overlay the graphs or create a multi-graph layout. See *Overlaying Graphs* on page 16-16 and *Creating a Multi-Graph Layout* on page 16-20.

▶ **To create several graphs at once**

1 In row 1 of the **Graph variables** table, enter the variables for the first graph. Some core graphs require two variables, and some require only one.

Each row creates a different graph.

2 In row 2 of the **Graph variables** table, enter the variables for the second graph.

3 Continue specifying sets of variables. You can specify up to 100 sets, to create up to 100 graphs.

4 If you like, change the attributes for the data display elements for each graph (see below).

5 If you like, set the scales to be the same on all graphs. For details, see *Keeping the same scales across graphs* on page 16-14.

Assigning data display attributes to multiple graphs

Each graph receives all the data display elements specified in the **Data display** table. By default, each of those elements have the same attributes. You can override the defaults and set different data display attributes for each graph. For example, you can set symbols to display as solid circles for the first graph, plus signs for the second graph, and so on.

Note │ If you specify more than one graph in the **Graph variables** table, then use grouping variables with data display elements, attributes are assigned to the groups and not the graphs. For an example, see *Example of editing attributes for groups with multiple overlayed graphs* on page 16-18.

▶ **To change data display attributes for each graph**

1 In the core graph's **Data display** table, click in the row of the data display element you want to change.

2 Choose **For each ▶ Graph**.

3 Click **Edit Attributes**.

The Attributes dialog box will contain one row for each graph specified in the **Graph variables** table. The first row in the attributes dialog box applies to the first graph variables table; the second row applies to the second graph, and so on. For example, here is the symbol attributes dialog box for three graphs:

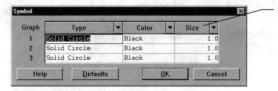

To change an attribute setting for all the graphs at once, click on the column header, then pick a setting from the drop-down menu.

4 Change any of the attributes and click **OK**.

▷ Example of setting different data display attributes for two graphs

In the plots below, the first graph will have circle symbols, and the second graph will have plus symbols.

1 Open the worksheet MARKET.MTW.

2 Choose **Graph ➤ Plot**.

3 In row 1 of **Graph variables**, enter *Sales* in **Y** and *Index* in **X**. In row 2, enter *Advertis* in **Y** and *Index* in **X**.

4 Click **Edit Attributes**.

5 In row 1, choose **Type ➤ Circle**. In row 2, choose **Type ➤ Plus**. Click **OK** in each dialog box.

Graph window output

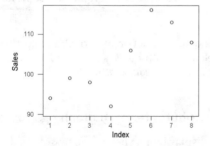
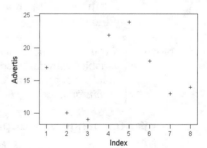

Keeping the same scales across graphs

When you generate multiple graphs from the same dialog box, you can keep one or both axis scales the same for all the graphs. This is very useful when you want to make comparisons across several graphs.

Note | This option is also not available when you overlay multiple graphs on the same page.

▶ **To keep the same scales across graphs**

1 From the core graph main dialog box, choose **Frame ➤ Multiple Graphs**.

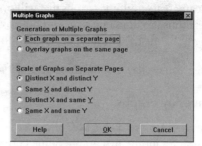

2 Under **Scale of Graphs on Separate Pages**, choose one of the options to keep the same X scale, same Y scale, or the same X and Y scales. Click **OK**.

▶ **Example of generating multiple graphs with the same scale**

1 Open the worksheet MARKET.MTW.

2 Choose **Graph ➤ Time Series Plot**.

3 Under **Y**, enter *Sales* in row 1, *Advertis* in row 2, and *Capital* in row 3.

4 Choose **Frame ➤ Multiple Graphs**.

5 Select **Same X and same Y**. Click **OK** in each dialog box.

Graph window output

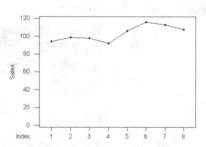

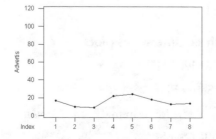

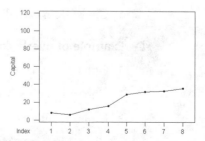

Overlaying Graphs

You can create multiple graphs that will overlay each other in the same Graph window. The graphs use the same scales on both axes. By default, the label for the Y axis is the name of the first Y axis variable listed in the **Graph variables** table.

Note | When you overlay graphs, you do not get a legend.

▶ **To overlay graphs**

1 In a core graph dialog box, click in row 1 of the **Graph variables** table. Enter the variables for the first graph. Some core graphs require two variables, and some require only one.

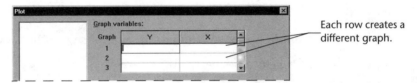

Each row creates a different graph.

2 In row 2 of the **Graph variables** table, enter the variables for the second graph; in row 3, enter the variables for the third graph, and so on.

Continue specifying sets of variables. You can specify up to 100 sets, to create up to 100 graphs.

3 Choose **Frame ➤ Multiple Graphs**.

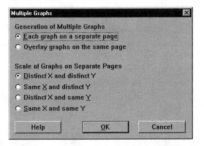

4 Under **Generation of Multiple Graphs**, choose **Overlay graphs on the same page**.

5 Click **OK** in each dialog box.

▷ **Example of overlaying three time series plots**

1 Open the worksheet MARKET.MTW.

2 Choose **Graph ➤ Time Series Plot**.

3 Under **Y**, enter *Sales* in row 1, *Advertis* in row 2, and *Capital* in row 3.

4 Choose **Frame ➤ Multiple Graphs**.

5 Under **Generation of Multiple Graphs**, choose **Overlay graphs on the same page**. Click **OK**.

6 Choose **Frame ➤ Axis**.

7 In row 2 of **Label**, type a quotation mark, space, and quotation mark, like this " ". Click **OK** in each dialog box.

Graph window output

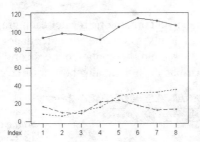

Note | If you typed a space in **Label** without the quotation marks, MINITAB would interpret that as a null entry, and would substitute the default label on the graph.

But why create a blank label for the Y axis at all? Because the default label is the name of the first Y axis variable in the **Graph variables** table, in this case "Sales." That label would be incorrect because the Y axis for an overlayed graph covers the combined range of all the Y variables, from the lowest value in any of the variables to the highest value.

Assigning data display attributes to overlayed graphs

All graphs receive all the data display elements specified in the **Data display** table. By default, each element will have a different *type* attribute for each graph. For example, if the data display element is symbols, the first graph will have symbols that are solid circles, the second graph will have symbols that are plus signs, and so on. All other attributes, such as size and color, are the same across all graphs. However, you can override the defaults and edit the data display attributes for each graph (see below). For more information on data display attributes, see the description of each data display element in Chapter 15, *Core Graphs: Displaying Data*.

Note | If you specify more than one graph in the **Graph variables** table, then use grouping variables with data display elements, attributes are assigned to the groups and not the graphs. For an example, see *Example of editing attributes for groups with multiple overlayed graphs* on page 16-18.

▶ **To change data display attributes for each graph**

1 In the core graph's **Data display** table, click in the row of the data display element you want to change.

2 Choose **For each ➤ Graph**.

3 Click **Edit Attributes**.

The Attributes dialog box will contain one row for each graph specified in the **Graph variables** table. The first row in the attributes dialog box applies to the first graph variables table; the second row applies to the second graph, and so on For example, here is the symbol attributes dialog box for three graphs:

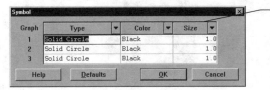

To change an attribute setting for all the graphs at once, click on the column header, then pick a setting from the drop-down menu.

4 Change any of the attributes and click **OK**.

▷ **Example of editing attributes for groups with multiple overlayed graphs**

In this example, two graphs are overlaid. The connection line data display element does not use a grouping variable, so different line types are assigned to each graph. The symbol element, however, has a group variable, AdAgency, so the two symbol types are assigned to the two ad agencies. The default y-axis label is the name of the first variable specified under **Y**.

1 Open the worksheet MARKET.MTW.

2 Choose **Graph ➤ Plot**.

3 In row 1 of **Graph variables,** enter *Sales* in **Y** and *Index* in **X**.

4 In row 2 of **Graph variables,** enter *Advertis* in **Y** and *Index* in **X**.

5 In row 1 of **Data display,** choose **For each ➤ Group** and enter *AdAgency* in **Group variables**.

6 Click **Edit Attributes**.

7 In the **Alpha** row, choose **Type ➤ More Types ➤ Square**. Click **OK** in each dialog box.

8 In row 2 of **Data display,** choose **Display ➤ Connect** and **For Each ➤ Graph**.

9 Choose **Frame ➤ Multiple Graphs**.

10 Under **Generation of Multiple Graphs**, choose **Overlay graphs on the same page**. Click **OK** in each dialog box.

Graph window output

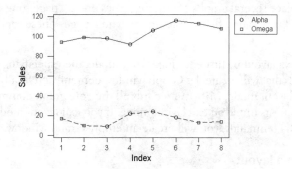

Overlaying charts and boxplots

When overlaying charts or boxplots, MINITAB generates a tick on the x-axis for each unique category in any of the graphs. For example, here is a graph of two overlayed charts. The y-axis for both graphs is Sales. The x-axis for the first graph is Quarter (which has four categories), and the x-axis for the other graph is Year (which as two categories).

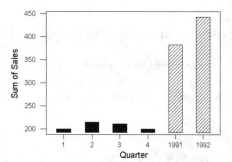

Overlaying charts will not work in two cases:

- when you use the chart ordering options **Increasing Y** or **Decreasing Y**, the graph will not be created unless all charts use the same categorical (X) variable. For example, the graph above has two categorical variables, Quarter and Year. If either ordering option was activated, the graph would not be created, and you would receive an error message.

- when you use the chart with mixed numeric and text categories. For example, you could not create a chart of Sales by Quarter overlayed on a chart of Sales by AdAgency. The graph will not be created, and you will receive an error message.

Creating a Multi-Graph Layout

You can place several graphs of differing types on one page (one Graph window), as well as add annotation that applies to the whole page. These sophisticated displays are called *layouts*.

You create a layout by first entering layout mode, then specifying the graphics commands that will create the Graph window content, and finally exiting layout mode. While in layout mode, MINITAB records all the core graph commands you use. No content appears until you exit layout mode. If you exit layout mode without issuing any core graph commands, you will create an empty Graph window.

▶ **To create a layout**

1 Choose **Graph ➤ Layout**. This opens the Layout dialog box.

2 In the Layout dialog box, specify any annotation you want to apply to the entire Graph window, such as titles, footnotes, reference lines, and other graphical and text items—see *Adding annotation to a page* on page 16-23.

3 In the Layout dialog box, click **OK**. This puts MINITAB in layout mode.

4 Create each core graph, specifying its position in the Graph window by setting the coordinates of its figure region—see *Positioning graphs on the page* on page 16-20.

5 Choose **Graph ➤ End Layout**. This exits layout mode. The graphs and annotation then appear in one Graph window.

Positioning graphs on the page

You can place multiple graphs on one page (or Graph window) by controlling the size and location of each graph's *figure region*. The size and location of each figure region is set by *page coordinates* that you specify.

What is a figure region?

A figure region is the total area that a single graph takes up within the page. The figure region contains the data region (the interior of the plot or chart where the data points are displayed), axes, and axis labels—as well as any titles and footnotes that are specific to that graph.

Simple graphs have one figure region that, by default, takes up the whole page. In layout mode, you can have more than one figure region on a page. The example on the left shows the figure region for a simple graph in a shaded area. The example on the right shows two figure regions on the same page in the shaded areas, with a dotted line to show the extent of the page:

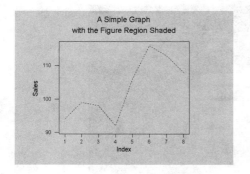

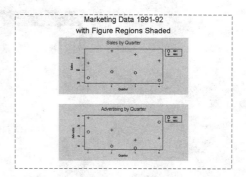

Using page coordinates

You size and place a figure region by specifying minimum and maximum x- and y-coordinates. The coordinates are in terms of the page, and run from 0 to 1 in each direction. In the x-direction, 0 is the left edge of the page, 1 is the right edge. In the y-direction, 0 is the bottom edge, and 1 is the top edge.

The graph page below has three graphs. The page has a dark outline, and each figure region has a dashed outline. Notice how the coordinates change for each graph, and how the coordinates change the shape of the graph.

X- minimum: 0.1, X-maximum: 0.45   X- minimum: 0.55, X-maximum: 0.9
Y-minimum: 0.6, Y-maximum: 0.9   Y-minimum: 0.6, Y-maximum: 0.9

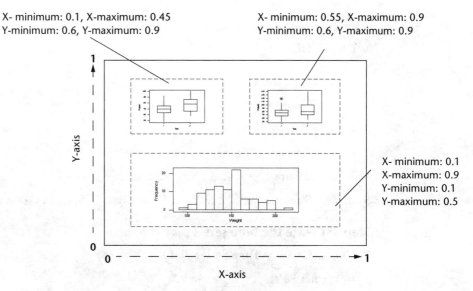

X- minimum: 0.1
X-maximum: 0.9
Y-minimum: 0.1
Y-maximum: 0.5

More | You can not only set the figure region's size and position, but also its color, fill type, edge type, and more. See *Figure Regions* on page 19-10.

▶ **To change the figure region size and position**

1 In a core graph main dialog box, choose **Regions ➤ Figure**.

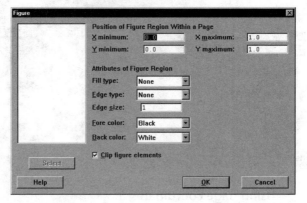

2 Under **Position of Figure Region Within a Page**, enter the minimum and maximum values for X and Y. Values can be any real number from 0 to 1.

▶ **Example of a two-graph layout**

The following example places two graphs on one page. Notice how the x- and y-coordinates specify where to place the graphs on the page. For illustration, the page region in the example is surrounded by a dashed line, but the dashed line does not appear in the actual output.

Step 1: Enter layout mode

1 Choose **Graph ➤ Layout**. Click **OK**.

Step 2: Create the chart

1 Choose **Graph ➤ Chart**.

2 In **Y**, enter *Sales*. In **X**, enter *Year*.

3 Choose **Regions ➤ Figure**.

4 In **X minimum**, type *0.02*. In **X maximum**, type *0.48*.

5 In **Y minimum**, type *0.25*. In **Y maximum**, type *0.75*. Click **OK** in each dialog box.

Step 3: Create the time series plot

1 Choose **Graph ➤ Time Series Plot**.

2 In **Y**, enter *Sales*.

3 Choose **Regions ➤ Figure**.

4 In **X minimum**, type *0.52*. In **X maximum**, type *0.98*.

5 In **Y minimum**, type *0.25*. In **Y maximum**, type *0.75*. Click **OK** in each dialog box.

Step 4: End layout mode

1 Choose **Graph ➤ End Layout**.

Graph window output

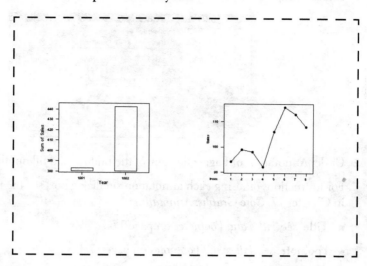

Adding annotation to a page

With a multi-graph layout, you sometimes want titles, footnotes, and other annotation to apply to the entire page, not just individual graphs. The methods for annotating the page are the same as those for annotating a graph, with two exceptions:

- the annotation commands are found in the Layout dialog box, not in a core graph dialog box.

- annotation items that are placed using coordinates will be placed in relation to the entire page, not in relation to the graph figure region. For an explanation of page coordinates, see *Using page coordinates* on page 16-21.

Tip You can use layout annotation features to create slides or drawings that do not even have to use graphs. Just choose **Graph ➤ Layout**, annotate the page, click **OK**, and choose **Graph ➤ End Layout**.

▶ **To annotate the page**

1 Choose **Graph ➤ Layout**.

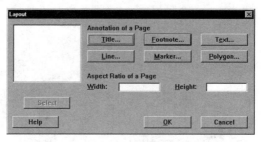

2 Under **Annotation of Page**, click any of the buttons and fill out the dialog box.

For instructions on using each annotation subdialog box, see the following sections in Chapter 17, *Core Graphs: Annotating*:

- **Title**: see *Titles and Footnotes* on page 17-4

- **Footnote**: see *Titles and Footnotes* on page 17-4

- **Text**: see *Text* on page 17-5

- **Line**: see *Lines* on page 17-10

- **Marker**: see *Markers* on page 17-14

- **Polygon**: see *Polygons* on page 17-12

▶ **Example of adding annotation to a multi-graph layout**

This example builds on the example shown on page 16-22. You will add a title and a footnote that describe the entire page. For illustration, the page region in the example is surrounded by a dashed line, but the dashed line does not appear in the actual output.

Step 1: Enter layout mode and create annotation

1 Choose **Graph ➤ Layout**.

2 Click **Title**.

3 In **Title**, type *Sales Data for 1991-1992*. From **Text Size**, choose **2.0**. Click **OK**.

4 Click **Footnote**.

5 In **Footnote**, type *Source: Marketing Data*. Click **OK** in each dialog box.

Step 2: Create the chart

1 Choose **Graph ➤ Chart**.

2 In **Y**, enter *Sales*. In **X**, enter *Year*.

3 Choose **Regions ➤ Figure**.

4 In **X minimum**, type *0.02*. In **X maximum**, type *0.48*.

5 In **Y minimum**, type *0.25*. In **Y maximum**, type *0.75*. Click **OK** in each dialog box.

Step 3: Create the time series plot

1 Choose **Graph ➤ Time Series Plot**.

2 In **Y**, enter *Sales*.

3 Choose **Regions ➤ Figure**.

4 In **X minimum**, type *0.52*. In **X maximum**, type *0.98*.

5 In **Y minimum**, type *0.25*. In **Y maximum**, type *0.75*. Click **OK** in each dialog box.

Step 4: End layout mode

1 Choose **Graph ➤ End Layout**.

Graph window output

17

Core Graphs: Annotating

Annotating Overview

The graphics options in this chapter are for annotating graphs—adding text, lines, and other graphical objects to the graph to help explain it.

Often you will find it easier to add annotation using the graph editing tools (Chapter 24) rather than the dialog box options described in this chapter. However, the dialog box options are useful when you want to repeat annotation on many graphs, or place annotation with precise coordinates rather than dragging items into place with the graph editing tools. For example, you may want to repeatedly produce a graph with markers in the same positions, or place markers in exact locations using predefined points.

Note | Axes, ticks, grid lines, and reference lines are considered part of the frame of the graph, not stand-alone annotation items. For details, see Chapter 18, *Core Graphs: Customizing the Frame*.

Graphs that use annotation options

Annotation options are available in the Layout dialog box when you choose **Graph ➤ Layout**. The options are also available in the main dialog boxes of the following graphs:

- core graphs - Plots, Time Series Plots, Charts, Histograms, Boxplots, Matrix Plots, Draftsman Plots, Contour Plots

- control charts - Xbar, R, S, Individuals, Moving Range, EWMA, Moving Average, P, NP, C, U

Using Region Coordinates for Annotation

One of the benefits of using the annotation options in the graph dialog boxes is the ability to place text and graphical elements at precise x- and y-coordinates. The coordinates you enter depend on which *region* the annotation is in.

Note | Titles, footnotes, and data labels by default do not require you to specify any coordinates.

MINITAB graphs have at least three regions—the page region, the figure region, and the data region—and sometimes have a fourth region for the legend. These regions are explained in detail in Chapter 19, *Core Graphs: Controlling Regions*.

Titles and footnotes are in the figure region and so are placed using figure units. For an explanation of figure units, see *Using figure units and coordinates* on page 19-4.

Text, lines, markers, and polygons are all in the data region and are placed using data units, explained below.

Most annotation is placed in data units

For text, lines, markers, and polygons, the coordinates are in data units, that is, the actual values of data points as shown on the x- and y-axes of a graph. For example, here is a text item that is placed using the data units of 5 on the x-axis and 105 on the y-axis.

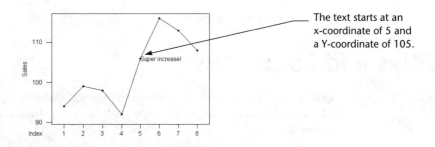

The text starts at an x-coordinate of 5 and a Y-coordinate of 105.

When the x-axis represents categories (as with charts, boxplots, and time series plots that use an x-axis other than an index), specify the categories as axis positions 1, 2, …, c (where c is the total number of categories) as they appear on the graph from left to right. For example, say that the time series plot above used the category of quarters instead of an index.

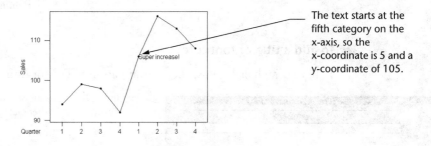

The text starts at the fifth category on the x-axis, so the x-coordinate is 5 and a y-coordinate of 105.

To place the text "Super increase!" at the first quarter of the second year, you would count the number of categories and see that the second instance of quarter 1 is the fifth category. Therefore, the coordinates you would enter would be 5 for the x-coordinate, and 105 for the y-coordinate.

You can specify points between categories. For example, a point midway between the first and second quarter of the second year would be an x-coordinate of 5.5.

Substitute other units for data units in three cases

For text, lines, markers, and polygons, coordinates that are normally in data units will use page units or figure units in three cases: in the **Graph ➤ Layout** dialog box, the coordinates are specified in page units; in the **Graph ➤ Matrix Plot** and **Draftsman Plot** dialog boxes, the coordinates are in figure units. For an explanation of page and figure units, see *Region Coordinate Systems* on page 19-3.

Titles and Footnotes

A title is simply text placed above the data region; a footnote is text placed below the data region. You can have multiple rows of titles and footnotes, and each row can have its own format.

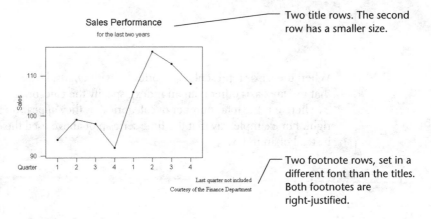

Two title rows. The second row has a smaller size.

Two footnote rows, set in a different font than the titles. Both footnotes are right-justified.

▶ **To add a title or footnote**

1 In the graph dialog box, choose **Annotation ➤ Title** or **Annotation ➤ Footnote**.

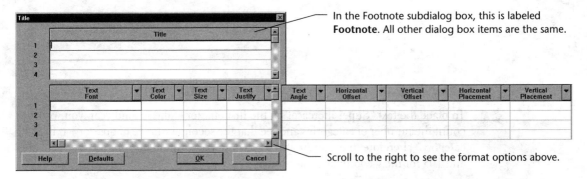

In the Footnote subdialog box, this is labeled **Footnote**. All other dialog box items are the same.

Scroll to the right to see the format options above.

2 In row 1 under **Title** (or **Footnote**), type the text you want. If want additional title or footnote rows, type text into rows 2, 3, and so on.

3 If you like, use any of the text format options. The options you specify in a row at the bottom of the dialog box will be applied to the corresponding row of text at the top of the dialog box. Click **OK**.

Options

You can change the format of each row of text. The format applies to the entire row; you cannot change individual characters in a row to a different format. If you do not specify a format, MINITAB will use default formats. You can specify:

- font, color, and size

- justification (left, center, or right—center is the default)

- angle (rotation)

- horizontal and vertical offset (coordinates for exactly positioning text, in figure units—see *Using Region Coordinates for Annotation* on page 17-2)

- horizontal and vertical placement (how the text is placed in relation to the offset coordinates—above, below, to the right, etc.)

More | For details on using these options, see Help.

Text

While the Title and Footnote options let you easily place text above and below a graph's data region, the Text option lets you place text anywhere on the graph using precise x- and y- coordinates.

▶ To add text

1 In the graph dialog box, choose **Annotation ➤ Text**.

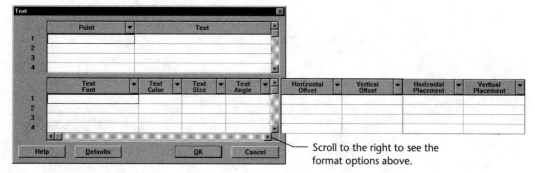

Scroll to the right to see the format options above.

2 In row 1 of **Point**, enter an x-coordinate (such as 5) and a y-coordinate (such as 105), separated by a space. Specify coordinates for other text in rows 2, 3, etc.

Coordinates are in data units, except in three cases—see *Using Region Coordinates for Annotation* on page 17-2.

3 In row 1 of **Text**, type the characters you want to appear. Enter characters for other text in rows 2, 3, etc.

4 If you like, use any of the text format options. The options you specify in a row at the bottom of the dialog box will be applied to the corresponding row of text at the top of the dialog box. Click **OK**.

Options

You can change the format of each row of text. The format applies to the entire row; you cannot change individual characters in a row to a different format. If you do not specify a format, MINITAB will use format defaults.

■ font, color, and size

■ justification (left, center, or right—center is the default)

■ angle (rotation)

■ horizontal and vertical offset (positive or negative values that position text away from the x- and y-coordinates specified in **Point**, which is handy for nudging text away from nearby data points)

■ horizontal and vertical placement (how the text is placed in relation to the offset coordinates—above, below, to the right, etc.)

More | For details on using these options, see Help.

For an example of using annotation text, see *Example of a graph with annotation lines and text* on page 17-11.

Data Labels

Data labels are text or numbers you can display with each data point. The labels can be y-axis values, row numbers, values stored in a column, or values you enter in the dialog box. For example, here is a graph labeled with the y-values of the data points.

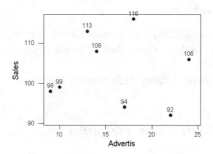

▶ **To show data labels**

1 In the graph dialog box, choose **Annotation ▶ Data Labels**.

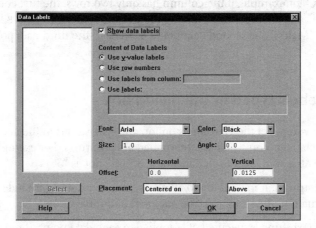

2 Check **Show data labels**.

3 Under **Content of Data Labels**, pick one of the options. If you choose **Use labels from column** or **Use labels**, see the sections on these topics below.

4 If you like, use one of the format options, and click **OK**.

Options

For each data label, you can change the:

- font, color, or size
- angle (rotation)
- horizontal and vertical offset (positive or negative values that position text away from the data point)
- horizontal and vertical placement (how the text is placed in relation to the offset coordinates—above, below, to the right, etc.)

More | For details on using these options, see Help.

Using labels from a column

When you choose the option Use labels from column, you can enter a numeric, text, or date/time column that contains the labels you want. The values in the column are distributed to the points in the order that they appear in the column.

If there are less values than data points, the data points cycle through the available values. For example, if the column has only two rows, the first containing the word "Male" and the second containing the word "Female," MINITAB labels the first data point "Males," the second data point "Females," the third data point "Males," and so on.

Using labels typed in the dialog box

When you select the **Use labels** option and type values in the accompanying text box, the characters you typed are interpreted as text strings. For example, if you typed *1-4*, MINITAB would label each data point as "1-4" not as "3."

A text string can include up to 80 characters. If the string includes spaces or punctuation, the string must be enclosed in double quotes.

If one text string is specified, it is applied to each data point. If more than one text string is specified, the labels are applied iteratively. For example, entering *Male Female* labels the first data point "Males," the second data point "Females," the third data point "Males," and so on.

▷ Example of a graph with data labels

This example gives labels to individual points from the text column AdAgency. The labels are formatted in several ways. First, the offset is changed to move labels a little to the right and down, so that labels do not cover the data points. Then horizontal and vertical placement is changed to move the labels to the lower right of the offset point. Finally, the angle of the text is changed so that the labels are rotated 45° clockwise.

1 Open the worksheet MARKET.MTW.

2 Choose **Graph ➤ Plot**.

3 In **Y**, enter *Sales*. In **X**, enter *Advertis*.

4 Choose **Annotation ➤ Data Labels**.

5 Check **Show data labels**.

6 Click **Use labels from column** and enter *AdAgency*.

7 In **Angle**, type *-45*.

8 In **Horizontal Offset** type *0.02*. In **Vertical Offset** type *-0.01*.

9 Choose **Horizontal Placement ➤ To the Right of**. Choose **Vertical Placement ➤ Below**. Click **OK** in each dialog box.

Graph window output

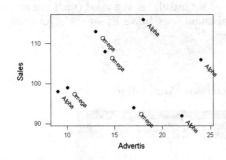

Lines

Use this option to draw a line from one point to another, or to connect a series of points. The line can be in different types (for example, solid or dashed), colors, and sizes. Lines are often used with text, as below.

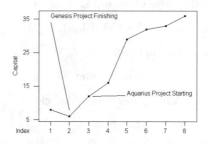

Note | If you place annotation lines beyond the data's minimum or maximum, by default MINITAB will automatically expand the scale to include those lines. For details, see *Ticks and other items may affect the scale* on page 18-28.

Tip | Annotation lines are different from *reference lines*. Reference lines (discussed in *Reference Lines and Labels* on page 18-22) are horizontal and vertical lines that span the data region of the graph. Reference lines are usually set at a value (such as a mean) that you want to compare to all values. Annotation lines, however, are useful for pointing out miscellaneous data points.

▶ To create a line

1 In the graph dialog box, choose **Annotation ➤ Line**.

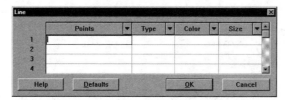

2 In row 1 of **Points**, enter an x-coordinate (such as 5) and a y-coordinate (such as 105), separated by a space. Then specify an x- and y-coordinate for the second point. If you like, specify more points in the line.

Coordinates are in data units, except in three cases—see *Using Region Coordinates for Annotation* on page 17-2.

3 If you like, specify sets of coordinates for other lines in rows 2, 3, etc.

4 If you like, choose any of the format options, and click **OK**.

Tip | For a line with many points, you can put x-coordinates in one column and y-coordinates in another. Then, in **Points** choose **Use variables** and select those columns.

Options

For each line, you can specify:

- the type and color by choosing from the drop-down list. For a list of line types and colors, see *Lists of Symbols, Colors, Lines, and Fills* on page 17-17.

- the size (width) by choosing from the drop-down list or entering a value. The value can be any positive real number. Lines with larger sizes are wider than lines with smaller sizes. The default size is 1.

▷ **Example of a graph with annotation lines and text**

1 Open the worksheet MARKET.MTW.

2 Choose **Graph ➤ Time Series Plot**.

3 In **Y**, enter *Sales*.

4 Choose **Annotation ➤ Text**.

5 In the top portion of the dialog box, do the following:

In Row	under Point	under Text
1	type *5 95*	type *The Last of Old Product*
2	type *3.9 110*	type *A New Product Jump!*

6 In the bottom portion of the dialog box, do the following:

In Row	under Horizontal Placement	under Vertical Placement
1	leave the defaults	leave the defaults
2	choose **To the left of**	choose **Centered on**

7 Click **OK**.

8 Choose **Annotation ➤ Line**. Do the following:

In Row	under Points	under Type	Size
1	type *6.5 94.8 6.5 92.2 4.2 92.2*	choose **Dash**	choose **3**
2	type *4 110 4.5 110 4.8 107*	choose **Dash 1-Dot**	

9 Click **OK** in each dialog box.

*Graph
window
output*

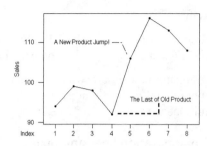

Polygons

Use this option to draw a series of lines from one point to another, which connect to form a closed polygon. You can change the edge lines of the polygon to another color, size (width), or type (such as solid or dashed). You can also fill the interior of the polygon with patterns and colors. The following simple polygon used to highlight three data points, along with some annotation text.

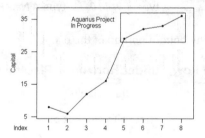

Note | If you place polygons beyond the data's minimum or maximum, by default MINITAB will automatically expand the scale to include those polygons. For details, see *Ticks and other items may affect the scale* on page 18-28.

▶ **To create a polygon**

1 In the graph dialog box, choose **Annotation ➤ Polygon**.

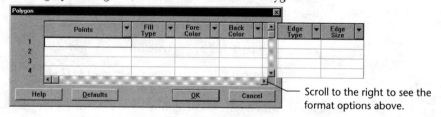

Scroll to the right to see the
format options above.

2 In row 1 of **Points**, enter an x-coordinate (such as 5) and a y-coordinate (such as 105), separated by a space. Then specify a set of x- and y-coordinates for the second and third points. If you like, create complex polygons by specifying more points.

Each succeeding point connects to the last to form the polygon edges. The first and last points connect to close the polygon.

Coordinates are in data units, except in three cases—see *Using Region Coordinates for Annotation* on page 17-2.

3 If you like, specify sets of coordinates for other polygons in rows 2, 3, etc.

4 If you like, choose any of the format options, and click **OK**.

Tip | For a polygon with many points, you can put x-coordinates in one column and y-coordinates in another. Then, in **Points** choose **Use variables** and select those columns.

Options

■ For each polygon, choose a fill type, fore color, back color, or edge type. For a list of line types and colors, see *Lists of Symbols, Colors, Lines, and Fills* on page 17-17.

Note | The fore color is the color of the edge line *and* the foreground color of any fill pattern.

■ For polygon, choose an edge size (width). Choose from the drop-down list or enter a value. The value can be any positive real number. Edges with larger sizes are wider than lines with smaller sizes. The default size is 1.

▷ **Example of a graph with polygons and text**

1 Open the worksheet MARKET.MTW.

2 Choose **Graph ➤ Time Series Plot**.

3 In **Y**, enter *Sales*.

4 Choose **Annotation ➤ Title**.

5 In **Title**, type *Sales Patterns 1991-1992*. Click **OK**.

6 Choose **Annotation ➤ Text**.

7 In the top portion of the dialog box, do the following, and click **OK**:

In Row	under Point	under Text
1	type *5 103.5*	type *Genesis In Field*
2	type *0.8 101*	type *Old Product In Field*

8 Choose **Annotation ➤ Polygon**. Do the following:

In Row	under Points	under Edge Type
1	type *4.8 105 4.8 116.5 8.2 116.5 8.2 105*	choose **Dash**
2	type *0.8 91.5 0.8 100 4.2 100 4.2 91.5*	choose **Dash 1-Dot**

9 Click **OK** in each dialog box.

Graph window output

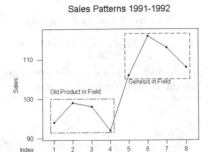

Sales Patterns 1991-1992

Markers

Markers are symbols you can place at precise points in your graph. You can set the symbol type, color, and size of each marker.

Note   If you place markers beyond the data's minimum or maximum, by default MINITAB will automatically expand the scale to include those markers. For details, see *Ticks and other items may affect the scale* on page 18-28.

▶ **To create a marker**

1 In the graph dialog box, choose **Annotation ➤ Marker**.

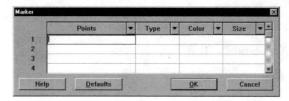

2 In row 1 of **Points**, enter an x-coordinate (such as 5) and a y-coordinate (such as 105), separated by a space.

Coordinates are in data units, except in three cases—see *Using Region Coordinates for Annotation* on page 17-2.

3 If you like, specify sets of coordinates for other markers in rows 2, 3, etc.

4 If you like, choose any of the format options, and click **OK**.

Tip | To place many markers, you can put x-coordinates in one column and y-coordinates in another. Then, in **Points** choose **Use variables** and select those columns.

Options

- For each marker, specify a symbol type and color by choosing from the drop-down list. For a list of symbol types and colors, see *Lists of Symbols, Colors, Lines, and Fills* on page 17-17.

- For each marker, specify a size by choosing from the drop-down list or entering a value. The value can be any positive real number. Markers with larger sizes are wider than markers with smaller sizes. The default size is 1.

▷ **Example of using a marker with text**

Since you can place markers anywhere on a graph, they can represent data points that did not occur in the data, such as goals or danger points. In this graph, we use a marker and some explanatory text to show where the Alpha advertising agency exceeded their budget.

1 Open the worksheet MARKET.MTW.

2 Choose **Graph ➤ Chart**.

3 In **Y**, enter *Advertis*. In **X**, enter *AdAgency*.

4 Choose **Annotation ➤ Marker**.

5 Do the following, and click **OK**:

In Row	under Points	under Type	Size
1	type *1 65*	choose **More Types ➤ Cross Circle**	choose **2.0**.

6 Choose **Annotation ➤ Text**.

7 Do the following:

In Row	under Point	under Text	Horizontal Offset
1	type *1 65*	type *Budgeted expense: $65,000*	choose **0.02**

8 Click **OK** in each dialog box

Graph window output

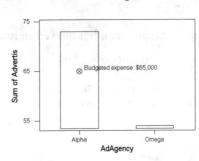

Lists of Symbols, Colors, Lines, and Fills

Symbol types

Applies to markers.

Code	Type	Name	Code	Type	Name
0		None			
1	○	Circle	16	◆	Solid Diamond
2	+	Plus	17	◇	Dot Diamond
3	×	Cross	18	⊕	Plus Diamond
4	✳	Asterisk	19	△	Triangle
5	·	Dot	20	▲	Solid Triangle
6	●	Solid Circle	21	△	Dot Triangle
7	⊙	Dot Circle	22	▷	Triangle Right
8	⊕	Plus Circle	23	▶	Solid Triangle Right
9	⊗	Cross Circle	24	▷	Dot Triangle Right
10	◎	Circle Circle	25	◁	Triangle Left
11	□	Square	26	◀	Solid Triangle Left
12	■	Solid Square	27	◁	Dot Triangle Left
13	⊡	Dot Square	28	▽	Triangle Down
14	⊠	Cross Square	29	▼	Solid Triangle Down
15	◇	Diamond	30	▽	Dot Triangle Down

Colors

Applies to:

- titles and footnotes
- text
- lines
- markers
- polygon fore colors and back colors

Code	Color	Code	Color	Code	Color
0	White				
1	Black	6	Magenta	11	Dark Cyan
2	Red	7	Yellow	12	Dark Magenta
3	Green	8	Dark Red	13	Dark Yellow
4	Blue	9	Dark Green	14	Dark Gray
5	Cyan	10	Dark Blue	15	Light Gray

Note | In polygons, the fore color is the color of the edge line *and* the foreground color of any fill pattern.

Line and edge types

Applies to:

- line types
- polygon edge types

Code	Line type	Name	Code	Line type	Name
0		None	4	— — — — –	Dash 1-Dot
1	————	Solid	5	— —·· — —·· —	Dash 2-Dot
2	— — — — —	Dash	6	—————————	Dash 3-Dot
3	- - - - - - - - -	Dot	7	— —— ——	Long Dash

Fill types

Applies to polygon fills.

Code	Fill type	Name	Code	Fill type	Name
0		None	5		Horizontal line
1		Solid (background is white)	6		Vertical line
2		Right slant	7		Cross line
3		Left slant	8		Dots
4		Cross slant	9		Squares

18

Core Graphs: Customizing the Frame

Customizing the Frame Overview

The *frame* of a graph surrounds the data region and sets the scale for the data. The following *frame elements* help you see how the data points relate to the scale:

- *axis lines* show the extent of the scale, while *axis labels* denote which variables were used to create the scale

- *tick lines and labels* show either scale increments or categories

- *grid lines* and *reference lines* help show how data points—especially those far away from tick lines and labels on the axes—relate to the scale

You can change the scale of the data by setting minimum and maximum data values, described on page 18-26. By default, MINITAB automatically adjusts the frame elements to scale. You can also override the defaults and place frame elements wherever you like along the scale.

The appearance of frame elements can also be customized. You can change the color, line type, size, fonts (for labels), and other properties of the various frame elements.

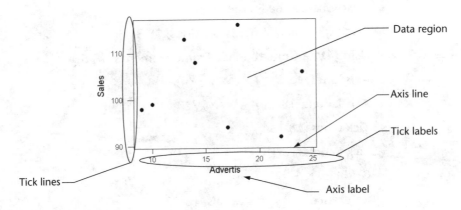

Graphs that use annotation options

Annotation options are available in the Layout dialog box when you choose **Graph ➤ Layout**. The options are also available in the main dialog boxes of the following graphs:

- core graphs - Plots, Time Series Plots, Charts, Histograms, Boxplots, Matrix Plots, Draftsman Plots, Contour Plots

- control charts - Xbar, R, S, Individuals, Moving Range, EWMA, Moving Average, P, NP, C, U

More | You can also modify axis lines and labels using the graph editing features described in Chapter 24, *Editing Graphs*. Using the graph editing features can be easier, unless you want to repeatedly produce a graph with the same line or label attributes, or you want to place axis lines or labels in exact locations using predefined points.

Placing Frame Elements on Sides

For each frame item—axis lines and labels, tick lines and labels, reference lines, or grid lines—you can specify which side of the frame you want to affect. In the dialog boxes, you do this by choosing a direction (X or Y), then a side (top, bottom, left, or right).

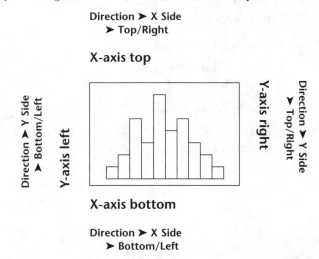

By default, MINITAB creates axis lines and labels and tick lines and labels on two sides: the X-axis bottom and the Y-axis left. You can modify those default frame elements, remove them, or add new frame elements on the other two sides. You can have frame elements on all four sides of the graph at once.

▶ To specify a side

1 In the graph main dialog box, choose **Frame ➤ Axis**, **Tick**, **Grid**, or **Reference**.

2 Under **Direction**, choose **X** or **Y**. (Time series plots have more x-axis choices—see *Specifying sides with time series plots* below).

3 Under **Side**, choose **Bottom/Left** or **Top/Right**. Click **OK**.

Note   **Bottom/Left** means bottom *or* left, depending on the direction. Likewise, **Top/Right** means top *or* right. For example, if you chose a **Direction** of **X**, **Bottom/Left** means that you are picking the bottom side. If you chose a **Direction** of **Y**, **Bottom/Left** means that are picking the left side.

Axis lines and labels are independent of tick lines and labels

Axis lines and labels are drawn independently of tick lines and labels. Therefore, if you want to have both axes and ticks appear on a side that does not have them by default (such as the top and right of a scatter plot), you must add both axis lines and labels in the **Frame ➤ Axis** subdialog box, and tick lines and labels in the **Frame ➤ Tick** subdialog box.

▷ Example of moving axes and ticks to the opposite side of a frame

First you specify a top-right axis, then you specify top-right tick lines and labels.

1 Open the worksheet MARKET.MTW.

2 Choose **Graph ➤ Plot**.

3 In **Y**, enter *Sales*. In **X** enter *Advertis*.

4 Choose **Frame ➤ Axis**.

5 Click the **Side** column header to highlight the column, then choose **Top/Right**. Click **OK**.

6 Choose **Frame ➤ Tick**.

7 Click the **Side** column header to highlight the column, then choose **Top/Right**. Click **OK** in each dialog box.

Graph window output

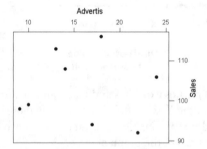

Specifying sides with time series plots

Time series plots can have up to three rows of axis labels and tick labels on the x-axis. Axis lines, tick lines, and grid lines can also be assigned to different rows. For example, the following time series plot has label rows for the month, quarter, and year. The plot also has larger ticks for each quarter, and a grid assigned to the Year row.

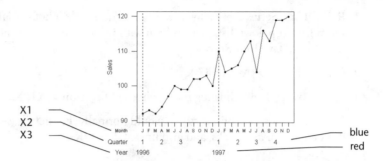

In the Axis, Tick, and Grid subdialog boxes, the rows are referred to as X1, X2, and X3:

X1   refers to the smallest time unit axis (for example, Month or Second)

X2   refers to the next largest time unit axis (for example, Quarter or Minute)

X3   refers to the largest time unit axis (for example, Year or Hour)

Axis and tick labels

Each row of labels can have its own format, and can appear on the top or bottom sides. In the graph above, the Month (X1) row has a smaller font than the other rows, the Quarter row (X2) is set to blue, and the Year row (X3) is set to red.

Lines

Axis lines for each row are placed on top of each other. Tick and grid lines that share positions are also placed on top of each other. X1 frame items are placed first (on the bottom), X2 items are placed next, and X3 items are placed last (on top). For example, look at the left-most tick on the x-axis below, the one for January (J), Quarter 1, 1996.

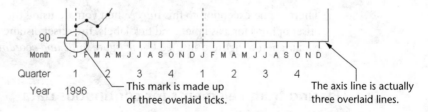

The mark looks like one tick, but there are actually three ticks placed exactly on top of each other. The ticks for quarters (X2) are set to a larger size, and they cover the ticks for months (X1). The tick for 1996 (X3) appears on top of the quarter 1 tick, but because it is the same color and of a smaller size, you cannot see it. If you edited this graph with the graph editing tools, you would be able to select and modify each tick separately.

The axis line also looks like one line—but it, too, is actually three overlaid lines.

▶ **To specify the format of rows for time series plots**

1 In the Time Series Plot dialog box, under **Time scale**, choose **Calendar** or **Clock**. From the drop down list, pick an item with two or three time units, such as **Day Month** or **Day Hour Second**.

2 Choose **Frame ➤ Axis** or **Tick**.

3 In the Axis or Tick subdialog boxes, choose **Direction ➤ X1, X2,** or **X3**.

4 Change any format options as you would normally. For details, see the sections in this chapter on axes, ticks, and grid lines. Click **OK**.

Note | If you create a label for **Direction ➤ X2** and only have one time unit specified in the main dialog box (such as **Hour**), or create a label for X3 and have only two time units specified, MINITAB will issue an error message about an "illegal argument" when you try to generate the graph. Re-edit the Axis or Tick subdialog box and remove the entries about X2 or X3.

Using Data Units to Place Frame Elements

One of the benefits of using the frame options in the graph dialog boxes, rather than the graph editing tools, is the ability to place elements at precise locations in relation to the data.

Tip | You may not need to read this section until after you choose the frame element you want to use. For example, you do not need to know how to place elements if you only want to change the text of an axis label or change the color of tick lines.

Frame elements are almost always placed in relation to the data, and so the location of elements are specified in *data units*. Y-axis elements are specified in terms of the data in the y-variable, and X-axis elements are specified in terms of the data in the x-variable.

There is one exception to this rule. When you are using the horizontal and vertical offset options for axis labels and tick labels, the offset distance is in *figure units*. For an explanation of figure units, see *Using figure units and coordinates* on page 19-4.

Placing frame elements for continuous data

For variables that have continuous data, you can place frame elements using any value that falls within the scale.

For example, say that the column Sales is the y-variable for your scatter plot. You want to place a reference line at the mean of that y-variable, so you can easily see which sales figures are above and below the average. Using MINITAB'S calculator, you find that the mean of Sales is 103.25. You would then place the reference line on the y-axis at a position of 103.25. For clarity, you give the reference line dashed line type and a label of "Mean = 103.25." (For step-by-step instructions for creating this graph, see *Example of creating a reference line based on a calculation* on page 18-24.)

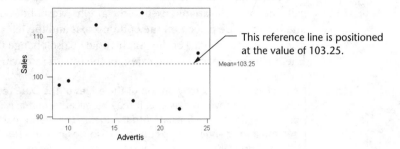

This reference line is positioned at the value of 103.25.

Placing frame elements with categorical data

When the x-axis represents categories (as with charts, boxplots, and time series plots that use an x-axis other than an index), specify the categories as axis positions 1, 2, ..., c (where c is the total number of categories) as they appear on the graph from left to right.

For example, say that a time series plot uses the categories of quarters and years instead of an index. (For step-by-step instructions for creating this graph, see *Example of placing reference lines for categorical data* on page 18-25.)

This reference line is placed at 4.5.

This reference line is placed at 6.

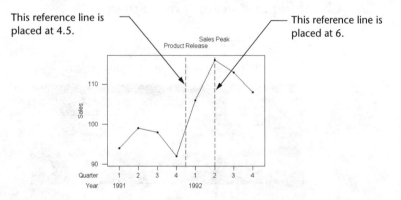

To place the first reference line (labeled "Product Release") between the last quarter of the first year and the first quarter of the second year, you would count the number of categories and see that the line should fall between categories 4 and 5, so the data unit value is 4.5. To place the second reference line (labeled "Sales Peak") at the second quarter of the second year, you would count six categories, and so use the data unit value of 6.

Axis Lines

You can create and modify the line for each axis. By default, MINITAB will create an axis line for each variable used in the graph. Most of the time, there are two variables, and the lines are placed on the bottom x-axis and the left y-axis. However, you can add axis lines to other sides of the graph. You can also change the appearance of each axis line, including changing the extent of the line or removing it completely.

Note | Axis lines display exactly on top of the edges of the Data region. If you cannot seem to change or remove an axis line, it may be because that axis line is actually a data region edge. To change the format of that edge, in the graph main dialog box choose **Regions ➤ Data** and change settings under **Attributes of Data Region**. To remove the edge, choose **Edge type ➤ None**. For details, see *Data Regions* on page 19-15.

Axis lines with matrix and draftsman plots

With matrix plots and draftsman plots, you can only modify axis lines on the outer edges of the plot. All the outer axis lines for a direction (x or y) will all have the same format. For example, if you specify in the dialog box that the x-axis line color is blue, all outer x-axis lines will be blue; if you specify that the y-axis line is red, all outer y-axis lines will be red. Inner axis lines will have the default settings: black, size 1.0, and full extent.

Changing and adding axis lines

▶ **To change default axis lines**

1 In the graph dialog box, choose **Frame ➤ Axis**.

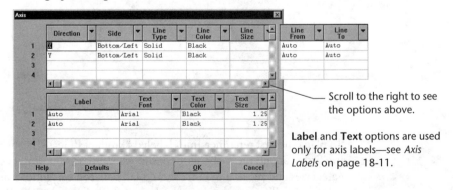

— Scroll to the right to see the options above.

Label and **Text** options are used only for axis labels—see *Axis Labels* on page 18-11.

2 If you like, use any of the options listed below, then click **OK**.

Tip | To display no line, choose **Line Type ➤ None**.

▶ **To add lines to other sides**

1 In the graph dialog box, choose **Frame ➤ Axis**.

2 Click in an empty row.

3 Under **Direction**, choose **X** or **Y**.

4 Under **Side**, choose **Top/Right**.

5 If you like, use any of the options listed below, then click **OK**.

Options

For each axis line, you can specify the:

■ side on which a line appears—see *Placing Frame Elements on Sides* on page 18-3

■ type and color—see *Lists of Colors and Lines* on page 18-32

■ size (width)

■ extent of the line from one data value to another—see *Controlling the extent of a line* on page 18-9

More | For more information on using these options, see Help.

Controlling the extent of a line

You can use this feature to highlight activity in a specific range. **Line from** and **Line to** specify (in data units) where to draw the axis line. By default, **Line from** is the minimum data value for the axis line, and **Line to** is the maximum data value. You can limit the extent of the line by changing the values of these settings.

Note | Because the axis line is drawn directly over the top of the data region edge line, you may not see that you have changed the extent of the axis line. You can either change the axis line attributes or suppress the data region edge line—see the example below.

Changing the axis line extent does not change the graph's scale

Changing the extent of the axis line does not change the scale of the graph. Nor does it change the placement of tick lines and labels.

If you set **Line from** to less than the data minimum, or set **Line to** greater than the data maximum, the axis line stops at the limit of the data; the line does not extend past the minimum or maximum data values. Of course, if you change the minimum or maximum of the scale, you will then be able to see the full extent of the line—see *Changing the Scale with Minimum and Maximum Values* on page 18-26.

If you want to change the x-axis line length when the x-axis represents categories (as with charts, boxplots, and time series plots), you need to specify the beginning and end values differently. For details, see *Placing frame elements with categorical data* on page 18-7.

▷ **Example of restricting the extent of the axis line**

In the example below, the data region's edge type is set to none, so that we can clearly see the axis lines. Then the axis line size is widened. Finally, the extent of the axis line is shortened so that it extends only from position 12 to position 22.

1 Open the worksheet MARKET.MTW.

2 Choose **Graph ➤ Plot**.

3 In **Y**, enter *Sales*. In **X**, enter *Advertis*.

4 Choose **Regions ➤ Data**. Choose **Edge type ➤ None**. Click **OK**.

5 Choose **Frame ➤ Axis**.

6 In the top portion of the dialog box, enter row values for the following items as shown:

Row	Line Size	Line From	Line To
1	choose **3.0**	type *12*	type *22*

7 In the bottom portion of the dialog box, enter row values for the following items as shown:

Row	Label	Text Font
1	type *Advertising Expenses*	choose **Times New Roman**
2	type *Sales Revenues*	choose **Times New Roman**

Tip You can change both rows of **Text Font** at once by clicking on the column header (which selects all the rows in that column), then choosing **Times New Roman**.

8 Click **OK** in each dialog box.

Graph window output

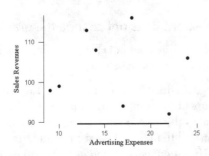

Axis Labels

You can create and modify the label for each axis. By default, MINITAB will create a label for each variable used in the graph. Most of the time, there are two variables, and the labels are placed on the bottom x-axis and the left y-axis.

The default label for a variable is usually that variable's name, such as "Sales." If the column name is long, MINITAB will truncate the name on the axis label to 12 characters. If the variable is not named, the label will be the variable's column number, such as C2. Labels for some graphs, like charts, may include the function used on that axis, such as "Sum of Sales." For example, here are two charts for the column Sales as the y-variable and the column Quarter as the x-variable.

Graph with default labels   **Graph with customized labels**

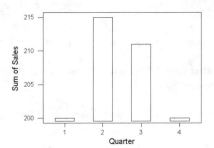 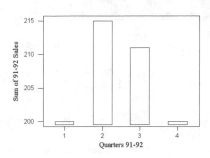

You can change the text of default labels, as well as the label's format and positioning, or hide the label. You can place labels on the default sides of the frame and on additional sides.

Axis labels with matrix and draftsman plots

With matrix plots, one axis label applies to both x- and y-axes. The format for that label is set in the x-axis row in the Axis subdialog box. The y-axis label settings have no effect on the graph. All labels share the same format. For example, if you specify in the dialog box that the x-axis label color is blue, all labels will be blue. If you change the label text from **Auto** to a text string, that text string will apply to each axis label—which can make your graph very confusing.

With draftsman plots, the format that you set for the x-axis label applies to all x-axis labels, and the format that you set for the y-axis label applies to all y-axis labels. If you change the text of the label from **Auto** to a text string, that text string will become the label for all the labels in that direction.

Changing and adding axis labels

▶ To change default axis labels

1 In the graph dialog box, choose **Frame ➤ Axis**.

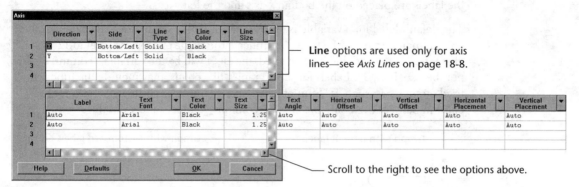

Line options are used only for axis lines—see *Axis Lines* on page 18-8.

Scroll to the right to see the options above.

2 Under **Label**, click in the row you want to affect, and enter text for a new label.

Tip To display no label, under **Label** type " " (double-quote, space, double-quote). Or, under **Text Font**, choose **None**.

3 If you like, use any of the options listed below, then click **OK**.

▶ To add labels to other sides

1 In the graph dialog box, choose **Frame ➤ Axis**.

2 Click in an empty row.

3 Under **Direction**, choose **X** or **Y**.

4 Under **Side**, choose **Top/Right**.

5 If you like, use any of the options listed below, then click **OK**.

Options

For each axis label, you can specify the:

- side on which the label appears—see *Placing Frame Elements on Sides* on page 18-3

- font and size

- color—see *Lists of Colors and Lines* on page 18-32

- angle (rotation), in degrees, going counter-clockwise

- horizontal and vertical offset (values from −1 to 1 which place the label away from the default position, in figure units)

- horizontal and vertical placement (how the label is placed in relation to the reference point—above, below, to the right of, etc.)

More | For more information on using these options, see Help.

▶ **Example of modifying axis labels**

In this example, both axis labels are changed from the defaults.

1 Open the worksheet MARKET.MTW.

2 Choose **Graph ➤ Plot**.

3 In **Y**, enter *Sales*. In **X**, enter *Advertis*.

4 Choose **Frame ➤ Axis**.

5 Under **Label**, in row 1 type *Advertising Expenditures*. In row 2, type *Sales Revenue*. Click **OK** in each dialog box.

Graph window output

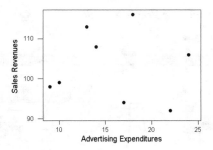

Tick Lines

Tick lines are sometimes called "tick marks," or simply "ticks." MINITAB has two types of tick lines: major tick lines, which denote intervals on the scale or denote categories; and minor tick lines, which are usually shorter lines, that denote smaller intervals between the major ticks. Major ticks also have labels (for details, see *Tick Labels* on page 18-18); minor ticks have no labels. Minor ticks can only be used with measurement, but not with categorical scales.

By default, MINITAB will create major tick lines for each axis. MINITAB will try to place the ticks at intervals that make sense for the data.

You can override the defaults and control the number, placement, and appearance of major tick lines. You can also add minor tick lines, and control their properties as well.

Tick lines can change the scale

If you place tick lines beyond the data's minimum or maximum, by default MINITAB will automatically expand the scale to include those items. For details, see *Ticks and other items may affect the scale* on page 18-28.

Tick lines with matrix and draftsman plots

With matrix plots and draftsman plots, tick lines appear only on the outer axes of the plots. In the dialog box, you can set properties for the set of x-axis ticks and the set of y-axis ticks. All x-axis tick lines on the graph share the same properties, and all y-axis tick lines share the same properties.

Changing and adding tick lines

▶ To change default tick lines

1 In the graph dialog box, choose **Frame ➤ Tick**.

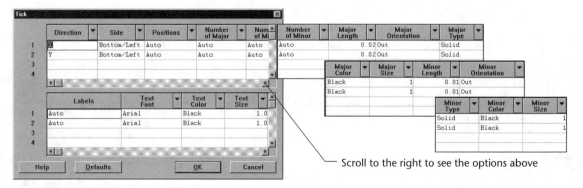

Scroll to the right to see the options above

2 If you like, use any of the options listed below, then click **OK**.

Tip To display no major tick lines, choose **Major Type ➤ None**. The tick label will still display unless you choose **Text Font ➤ None**.

Options

For major and minor tick lines, you can specify the:

■ side on which ticks appear—see *Placing Frame Elements on Sides* on page 18-3

■ exact positions or the number of tick lines—see *Setting the position and number of tick lines* on page 18-15

■ line type and color—see *Lists of Colors and Lines* on page 18-32

- orientation of the tick line: pointing out of the data region, in, or both in and out

- length and size (width), in figure units

More | For more information on using these options, see Help.

▶ **To add tick lines to other sides**

1 In the graph dialog box, choose **Frame ➤ Tick**.

2 Click in an empty row.

3 Under **Direction**, choose **X** or **Y**.

4 Under **Side**, choose **Top/Right**.

5 If you like, use any of the options listed above, then click **OK**.

Setting the position and number of tick lines

By default, MINITAB will create major tick lines for each axis, and no minor ticks. MINITAB will try to place the major ticks at intervals that make sense for the data.

For major tick lines, you can override the default placement in one of two ways:

- You can set the exact position of each tick line, or

- You can also set the number of tick lines that you want, letting MINITAB set the position of that number of ticks at evenly spaced intervals. If you set both the position and number of major ticks, the number of ticks setting is ignored.

For minor tick lines, you can set only the number of minor ticks that you want to appear between each pair of major ticks. You cannot have minor ticks when the axes represent categories.

Abbreviating ranges for tick positions

In the Tick subdialog box, you can enter a series of numbers to specify the position of each tick. To save space, you can use two punctuation marks to indicate ranges and increments.

A colon (:) between two numbers indicates a range. A slash (/) after a range indicates an increment amount. Consider the following examples:

Entering this set of numbers	Creates ticks at these positions
10 20 50	10, 20, 50
10 20 50:52	10, 20, 50, 51, 52
10 20 50:52/0.5	10, 20, 50, 50.5, 51, 51.5, 52
10 20:17 50	10, 20, 19, 18, 17, 50

▶ **Example of changing tick line positions**

1 Open the worksheet MARKET.MTW.

2 Choose **Graph ➤ Plot**.

3 In **Y**, enter *Sales*. In **X** enter *Advertis*.

4 Choose **Frame ➤ Tick**.

5 Under **Positions**, in row 1 type *10:25/3*. In row 2 type *95:115/5*.

   10:25/3 means all the positions from 10 to 25, by threes. Tick lines will be placed at the positions 10, 13, 16, 19, 22, and 25. Likewise, *95:115/5* means all the positions from 95 to 115, by fives, as in 95, 100, 105, 110, and 115.

6 Click **OK** in each dialog box.

Graph window output

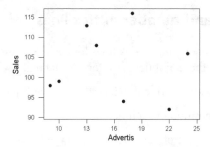

▶ **Example of setting the number and orientation of tick lines**

In this example, you set the number of major and minor tick lines, as well as their orientation.

1 Open the worksheet MARKET.MTW.

2 Choose **Graph ➤ Plot**.

3 In **Y**, enter *Sales*. In **X** enter *Advertis*.

4 Choose **Frame ➤ Tick**.

5 In the top portion of the dialog box, enter row values for the following items as shown:

Row	Number of Major	Number of Minor	Major Orientation	Minor Orientation
1	choose **4**	choose **4**	choose **Out and In**	choose **In**
2	choose **6**	choose **4**	choose **Out and In**	choose **In**

Tip | When all rows under a dialog box item need to be changed to the same value, such as **Number of Minor** being set to **4** for both rows, click the column header (which selects all the rows in that column), then choose the value from the column's drop-down list.

6 Click **OK** in each dialog box.

Graph window output

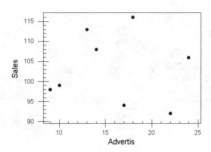

Placing tick lines for categorical data

You cannot change the *positions* of ticks on an x-axis that represents categories (for example, charts, boxplots, and time series plots). You cannot have minor ticks when the axes represent categories.

You can, however, specify which of the major tick lines on a category axis display and change their line and label attributes. You could, for example, display only the ticks for the third and fifth categories from the left of the graph by entering positions of 3 and 5.

For details on specifying which tick lines you want to affect, see *Placing frame elements with categorical data* on page 18-7.

▷ Example of changing tick lines and labels for categorical data

In this example, you will double the x-axis tick length to twice the default, then change the x-axis tick label text and size. Notice that the axis label (Sex) automatically moves down to account for the new tick label size and tick length.

1 Open the worksheet PULSE.MTW.

2 Choose **Graph ➤ Boxplot**.

3 In **Y**, enter *Weight*. In **X**, enter *Sex*.

4 Choose **Frame ➤ Tick**.

5 In top half of the dialog box, in row 1, choose **Major Length ➤ 0.04**.

6 In the bottom half of the dialog box, in row 1, type *Males Females* in **Label**, and
choose **Text Size ➤ 2.0**. Click **OK** in each dialog box.

*Graph
window
output*

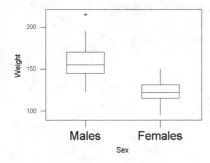

Tick Labels

Major tick lines have labels; minor tick lines do not. By default, MINITAB will create a
label for each tick line. The label text is that tick's data value. You can change the text
used for each label, as well as a label's format. You can also have labels appear even
when you have turned off tick lines.

Tick labels with matrix and draftsman plots

With matrix plots and draftsman plots, the format you set for the x-axis tick label applies
to all x-axis labels, and the format you set for the y-axis tick label applies to all y-axis
labels. If you change the text of the label from **Auto** to a text string, that text string will
become the label for all the tick labels in that direction.

Changing and adding tick labels

▶ **To change default tick labels**

1 In the graph dialog box, choose **Frame ➤ Tick**.

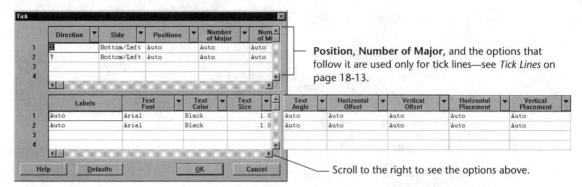

Position, **Number of Major,** and the options that follow it are used only for tick lines—see *Tick Lines* on page 18-13.

Scroll to the right to see the options above.

2 Under **Label**, click in the row you want to affect, and enter text for a new label.

Type characters for each label you want to create, separating labels with a space. You can enter up to 80 characters, including spaces.

If you want the label to include spaces, enclose the label in quotes, as in "*1st Qtr*" "*2nd Qtr*" "*3rd Qtr*" "*4th Qtr*"

If you do not enclose labels in quotes, each word is interpreted as a separate label. For example, entering *1st Qtr 2nd Qtr 3rd Qtr 4th Qtr* results in an axis that looks like this:

You can also store tick labels in a text column in the worksheet, and enter a column name or number.

Tip | To display no label, under **Label** type " " (double-quote, space, double-quote). Or, under **Text Font**, choose **None**.

3 If you like, use any of the options listed below, then click **OK**.

Options

For each tick label, you can specify the:

- side on which the label appears—see *Placing Frame Elements on Sides* on page 18-3

- font and size

- color—see *Lists of Colors and Lines* on page 18-32

- angle (rotation), in degrees, going counter-clockwise

- horizontal and vertical offset (values from −1 to 1 which place the label away from the default position, in figure units)

- horizontal and vertical placement (how the label is placed in relation to the reference point—above, below, to the right of, etc.)

More | For more information on using these options, see Help.

▶ **To add tick labels to other sides**

1 In the graph dialog box, choose **Frame ➤ Tick**.

2 Click in an empty row.

3 Under **Direction**, choose **X** or **Y**.

4 Under **Side**, choose **Top/Right**.

5 If you like, use any of the options listed above, then click **OK**.

▶ **Example of rotating tick labels using angle, offset, and placement options**

In this example, the y-axis tick labels are rotated 90 degrees to take up less room. The placement value attaches the tick labels at the middle right of the text. The axis label offset then brings the y-axis label closer to the axis.

1 Open the worksheet MARKET.MTW.

2 Choose **Graph ➤ Plot**.

3 In **Y**, enter *Sales*. In **X** enter *Advertis*.

4 Choose **Frame ➤ Tick**.

5 In row 2, choose **Text Angle ➤ 90**, **Horizontal Placement ➤ Centered on**, and **Vertical Placement ➤ Above**. Click **OK**.

6 Choose **Frame ➤ Axis**.

7 In row 2, type *−0.07* in **Horizontal Offset** and choose **Vertical Offset ➤ 0.0**.

8 Click **OK** in each dialog box.

Graph window output

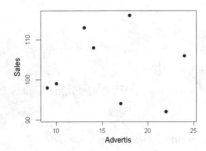

Grid Lines

Grid lines are horizontal or vertical lines that extend across the graph from the tick positions. The grid lines can extend in the y direction (from y-axis to y-axis) or the x direction (from x-axis to x-axis). You can create two grid lines, one in each direction, to to get a both horizontal and vertical lines.

Horizontal grid lines: the y-direction

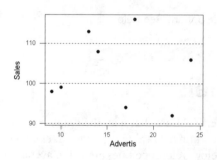

Horizontal and vertical grid lines: y- and x-direction

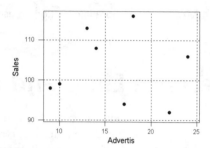

If your graph has minor ticks (see *Tick Lines* on page 18-13), you can customize the grid lines for minor ticks separately from major ticks. If your graph has both major and minor ticks, but you want grid lines to appear only for the major ticks, choose **Minor Type ➤ None**.

▶ **To add grid lines**

1 In the graph dialog box, choose **Frame ➤ Grid**.

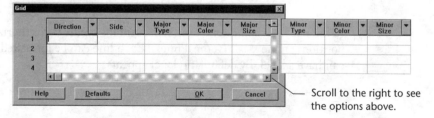

Scroll to the right to see the options above.

2 In **Direction**, choose **X** or **Y**.

To create grid lines in both directions, in row 1, choose **Direction ➤ X**; in row 2 choose **Direction ➤ Y**.

3 If you like, use any of the options listed below, then click **OK**.

Options

For each grid line, you can control the:

- side that grid lines project from. By default, **Side** is set to **Bottom/Left**. Choose **Side ▸ Top/Right** only if you have also placed tick lines on the top or right of the graph, and you want the grid lines to extend from those tick lines.

- major and minor line types and colors—see *Lists of Colors and Lines* on page 18-32.

- major and minor size (width) of the lines, in figure units.

More | For more information on using these options, see Help.

Reference Lines and Labels

Reference lines are horizontal or vertical lines that span the graph from one side to another. A reference line is set to a certain data value to provide a reference for the data points. For example, in the chart below, reference lines are at the average and target values so you can better see how closely each plant approaches those values.

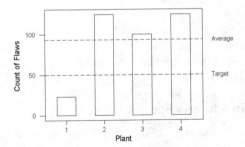

Reference lines can extend from tick positions on the y-axis (horizontal lines) or tick positions on the x-axis (vertical lines). Each line can be formatted in various ways, and can have a label. By default, no label appears.

▶ **To add reference lines and labels**

1 In the graph dialog box, choose **Frame ➤ Reference**.

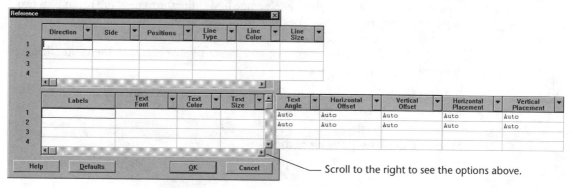

Scroll to the right to see the options above.

2 Click in an empty row.

3 Under **Direction**, choose **X** or **Y**.

Notice that as soon as you pick a direction, MINITAB fills in that row of the dialog box with default values.

4 If you want the reference line to have a label, click in the row you want to affect under **Labels**, and enter text.

If the text for your label includes spaces, such as *1st Qtr*, enclose the label in quotes, as in "*1st Qtr*". If you do not enclose the label in quotes, each word is interpreted as a separate label. For example, entering *1st Qtr* would create two labels, "1st" and "Qtr."

5 If you like, use any of the options listed below, then click **OK**.

Options

For each reference line and label, you can specify the:

- side on which the line and label appear—see *Placing Frame Elements on Sides* on page 18-3

- font and size of the label

- color—see *Lists of Colors and Lines* on page 18-32

- angle (rotation) of the label, in degrees, going counter-clockwise

- horizontal and vertical offset for the label (values from −1 to 1 which place the label away from the default position, in figure units)

- horizontal and vertical placement of the label (how the label is placed in relation to the reference point—above, below, to the right of, etc.)

More | For more information on using these options, see Help.

☞ Example of creating a reference line based on a calculation

Often, you will want to set a reference line at a value that needs to be calculated. For example, you may want to show a reference line at the mean or at the mean plus two standard deviations. In those cases, you can calculate the value with MINITAB's calculator. Then, either remember that calculated value and enter it in the Reference subdialog box, or have the calculator store the result in a constant, then enter that constant in the subdialog box.

In the example below, the mean of a variable is stored in a constant, and that constant is used in the Reference subdialog box.

Step 1: Open the data worksheet

1 Open the worksheet MARKET.MTW.

Step 2: Calculate the mean and store it in a constant

1 Choose **Calc ➤ Calculator**.

2 In **Store result in variable**, type *K1*.

3 In **Expression**, enter *MEAN(Sales)*. Click **OK**.

4 Click on the Constants folder in the Project manager. You see that K1 has a value of 103.25.

Step 3: Create the graph

1 Choose **Graph ➤ Plot**.

2 In **Y**, enter *Sales*. In **X**, enter *Advertis*.

3 Choose **Frame ➤ Reference**.

4 Choose **Direction ➤ Y**.

5 In **Positions**, enter *K1*.

6 Choose **Line Type ➤ Dash**.

7 In **Labels**, type "*Mean = 103.25*" (with double quotes). Click **OK** in each dialog box.

Graph window output

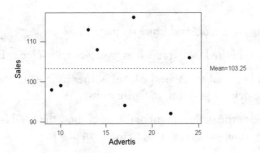

▷ Example of placing reference lines for categorical data

In the example below, two vertical reference lines denote the introduction of a new product and the peak of sales. Note that the second reference label is placed at position 6 from the left since the time units are treated as categories (for details, see *Placing frame elements with categorical data* on page 18-7). The "Sales Peak" label is offset higher so it does not interfere with the "Product Release" label.

1 Open the worksheet MARKET.MTW.

2 Choose **Graph ➤ Time Series Plot**.

3 In **Y**, enter *Sales*.

4 Click **Calendar** and choose **Quarter Year**.

5 Click **Options**.

6 Under **Start time**, type *1* in **Quarter** and *1991* in **Year**. Click **OK**.

7 Choose **Frame ➤ Reference**.

8 In the top half of the dialog box, enter row values for the following items as shown:

Row	Direction	Positions	Line Type
1	choose **X**	type *4.5*	choose **Dash**
2	choose **X**	type *6*	choose **Dash**

Tip When all rows under a dialog box item need to be changed to the same value, such as **Line Type** being set to **Dash** for both rows, click the column header (which selects all the rows in that column), then choose the value from the column's drop-down list.

9 In the bottom half of the dialog box, enter row values for the following items as shown:

Row	Labels	Horizontal Offset	Vertical Offset
1	type *"Product Release"* (with double quotes)	Auto	Auto
2	type *"Sales Peak"* (with double quotes)	choose **0.0**	type *0.07*

10 Click **OK** in each dialog box.

*Graph
window
output*

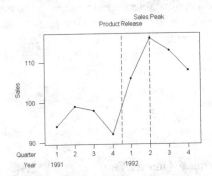

Changing the Scale with Minimum and Maximum Values

By default, the scale of an axis is set by the range of data in that axis variable, from the smallest data value (minimum) to the largest (maximum). In some cases, the scale may be extend beyond the data's minimum and maximum to include some frame elements and annotation items (see *Ticks and other items may affect the scale* on page 18-28).

You can change the scale of an axis by setting your own minimum and maximum values for each scale. The scale for each axis can be expanded or restricted.

For example, here is a scatter plot with a default scale, and the same scatter plot with an expanded scale: for each axis, the minimum is set to be smaller than the smallest value in the variable, and the maximum is set to be larger than the largest value in the variable.

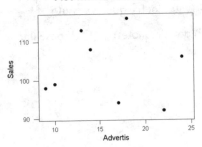

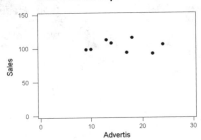

For step-by-step instructions for creating this graph, see *Example of changing the scale of a graph* on page 18-28.

If you restrict the scale of the graph, data points that fall outside the scale are by default "clipped" from the data region. Clipped objects are omitted from the graph. You can turn off clipping in the data region—see *Data Regions* on page 19-15.

Tip | Because data outside the scale are clipped, restricting the scale is an easy way to show just the data points you are interested in.

Note | You cannot change the scale for:
- any axis of matrix plots or draftsman plots
- an axis based on a column of date/time data

▶ To change the scale of an axis

1 In the graph dialog box, choose **Frame ➤ Min and Max**.

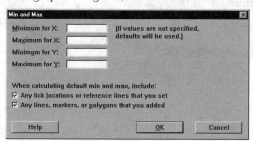

If you are using the Plots main dialog box, this subdialog box will look different. Plots have an extra option that appears here. See *Setting the same scale for X and Y— plots only* on page 18-30.

2 In the four text boxes, set the minimum and maximum data values for the axes you want to affect.

Note | If you set a minimum or maximum for an axis, your new scale will stop at your settings, ignoring tick locations and the other items listed in the dialog box under **When calculating default min and max, include**. For details, see *Ticks and other items may affect the scale* on page 18-28.

3 If you like, use any of the options listed below, then click **OK**.

Options

- You can make the default scale ignore frame elements or annotation items which might expand the scale. See *Ticks and other items may affect the scale* on page 18-28.

- If you are creating a graph using the **Graph ➤ Plot** command, you can set x- and y-axes to use the same minimum and maximum. See *Setting the same scale for X and Y—plots only* on page 18-30.

➤ **Example of changing the scale of a graph**

1 Open the worksheet MARKET.MTW.

2 Choose **Graph ➤ Plot**.

3 In **Y**, enter *Sales*. In **X**, enter *Advertis*.

4 Choose **Frame ➤ Min and Max**.

5 Choose **Separate minimum and maximum for X and Y axes**, then do the following:

   ■ In **X minimum**, type *0*.

   ■ In **X maximum**, type *30*.

   ■ In **Y minimum**, type *0*.

   ■ In **Y maximum**, type *150*.

6 Click **OK** in each dialog box.

Graph window output

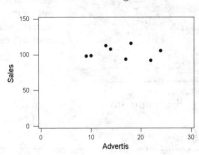

Ticks and other items may affect the scale

There are several frame elements and annotation items that can affect the default scale of an axis:

■ two frame elements: tick lines and reference lines (discussed in this chapter)

■ three annotation items: lines, markers, and polygons (discussed in Chapter 17, *Core Graphs: Annotating*)

The *default scale* of an axis is set by the range of data in that axis variable, from the smallest data value (the minimum) to the largest (the maximum). In your graph, you can add tick lines (and other items listed above) that are positioned beyond the default scale.

How MINITAB handles those items that are beyond the scale depends on whether or not you have overridden the default scale. The default scale is overridden when you set your own minimum and maximum for an axis in the Min and Max subdialog box.

If you do not override the default scale

If you do not override the default scale, by default MINITAB will expand the default scale to include the full extent of those ticks and other items. You can tell MINITAB to ignore those items that go beyond the scale (described below).

For example, say that the data's minimum for the x-axis variable is 9 and the maximum is 24. If you open the **Frame ➤ Tick** subdialog box and specify x-axis tick lines at positions of 0, 10, 15, 30, and 40, MINITAB will automatically change the scale of the x-axis in both directions to account for a minimum of 0 and a maximum of 40. Here is the default graph next to the graph with specified tick positions.

Plot with default scale   **Plot with a scale expanded by specified tick positions**

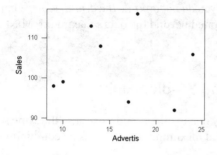
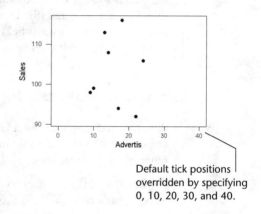

Default tick positions
overridden by specifying
0, 10, 20, 30, and 40.

▶ **To make the default scale ignore frame elements and annotation items**

1 In the graph dialog box, choose **Frame ➤ Min and Max**.

2 Under **When calculating default min and max, include**, do one or both of the following, then click **OK**.

   ■ uncheck **Any tick locations or reference lines that you set**

   ■ uncheck **Any lines, marker, or polygons that you added**

When the ticks and reference lines that exceed the default scale are not included, the portions of those items that exceed the scale are "clipped." Clipped portions (or items, if the entire item lies beyond the scale) are removed from the graph. Annotation items, including lines, markers, and polygons, are not clipped.

For example, say that the default scale of the x-axis goes from 9 to 24. If you specify in the Tick subdialog box to place x-axis tick lines in positions of 0, 10, 15, 30, and 40, then uncheck **Any tick locations or reference lines that you set**, the x-axis will display only the tick lines at positions 10 and 15.

If you override the default scale

If you override the default scale (by setting a minimum or maximum for that axis in the Min and Max subdialog box), the ticks and other items that exceed the specified range will be "clipped," no matter what checkboxes are checked or unchecked under **When calculating default min and max, include**. Clipped items are removed from the graph.

For example, say that you specify x-axis tick lines at positions of 0, 10, 15, 30, and 40. If you then set the x-axis minimum to be 15, the tick lines at 0 and 10 will be clipped. If you also set the x-axis maximum to 30, the tick line at position 40 will also be clipped.

Remember that any minimum or maximum (for either axis) that you do not specify will use the defaults. For example, if you specify only an x-axis minimum, the x-axis maximum will use the maximum of the default scale, and will therefore follow the rules for expansion described under *If you do not override the default scale*. That means that if there were any x-axis ticks positioned beyond the data's maximum, MINITAB will expand the scale to include those ticks.

Setting the same scale for X and Y—plots only

Plots have a dialog box option for easily making the x- and y-axes use the same scale. By default, MINITAB sets the minimum and maximum for each axis by combining the range of the two variables.

For example, if the x-axis variable Sales has a range of 9 to 24, and the y-variable Advertis has a range of 92 to 116, the combined range is 9 to 116: both axes will have a minimum of 9 and a maximum of 116.

You can also set your own minimum or maximum for x and y to share.

▶ **To set the same scale for X and Y**

1 Choose **Graph ➤ Plot**.

2 Choose **Frame ➤ Min and Max**.

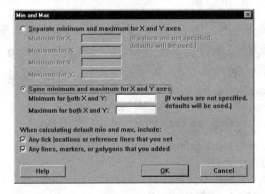

3   Choose **Same minimum and maximum for X and Y axes**.

4   If you like, enter values in the two text boxes to set the minimum for X and Y, the maximum for X and Y, or both. If you leave the text boxes blank, they will use the combined minimum or maximum values of the data.

5   If you like, choose how to calculate the default scale as described in *Ticks and other items may affect the scale* on page 18-28. Then click **OK**.

Suppressing and Showing All Frame Elements at Once

You can remove all axis, tick, grid, and reference lines and labels at once.

Plot with default frame elements

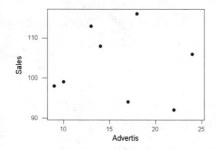

Plot with suppressed frame elements

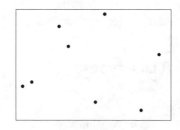

▶ **To suppress all frame elements**

1   In the graph dialog box, choose **Regions ➤ Data**.

2   Uncheck **Show frame elements**. Click **OK** in each dialog box.

More | You can also remove the box that surrounds the data. In the graph dialog box, choose **Regions ➤ Data**, then choose **Edge type ➤ None**.

Lists of Colors and Lines

Colors

Apply to:

- Axis lines and labels
- Tick lines and labels
- Reference lines and labels
- Grid lines

Code	Color	Code	Color	Code	Color
0	White				
1	Black	6	Magenta	11	Dark Cyan
2	Red	7	Yellow	12	Dark Magenta
3	Green	8	Dark Red	13	Dark Yellow
4	Blue	9	Dark Green	14	Dark Gray
5	Cyan	10	Dark Blue	15	Light Gray

Line types

Apply to:

- Axis lines
- Tick lines
- Grid lines
- Reference lines

Code	Line type	Name	Code	Line type	Name
0		None	4	— – — – –	Dash 1-Dot
1	————————	Solid	5	—– – – —– – –	Dash 2-Dot
2	— — — — — —	Dash	6	——————————	Dash 3-Dot
3	- - - - - - - - - - -	Dot	7	—— —— ——	Long Dash

19

Core Graphs: Controlling Regions

Graph Regions Overview

Each graph window is one *page*, or *page region*. Each page can contain three other types of regions:

- *figure* regions (one for each graph on the page)

- *data* regions (one inside each figure region)

- and in some cases, a *legend* region. Legends are created only when you use the data display option of assigning different display attributes to each group.

The **page region** contains all three graphs.

Each graph is enclosed by a **figure region**, shown here with dashed lines.

The **data region** includes all the data points within the frame.

The **legend region** contains the legend.

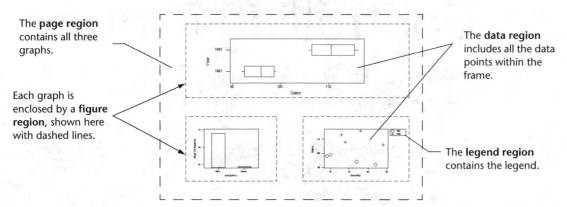

The page region always fits the Graph window. Each region within the page can be resized, relocated on the page, and formatted with color, fill patterns, edge line types, and more.

Region coordinate systems

Each region has its own coordinate system. By using x- and y-region coordinates, you can place annotation items and frame elements—such as titles and reference lines—relative to the region that they are in. You can also place regions within other regions.

For example, say that you have a page with many graphs on it. A title that explains all the graphs can be placed relative to the entire page by using page units. Each graph (or figure) can have its own title, which is placed in figure units. On one graph, a data label can identify a particular point in the data region, and so use data units.

Graphs that use annotation options

Annotation options are available in the Layout dialog box when you choose **Graph ➤ Layout**. The options are also available in the main dialog boxes of the following graphs:

- core graphs - Plots, Time Series Plots, Charts, Histograms, Boxplots, Matrix Plots, Draftsman Plots, Contour Plots

- control charts - Xbar, R, S, Individuals, Moving Range, EWMA, Moving Average, P, NP, C, U

More | You can also modify axis lines and labels using the graph editing features described in Chapter 24, *Editing Graphs*. Using the graph editing features can be easier, unless you want to repeatedly produce a graph with the same line or label attributes, or you want to place axis lines or labels in exact locations using predefined points.

Region Coordinate Systems

The page, figure, and data regions each have their own coordinate systems. By using x- and y-region coordinates, you can place the figure and data regions where you want, or place annotation items, frame elements, and other regions relative to the region they affect.

For example, say that you have a page with many graphs on it. Each graph is placed on the page using page units. A title that explains all the graphs can also be placed relative to the entire page by using page units. Each graph (or figure) can have its own title, which is placed in figure units. On one graph, a data label can identify a particular point in the data region, and so uses data units.

Using page units and coordinates

Page units and the page coordinate system are used when you place

- one or more figure regions on a page—see *Changing the size and placement of the figure region* on page 19-10

- annotation items that are for the whole page, rather than one graph—see *Adding annotation to a page* on page 16-23

The page coordinate system ranges from 0 to 1 in each direction, x and y. In the x-direction, 0 is the left edge of the page and 1 is the right edge of the page. In the y-direction, 0 is the bottom edge of the page and 1 is the top edge of the page.

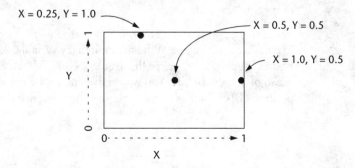

Using figure units and coordinates

Figure units are used when you place items specific to a particular graph, but whose location is independent of the data. For example, a title would not change position if the data changed, but a symbol label would move with the data. With figure units, you can place:

- the data region—see *Changing the size and placement of the data region* on page 19-16

- some annotation items, such as titles and footnotes—see *Titles and Footnotes* on page 17-4

- some frame elements, such as axis labels and tick labels—see *Axis Labels* on page 18-11 and *Tick Labels* on page 18-18

The figure coordinate system, like the page coordinate system, ranges from 0 to 1 in each direction, x and y. In the x direction, 0 is the left edge of the figure and 1 is the right edge of the figure. In the y direction, 0 is the bottom edge of the figure and 1 is the top edge of the figure.

Using data units and coordinates

Use data units when you want to place items relative to the data. Using data units you can place:

- annotation items such as text, lines, markers, and polygons—see *Using Region Coordinates for Annotation* on page 17-2

- frame elements, such as tick lines and reference lines—see *Using Data Units to Place Frame Elements* on page 18-6

The data coordinate system uses the data units of the x- and y-variables in a particular graph. If you add extra elements that will vary with the data in the graph—such as text, lines, symbols, or polygons—you place them using data coordinates.

Using data units with continuous data

For variables that have continuous data, you can place frame elements using the values of specific observations.

For example, say that the column Sales is the y-variable for your scatter plot. You want to place a reference line at the mean of that y-variable, so you can easily see which sales figures are above and below the average. Using MINITAB's calculator, you find that the mean of Sales is 103.25. You would then place the reference line on the y-axis at a position of 103.25. For clarity, you give the reference line dashed line type and a label of "Mean = 103.25." (For step-by-step instructions for creating this graph, see *Example of creating a reference line based on a calculation* on page 18-24.)

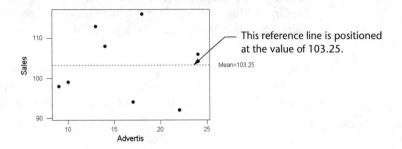

Using data units with categorical data

When the x-axis represents categories (as with charts, boxplots, and time series plots that use an x-axis other than an index), specify the categories as axis positions 1, 2, …, c (where c is the total number of categories) as they appear on the graph from left to right.

For example, say that a time series plot uses the categories of quarters and years instead of an index. (For step-by-step instructions for creating this graph, see *Example of placing reference lines for categorical data* on page 18-25.)

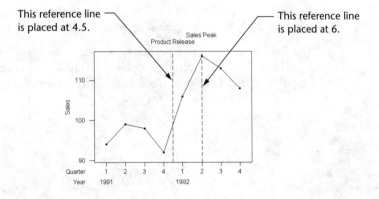

To place the first reference line (labeled "Product Release") between the last quarter of the first year and the first quarter of the second year, you would count the number of categories and see that the line should fall between categories 4 and 5, so the data unit value is 4.5. To place the second reference line (labeled "Sales Peak") at the second quarter of the second year, you would count six categories, and so use the data unit value of 6.

Page Regions

A *page* is the container of your graphs. On your screen, a page is the white area inside the Graph window; the gray area in the Graph window that is sometimes visible is outside the page. When you print a graph, the page region corresponds to one sheet of paper.

Using layout mode, you can place any number of graphs on a page, and also place annotation—such as a title, footnote, or line—that is not specific to any one graph. For example, here are two graphs on one page, with a page title.

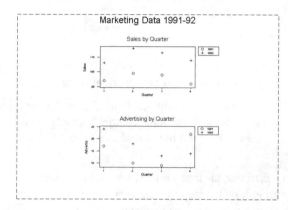

For details on using layout mode to place multiple graphs and add page annotation, see *Creating a Multi-Graph Layout* on page 16-20.

You can also change the aspect ratio of a page, described below. You can change the aspect ratio for one graph page, or change your defaults to use that aspect ratio for all graph pages. See *Changing the default aspect ratio* on page 19-9.

Changing the aspect ratio of a page

The aspect ratio is the ratio between the width (or x-dimension) and the height (or y-dimension) of the graph. For example, here are two graphs that use the same data, but have different aspect ratios. For clarity, the page edge is shown with a solid line.

Graph with aspect ratio of 3:2 (3 width to 2 height)   **Graph with aspect ratio of 4:1**

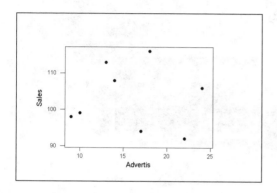
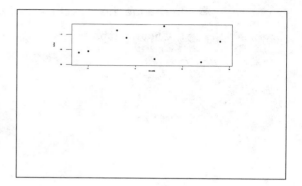

For step-by-step instructions on creating the graph on the right, see *Example of changing the aspect ratio of a graph* on page 19-8.

The default aspect ratio depends on your computer monitor's display size and the work area available in your desktop environment. The work area is the area of your screen between status bars, toolbars, and other screen objects, where a Graph window appears. A maximized Graph window fills the work area. A pleasing aspect ratio (and one probably close to what you see when you maximize a Graph window) may be 3:2.

You can change:

■ the aspect ratio for one graph

■ the default aspect ratio for all graphs in the current project

■ the default aspect ratio for all graphs in every project

Note | Once the graph is created, the aspect ratio of the graph page does not change. If you resize the Graph window, the graph page resizes, but the ratio stays the same. The ratio also stays the same when you print the graph or save the graph as a file.

Here are some common reasons for changing aspect ratios:

■ To make a similar unit be the same length on different axes. For example, if you have a range of 30 cm on the x-axis, 50 cm on the y-axis, and you want a centimeter to be the same length on both the x- and y-axes, you can set the aspect ratio to 50 for the x-axis, 30 for the y-axis.

- To make a graph of a certain shape. For example, an aspect ratio of 1:1 gives a square graph.

- To ensure that graph commands create graphs of the same shape when used on different computers. If you do not specify the same aspect ratio when creating the graph, the default aspect ratio may be different on the current computer, and the resulting graph will have a different aspect ratio.

▶ **To change the aspect ratio of a graph**

1 Choose **Graph ➤ Layout**.

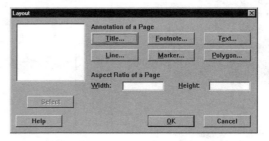

2 Under **Aspect Ratio of a Page**, enter a value for **Width** and a value for **Height**.

   Width and **Height** can be set to any positive value. For example, ratios of 3:2, 6:4, 0.3:0.2, and 1.5:1.0 all create a page region with a width that is 1.5 times its height.

3 Click **OK**.

4 Create the graph. For example, you could choose **Graph ➤ Plot**, specify two variables, and click **OK**.

5 Choose **Graph ➤ End Layout**.

▶ **Example of changing the aspect ratio of a graph**

In this example, the aspect ratio is set to 4:1, which has a width of four times that of height.

1 Open the worksheet MARKET.MTW.

2 Choose **Graph ➤ Layout**.

3 Under **Aspect Ratio of a Page**, in **Width** type *4*, and in **Height** type *1*. Click **OK**.

4 Choose **Graph ➤ Plot**.

5 In **Y**, enter *Sales*. In **X**, enter *Advertis*. Click **OK**.

6 Choose **Graph ➤ End Layout**.

*Graph
window
output*

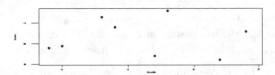

Changing the default aspect ratio

You can set a default aspect ratio so that all graphs in the current project will be created at that aspect ratio. You can then change your preferences so that when you create graphs in any other project, by default the graphs will have the aspect ratio you want.

▶ **To change the default aspect ratio for all graphs in the current project**

1 Create a graph at the aspect ratio you want—see *To change the aspect ratio of a graph* on page 19-8.

2 Using your mouse, resize the Graph window to fit the graph page as exactly as possible. When the fit is exact, no gray areas should be visible between the white graph page and the Graph window border.

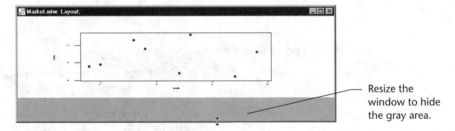

Resize the window to hide the gray area.

3 Choose **Window ➤ Set Graph Size/Location**.

▶ **To set a preference for aspect ratios to use in all projects**

1 Set the graph page aspect ratio for the current project—see *To change the default aspect ratio for all graphs in the current project* above.

2 Choose **Edit ➤ Preferences**.

3 Select **Window Layout**.

4 Check **Graph windows: last set size and location**. Click **OK**. Click **Save**.

Figure Regions

A *figure region* is the place within a page where you display a single graph. It contains everything specific to a particular graph: the data region, the legend region (if one exists) axes, axis labels, ticks, tick labels, titles, and footnotes.

Simple graphs have one figure region that, by default, takes up the whole page. In the layout mode, you can have more than one figure region on a page. The example on the left shows the figure region for a simple graph in a shaded area. The example on the right shows two figure regions on the same page in the shaded areas:

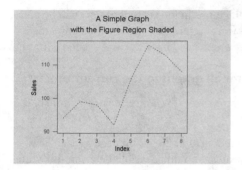
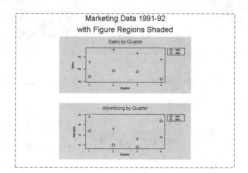

For each figure region you can control:

- the size and placement of the figure region on the page — see *Changing the size and placement of the figure region* on page 19-10

- the format of the figure region, including colors, fill type, and edge line type — see *Controlling the format of the figure region* on page 19-12

- whether or not to display annotation and data that extend beyond the figure region (clipping) — see *Clipping the display of items outside the figure region* on page 19-13

Changing the size and placement of the figure region

Figure regions are sized and placed using page coordinates — see *Using page units and coordinates* on page 19-3.

For each figure that you want to place, you specify four coordinates: a minimum for x, a maximum for x, a minimum for y, and a maximum for y. By default, the figure region is the same size as the page (the same as specifying x- and y- minimums of 0, and x- and y-maximums of 1).

When you change the size of the figure region, every item inside the figure region is resized proportionally. If you shrink a figure region, the axis and tick labels may become difficult to read on your screen.

The following examples show a graph with a default figure region that takes up the entire page, and the same graph with a smaller figure region. The dashed line shows the extent of the figure region on the page. In the first graph, the edge of the figure region is the same as the edge of the page. In the second graph, a solid line shows the page edge.

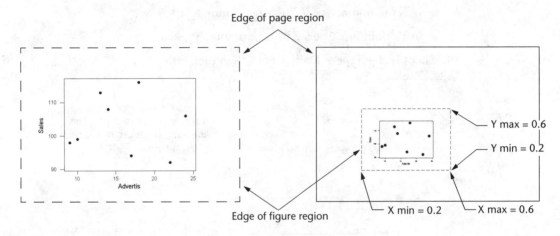

The smaller graph has a figure region set to x and y minimums of 0.2, and x and y maximums of 0.6. For step-by-step instructions on creating this graph, see *Example of changing the size of the figure region* on page 19-12.

▶ **To change the size and placement of the figure region**

1 In the graph dialog box, choose **Regions ➤ Figure**.

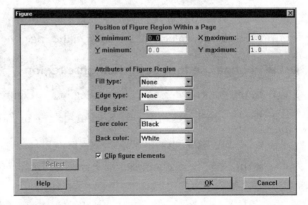

2 Under **Position of Figure Region Within a Page**, enter X and Y minimum and maximum values, in page units. Click **OK**.

▷ **Example of changing the size of the figure region**

1 Open the worksheet MARKET.MTW.

2 Choose **Graph ➤ Plot**.

3 In **Y**, enter *Sales*. In **X**, enter *Advertis*.

4 Choose **Regions ➤ Figure**.

5 Under **Position of Figure Region Within a Page**, do the following:

   ■ In **X minimum**, type *0.2* In **X maximum**, type *0.6*.

   ■ In **Y minimum**, type *0.2* In **Y maximum**, type *0.6*.

6 Choose **Edge Type ➤ Dash**. Click **OK** in each dialog box.

*Graph
window
output*

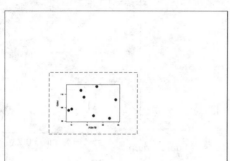

For clarity, the edge of the page is shown with a solid line. This line is not produced by the steps given above.

Controlling the format of the figure region

The figure region can be formatted in various ways. You can control:

■ the fill type and fill color

■ the line type, color, and thickness of the edge line around the figure region

▶ **To change the format of the figure region**

1 In the graph dialog box, choose **Regions ➤ Figure**.

2 Under **Attributes of Figure Region**, do one or more of the following, and click **OK**.

   ■ In **Fill type**, choose a type—see *Lists of Colors, Lines, and Fills* on page 19-25.

   ■ In **Edge type**, choose a line type—see *Lists of Colors, Lines, and Fills* on page 19-25.

   ■ In **Edge size**, enter a value for the thickness of the line, in pixels. The default of 1 gives an edge line that is one pixel wide.

- In **Fore color**, choose the color for the fill type pattern (if dots, for example, this will color the dots) and for the edge line.

- In **Back color**, choose a color for the background of the fill type pattern (if dots, for example, this will color the surface the dots are on). For a solid fill, click **Solid** from **Fill type** and choose a non-white **Back color**.

☞ Example of adding a background pattern to the figure

When you change the fill type and color of the figure region, the pattern or color covers the entire figure region, even the data region. But sometimes you may want to the figure pattern to appear only in the background, leaving the data region alone. In this example, the figure region fill pattern is created, and then the data region is given a solid white fill, so that it appears normally.

1 Open the worksheet MARKET.MTW.

2 Choose **Graph ➤ Plot**.

3 In **Y**, enter *Sales*. In **X**, enter *Advertis*.

4 Choose **Regions ➤ Figure**.

5 Choose **Fill Type ➤ Left Slant**. Click **OK**.

6 Choose **Regions ➤ Data**.

7 Choose **Fill Type ➤ Solid**. Click **OK** in each dialog box.

Graph window output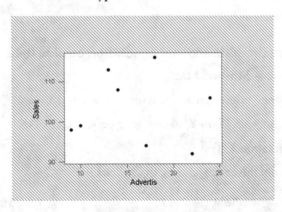

Clipping the display of items outside the figure region

Clipping suppresses the display of all data and annotation outside of the figure region. By default, clipping is turned on, but you can turn this option off. If you do not set the figure region to be smaller than the page region (describe in *Changing the size and placement of the figure region* on page 19-10), then turning off clipping appears to have no effect.

If you want to display data that fall outside the data region *and* outside the figure region, turn off data region clipping (see *Clipping the display of items outside the data region* on page 19-19) and turn off figure region clipping. For an example, see below.

Note | It is not possible for data points to fall outside the data region unless the scale of the graph has been restricted. This is uncommon. See *Changing the Scale with Minimum and Maximum Values* on page 18-26.

▶ **To turn figure region clipping on and off**

1 In the graph dialog box, choose **Regions ➤ Figure**.

2 Uncheck or check **Clip figure elements**. Click **OK**.

▷ **Example of turning off clipping in the figure and data regions**

In this plot, data points and some annotated text are allowed to fall outside the data and figure regions. After specifying the variables to plot, the scale is changed so that the maximum on the x-axis is 15 and the maximum on the y-axis is 105. Next, the figure region is reduced, and clipping is turned off in the figure and data regions.

Step 1: Choose the data to graph

1 Open the worksheet MARKET.MTW.

2 Choose **Graph ➤ Plot**.

3 In **Y**, enter *Sales*. In **X**, enter *Advertis*.

Step 2: Reduce the scale and add annotation outside the scale

1 Choose **Frame ➤ Min and Max**.

2 Choose **Separate minimum and maximum for X and Y axes**.

3 In **X maximum**, type *15*. In **Y maximum**, type *105*. Click **OK**.

4 Choose **Annotation ➤ Text**.

5 In row 1, fill out the cells as shown, then click **OK**:

Point	Text	Text Size
type *14 113*	type *MISCELLANEOUS TEXT*	choose **2.0**

The x-coordinate is 14 and the y-coordinate is 113 where the text begins, in data units.

Step 3: Reduce the figure region, then turn off clipping in both regions

1 Choose **Regions ➤ Figure**.

2 In **X minimum**, type *0.01*. In **X maximum**, type *0.6*.
In **Y minimum**, type *0.01*. In **Y maximum**, type *0.6*.

3 Uncheck **Clip figure elements**. Click **OK**.

4 Choose **Regions ➤ Data**.

5 Uncheck **Clip data elements**. Click **OK** in each dialog box.

*Graph
window
output*

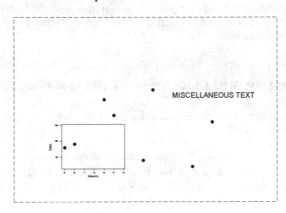

The outline of the
page is shown here for
illustrative purposes.

Data Regions

A *data region* is the place within a graph where you display your data. You can place
additional text, lines, symbols, and polygons within the data region. The following
examples show the data region in a simple graph and the data regions on a page with
two graphs:

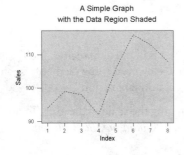

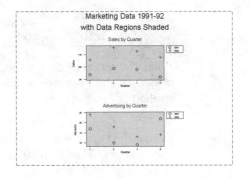

For each data region you can control:

- the size and placement of the data region within the figure region—see *Changing the size and placement of the data region* on page 19-16

- the format of the data region, including colors, fill type, and edge line type—see *Controlling the format of the data region* on page 19-18

- whether or not to display annotation and data that extend beyond the data region (clipping)—see *Clipping the display of items outside the data region* on page 19-19

More | In the Data Region subdialog box, you can also suppress all the frame elements at once, hiding axes, ticks, grid lines, and reference lines. See *Suppressing and Showing All Frame Elements at Once* on page 18-31.

Changing the size and placement of the data region

Data regions are sized and placed using figure units—see *Using figure units and coordinates* on page 19-4.

To resize or move the data region, you specify four coordinates: an x minimum and maximum, and a y minimum and maximum. By default, the data region extends from 0.2 to 0.8 (in figure units) in the x-direction and from 0.2 to 0.8 (in figure units) in the y-direction.

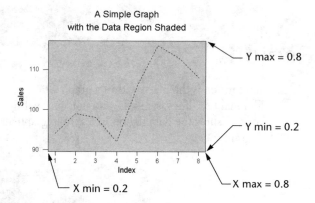

When you resize the data region, all data and elements of the data region, such as axes, ticks, data, and lines move to appropriate locations. However, some elements, such as symbols and text, remain the same size as in the default data region.

When you resize the data region, you are not changing the scale of the axes. To do that, you use the **Frame ➤ Min and Max** command—see *Changing the Scale with Minimum and Maximum Values* on page 18-26.

▶ **To change the size and placement of the data region**

1 In the graph dialog box, choose **Regions ➤ Data**.

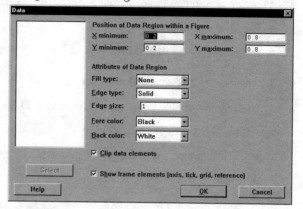

2 Under **Position of Data Region within a Figure**, enter X and Y minimum and maximum values, in figure units. Click **OK**.

▷ **Example of changing the size of the data region**

1 Open the worksheet MARKET.MTW.

2 Choose **Graph ➤ Plot**.

3 In **Y**, enter *Sales*. In **X**, enter *Advertis*.

4 Choose **Regions ➤ Data**.

5 Under **Position of Data Region Within a Figure**, do the following:

■ In **X minimum**, type *0.15* In **X maximum**, type *0.5*.

■ In **Y minimum**, type *0.15* In **Y maximum**, type *0.5*.

6 Click **OK** in each dialog box.

Graph window output

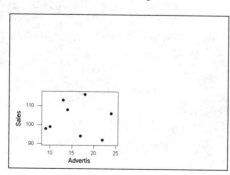

The outline of the page is shown here for illustrative purposes.

Controlling the format of the data region

The data region can be formatted in various ways. You can control:

- the fill type and fill color
- the line type, color, and thickness of the edge line around the data region

▶ **To change the format of the data region**

1 In the graph dialog box, choose **Regions ➤ Data**.

2 Under **Attributes of Data Region**, do one or more of the following, and click **OK**.

- In **Fill type**, choose a type—see *Lists of Colors, Lines, and Fills* on page 19-25.

- In **Edge type**, choose a line type—see *Lists of Colors, Lines, and Fills* on page 19-25.

- In **Edge size**, enter a value for the thickness of the line, in pixels. The default of 1 gives an edge line that is one pixel wide.

- In **Fore color**, choose the color for the fill type pattern (if dots, for example, this will color the dots) and for the edge line.

- In **Back color**, choose a color for the background of the fill type pattern (if dots, for example, this will color the surface the dots are on). For a solid fill, click **Solid** for **Fill type** and choose a non-white **Back color**.

▶ **Example of removing the data region edge line**

You can make the edge of the data region go away, leaving only the axes lines. Note that the axis and tick lines and labels still display. You can also turn off all the frame elements—including axis lines and labels and tick lines and labels—with one step. See *Suppressing and Showing All Frame Elements at Once* on page 18-31.

1 Open the worksheet MARKET.MTW.

2 Choose **Graph ➤ Plot**.

3 In **Y**, enter *Sales*. In **X**, enter *Advertis*.

4 Choose **Regions ➤ Data**.

5   Choose **Edge Type ➤ None**. Click **OK** in each dialog box.

Graph window output

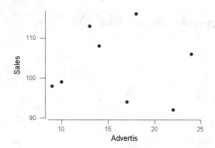

More   For an example of changing the fill pattern of the data region (as well as the figure region), see *Example of adding a background pattern to the figure* on page 19-13.

Clipping the display of items outside the data region

Clipping suppresses the display of all data outside of the data region, but does not suppress annotation items that extend out of the data region. By default, clipping is turned on, but you can turn this option off. For example, clipping has been turned off in the following graph.

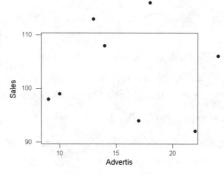

If you want to display data that fall outside data region *and* outside the figure region, turn off data region clipping and turn off figure region clipping. For an example, see *Example of turning off clipping in the figure and data regions* on page 19-14.

Note   It is not possible for data points to fall outside the data region unless the scale of the graph has been changed. See *Changing the Scale with Minimum and Maximum Values* on page 18-26.

▶ **To turn data region clipping on and off**

1 In the graph dialog box, choose **Regions ➤ Data**.

2 Uncheck or check **Clip data elements**. Click **OK**.

Legend Regions

A *legend region* displays when you display data differently for each group of a variable. For example, you can display all the data points for males as a solid circle, and all the data points for females as a triangle.

The legend tells the viewer what symbols, lines, or fills correspond to each group. It contains a sample of the data display elements along with group labels.

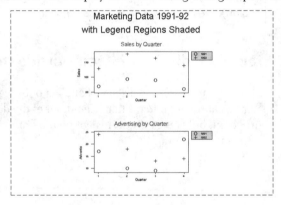

Specifically, a legend region appears when you:

- assign data display attributes in the graph dialog box using the **For each ➤ Group** option—for details, see *Displaying Data for Each Group* on page 16-5

- use contour plots (each contour level is a group—see *Contour Plots* on page 14-49)

A legend region does not appear when you overlay multiple graphs in the same window, or when you create a multi-graph layout, unless individual graphs in the window contain groups as described above. For an example of a multi-graph layout that contains legends, see the graph above.

Note | Even though you can choose **Regions ➤ Legend** at any time and enter values into the Legend subdialog box, the legend region does not appear until you meet the conditions above.

For each legend region, you can control:

- the position and size of the legend region

- the format of the legend region, including colors, fill type, and edge type, as well as the font, color, size, and positioning of text in the legend region

- whether or not to display the legend

- whether or not to clip legend text that extends outside of the legend region

Changing the size and placement of the legend region

Legend regions are sized and placed using figure units—see *Using figure units and coordinates* on page 19-4.

To resize or move the legend region, you specify four coordinates: an x minimum and maximum, and a y minimum and maximum.

By default, the location of the legend region is defined in the following manner:

- The top left corner of the legend region is 0.02 figure units to the right of the top right corner of the data region. When the data region is at its default location, the top left corner of the legend region is at the figure coordinate location (0.82, 0.8). When the data region moves, the legend region moves with it.

- The legend region expands to fit the group labels it contains. More groups stretch the legend region further down on the page. Long group labels stretch the legend region further to the right.

The default legend region can extend off the right or bottom of the figure by default when you have many groups or extremely long group names. When this happens, you can change legend region and data region locations and/or other attributes to try to bring the entire legend region on to the page.

Extremely large symbols or lines may extend outside of the default legend region regardless of the legend region's position.

▶ **To change the size and placement of the legend region**

1 In the graph dialog box, choose **Regions ➤ Legend**.

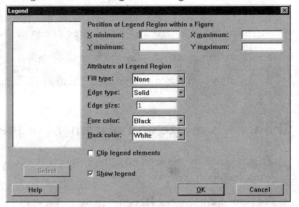

2 Under **Position of Legend Region within a Figure**, enter X and Y minimum and maximum values, in figure units. Click **OK**.

▷ **Example of changing the size and placement of the legend region**

For space reasons, you want to move the legend from the side of the graph to the top. To make the legend stand out, you turn the background of the legend to yellow.

1 Open the worksheet MARKET.MTW.

2 Choose **Graph ➤ Plot**.

3 In **Y**, enter *Sales*. In **X**, enter *Advertis*.

4 Choose **Display ➤ Connect**. Choose **For each ➤ Group**. In **Group variable**, enter *Year*.

5 Choose **Regions ➤ Legend**.

6 Under **Position of Legend Region within a Figure**, do the following:

■ In **X minimum**, type *0.4*. In **X maximum**, type *0.53*.

■ In **Y minimum**, type *0.81*. In **Y maximum**, type *0.91*.

7 Choose **Fill type** ➤ **Solid** and **Back color** ➤ **Yellow**. Click **OK** in each dialog box.

Graph window output

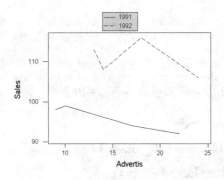

Controlling the format of the legend region

The legend region can be formatted in various ways. You can control:

- the fill type and fill color
- the line type, color, and thickness of the edge line around the legend region

Labels and data display items in the legend display on top of the fills. You cannot change the text or appearance of labels, except by using the graph editing tools described in Chapter 24, *Editing Graphs*.

▶ **To change the format of the legend region**

1 In the graph dialog box, choose **Regions** ➤ **Legend**.

2 Under **Attributes of Legend Region**, do one or more of the following, and click **OK**.

- In **Fill type**, choose a type—see *Lists of Colors, Lines, and Fills* on page 19-25.

- In **Edge type**, choose a line type—see *Lists of Colors, Lines, and Fills* on page 19-25.

- In **Edge size**, enter a value for the thickness of the line, in pixels. The default of 1 gives an edge line that is one pixel wide.

- In **Fore color**, choose the color for the fill type pattern (if dots, for example, this will color the dots) and for the edge line.

- In **Back color**, choose a color for the background of the fill type pattern (if dots, for example, this will color the surface the dots are on). For a solid fill, click **Solid** for **Fill type** and choose a non-white **Back color**.

More | For more details on these items, see Help.

Hiding and showing the legend

A legend is automatically generated when you create a graph that uses groups. If you do not want a legend to display, you can easily hide, or omit, the legend region.

If a legend is not showing up in your graph, check to see if the legend is set to show (described below), then check if your graph meets the conditions necessary for a legend, described under *Legend Regions* on page 19-20.

▶ **To hide or show the legend**

1　In the graph dialog box, choose **Regions ➤ Legend**.

2　Uncheck or check **Show legend**. Click **OK**.

Clipping the display of items outside the legend region

Clipping suppresses the display of text that extends out of the legend region.

▶ **To turn legend region clipping on and off**

1　In the graph dialog box, choose **Regions ➤ Legend**.

2　Check or uncheck **Clip legend elements**. Click **OK**.

Lists of Colors, Lines, and Fills

Colors

Apply to:

- fills for figure, data, and legend regions

- edge lines for figure, data, and legend regions

Code	Color	Code	Color	Code	Color
0	White				
1	Black	6	Magenta	11	Dark Cyan
2	Red	7	Yellow	12	Dark Magenta
3	Green	8	Dark Red	13	Dark Yellow
4	Blue	9	Dark Green	14	Dark Gray
5	Cyan	10	Dark Blue	15	Light Gray

Line and edge types

Applies to edge lines of figure, data, and legend regions.

Code	Line type	Name	Code	Line type	Name
0		None	4	— · — · —	Dash 1-Dot
1	———————	Solid	5	—— ·· —— ·· ——	Dash 2-Dot
2	— — — — —	Dash	6	—— ··· —— ···	Dash 3-Dot
3	- - - - - - - -	Dot	7	—— —— ——	Long Dash

Fill types

Applies to fills for figure, data, and legend regions.

Code	Fill type	Name	Code	Fill type	Name
0		None	5		Horizontal line
1		Solid (background is white)	6		Vertical line
2		Right slant	7		Cross line
3		Left slant	8		Dots
4		Cross slant	9		Squares

20

3D Graphs

3D Graphs Overview

You can create high-resolution three-dimensional graphs with MINITAB's 3D Graph commands. These graphs enable you to view a three-dimensional representation of three variables (x, y, and z). 3D graphs can represent the data in the form of a scatter plot, a surface plot, or a wireframe plot.

3D Scatter Plot   **3D Surface Plot**   **3D Wireframe Plot**

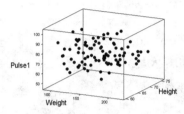   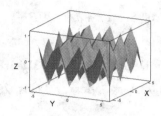   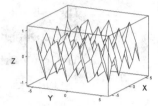

Scatter plots represent the data points on the plot as dots. Surface and wireframe plots generate a mesh of polygons composed of faces and edges that represent the x, y, and z data. As you can see, surface and wireframe plots are basically the same graph, with different defaults: by default, surface plots emphasize the faces of polygons, and wireframe plots emphasize the edges of faces.

For surface and wireframe plots, the x- and y-variables are displayed on the graph as a two-dimensional mesh with the data points plotted at the intersections of the mesh lines. The z data is then plotted on a vertical plane determined by its position relative to the x and y data.

Mesh of X and Y data   **Mesh with**
with Z data of all zeros   **two extreme Z points**

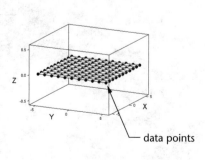   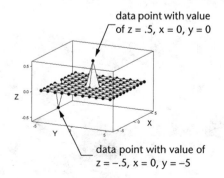

The mesh of x- and y-points on 3D graphs must be regular in shape, that is, a square mesh with evenly spaced intervals, with an equal number of intervals on the x and y axes. If your x and y data are regular in shape, MINITAB uses your data to create a regular mesh. If your data are irregular in shape, MINITAB automatically creates a mesh of new x and y data with the same range of values as your original x and y data, and then uses interpolation to calculate the position of your z-values for each point on the mesh. For more information, see *Regular and irregular mesh* on page 20-7.

If you need data to create your 3D surface and wireframe plots, you can create a regular mesh of x and y data using **Calc ➤ Make Mesh Data.** The command also allows you to create a z-variable using a function.

Three-Dimensional Scatter Plots

You can use 3D Plot to create three-dimensional scatter plots of your data.

Data

Three columns of numeric data for the x-, y-, and z-variables. Missing values are omitted from the graph.

▶ To make a three-dimensional scatter plot

1 Choose **Graph ➤ 3D Plot**.

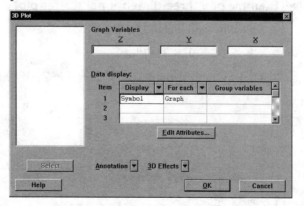

2 Under **Graph Variables**, enter data columns in **Z**, **Y**, and **X**.

3 If you like, use any of the options below, then click **OK**.

Options

Data display

- display points with symbols (default) or with projection lines. See *Symbols* on page 15-5 and *Projection Lines* on page 15-9.

- display different symbols or projection lines for different variable groups. You can use up to three variable groups. For additional information, see *Displaying Data for Each Group* on page 16-5.

- edit the attributes of both symbols and projection lines:
  - for symbols, you can change the symbol type, color, and size.
  - for projections, you can change the line type, color, and size; change the base location for each projection; and change the direction of the projections.

  For a list of attributes, see *Lists of Symbols, Colors, Lines, and Fills* on page 20-13.

Annotation

- customize the annotation of the title and footnote. See *Titles and Footnotes* on page 17-4.

3D effects

- adjust the viewing, lighting, and rendering options of the plot. See Chapter 21, *3D Graphs: Viewing Tools* and Chapter 22, *3D Graphs: Lighting and Rendering Tools*.

➤ Example of a three-dimensional scatter plot

1 Open the worksheet PULSE.MTW.

2 Choose **Graph ➤ 3D Plot**.

3 Under **Graph Variables**, enter *Pulse1* in **Z**, *Weight* in **Y**, and *Height* in **X**. Click **OK**.

Graph window output

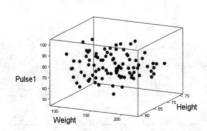

Three-Dimensional Surface and Wireframe Plots

You can generate a three-dimensional (3D) surface or wireframe plot for a z-variable based on a mesh determined from an x-variable and a y-variable.

The surface and wireframe plots use the same methods to plot data, and both offer most of the same options, although with different defaults. The main difference is that the 3D surface plot emphasizes the colored, shaded surfaces between z-values, and the 3D wireframe plot emphasizes the lines that connect z-values.

Surface plots are made up of polygons that have faces and edges. You can change the foreground fill patterns and color, and the background color, of the faces. You can also change the type, color, and size of the edges.

Wireframe plots have lines (or edges). You can also change the type, color, and size (width) of the lines.

Note | If you are creating experimental designs with MINITAB's DOE capabilities (see *part IV, Design of Experiments*, in MINITAB *User's Guide 2*), you should use the Contour/Surface (Wireframe) Plots commands found on the **Stat ➤ DOE** menu.

Data

Enter three columns that will be the x-, y-, and z-variables on the 3D graph.

▶ **To make a three-dimensional surface or wireframe plot**

1 Choose **Graph ➤ 3D Surface Plot** (or **Graph ➤ 3D Wireframe Plot**).

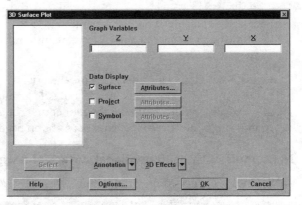

2 Under **Graph Variables**, enter data columns in **Z**, **Y**, and **X**.

3 If you like, use any of the options listed below, then click **OK**.

Options

Data display

■ adjust the fill and color attributes of the surface of the plot. See *Lists of Symbols, Colors, Lines, and Fills* on page 20-13.

■ adjust the edge color, type, and size. See *Lists of Symbols, Colors, Lines, and Fills* on page 20-13.

■ add customizable projection lines to the plot points on your graph. See *Lists of Symbols, Colors, Lines, and Fills* on page 20-13.

■ display customizable symbols on the plot points of your graph. See *Lists of Symbols, Colors, Lines, and Fills* on page 20-13.

Note | Faces and edges may appear to have colors different than the colors you specify. This is usually due to the presence/absence of lights and the type of light shading you use. For more information on lights and light shading methods, see *Light shading* on page 22-7.

Annotation

■ customize the title and footnote. See Chapter 17, *Core Graphs: Annotating*.

3D effects

■ adjust the viewing, lighting, and rendering options of the plot. See Chapter 21, *3D Graphs: Viewing Tools* and Chapter 22, *3D Graphs: Lighting and Rendering Tools*.

Options subdialog box

■ specify whether your data is regular in or irregular in shape. If your data is irregular in shape, MINITAB creates a new regular mesh based on the ranges of the original data. The default size of the new mesh is 15×15. MINITAB then calculates z-values on the mesh by interpolation. For more information, see *Regular and irregular mesh* on page 20-7.

■ if you are interpolating data because the original mesh was irregular, you can adjust the number of x or y positions (default is 15), adjust the x or y values (default is 15), or specify a z-value to use for the four corners of the grid. For more information on adjusting a mesh, see *Changing the mesh* on page 20-8.

▷ **Example of three-dimensional surface and wireframe plots**

1 Choose **Calc ➤ Make Mesh Data**.

2 Under **Store in X**, type X. Under **Store in Y**, type Y. Under **Store Z variable in**, type Z.

3 Select **Use function example** and choose **Egg Carton**. Click **OK**.

4 Choose **Graph ➤ 3D Surface Plot** or **Graph ➤ 3D Wireframe Plot**.

5 Under **Graph Variables**, enter Z in **Z**, Y in **Y**, and X in **X**. Click **OK**.

3D Surface Plot   **3D Wireframe Plot**

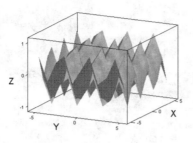 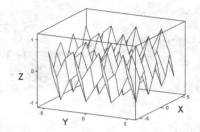

Regular and irregular mesh

For 3D surface and wireframe plots, MINITAB requires that x and y data be regular in shape. Data with a regular shape would produce a square grid with evenly spaced intervals, with an equal number of intervals on the x and y axes. Data with an irregular shape would theoretically create a non-square grid with unevenly spaced intervals or with an unequal number of intervals on the x and y axis.

If your x and y data are regular in shape, MINITAB uses your data to create a regular mesh. In this case, the points of the z-values that you provide will be located at the intersections of the gridlines. Data produced with the Make Mesh Data command is always regular in shape.

If your data are irregular in shape, MINITAB automatically creates a grid of new x and y data with the same range of values as your original x and y data. MINITAB then uses interpolation to calculate the z-positions for each polygon. By default, MINITAB creates a mesh with 15 points in the x direction and 15 points in the y direction. You can change the number of points in the mesh to create a mesh with a finer or coarser resolution. For more information on changing the number of points in the mesh, see *Changing the mesh* on page 20-8.

If you display symbols or projection lines, those items will display at the positions of the original data points, not necessarily at the intersection of mesh lines.

Mesh formed from regular data

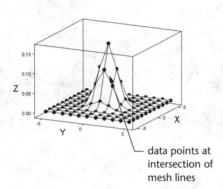

data points at intersection of mesh lines

Mesh formed from irregular data (interpolated)

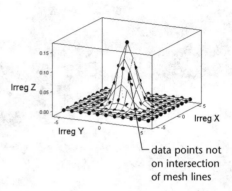

data points not on intersection of mesh lines

Changing the mesh

When the x and y data you provide are irregular in shape, by default, MINITAB creates a mesh with 15 points in the X direction and 15 points in the Y direction. Under Options, you can choose the number of points in the mesh. There are a number of reasons why you might want to change the number of points, but two primary reasons are:

- to improve the resolution of the graph—a mesh with more points results in a higher resolution
- improving the speed of drawing the graph—a mesh with fewer points results in faster drawing speed

▶ To improve 3D graph resolution

You can improve the graph resolution by defining a finer grid. MINITAB interpolates a z-value for each point on the grid and displays only these interpolated z-values on the graph.

1 In the 3D Surface Plot or 3D Wireframe Plot main dialog box, click **Options**.

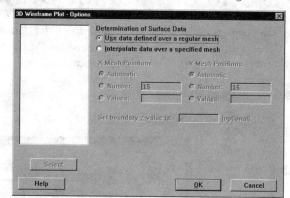

2 Choose **Interpolate data over a specified mesh**.

3 Under **X-Mesh Positions**, do one of the following:

- To increase the resolution while letting MINITAB choose the positions of points, choose **Number** and enter a value higher than 15.

- To increase the resolution while specifying the positions of points yourself, choose **Values** and enter between two and 101 data values in increasing order (or, enter the data values in a column and specify the column here).

4 Repeat step 3 for **Y-Mesh Positions**.

▶ **To improve the speed of drawing the 3D graph**

If you have many data points, you can to improve drawing speed:

1 In the 3D Surface Plot or 3D Wireframe Plot main dialog box, click **Options**.

2 Do either of the following, then click **OK**:

- If you know your x and y data are regular in shape, choose **Use data defined over a regular mesh**. That way, MINITAB will check for a regular mesh, and if it finds one, will display the graph without taking the time to calculate a z-value at each mesh point.

- Choose **Interpolate data over a specified mesh**, then specify a low number of x- and y-mesh positions, such as 10 and 10. The default for either the x- or y-position is Automatic, which uses a grid with 15 points in the direction of either the x- or y-position.

  You also can choose **Value** and enter specific positions. See *To improve 3D graph resolution* on page 20-8.

More | You can also set the boundary z-level. See Help for details.

Making a Grid of Data for Drawing 3D Graphs

You can create a regular (x, y) mesh to use for data input to contour plots (see *Contour Plots* on page 14-49), and three-dimensional surface and wireframe plots, with an option to create the z-variable using a function.

▶ **To make mesh data**

1 Choose **Calc ➤ Make Mesh Data**.

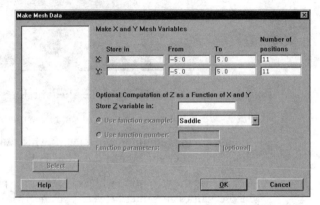

2 In **Store in**, enter the columns where you want to store the X and Y data.

3 Optionally, in **Store Z variable in**, enter a column. In **Use function example**, pick a function from the list.

4 If you like, choose one of the options described below, then click **OK**.

Options

- change the number of x- and y-positions. Meshes of between 7 and 15 points provide a good mix of performance and resolution for contour, 3D surface, and 3D wireframe plots. Additional points produce a finer grid, but the grid takes longer to plot.

- change the range of x- or y-values, from one value to another.

- enter a column to store x- or y-values.

- enter a column in which to store Z variables.

- select the function you want the generated z column to follow.

- select custom functions that you have created and stored as macros.

- enter custom parameters for functions you have selected.

For more information on functions and setting their parameters, see *Selecting example functions and setting parameters* on page 20-11.

☞ Example of making mesh data

This example creates three new columns named X, Y and Z. The Z variable will contain data to graph the bivariate normal function.

1 Choose **Calc ➤ Make Mesh Data**.

2 Under **Store in X:**, type X. Under **Store in Y:**, type Y. Under **Store Z variable in:**, type Z.

3 Select **Use function example:** and choose **Bivariate Normal**. Click **OK**.

4 Choose **Graph ➤ 3D Wireframe Plot**.

5 Under **Graph Variables**, enter Z in **Z**, Y in **Y**, and X in **X**. Click **OK**.

*Graph
window
output*

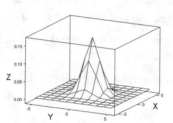

Selecting example functions and setting parameters

If you do not already have a column of Z data, you can generate Z data as a function of X and Y. Select the function you want to use and enter a column to store the Z data in. MINITAB provides a selection of functions with default parameters. You can change those parameters. You also can create your own functions and parameters.

Some of the functions make use of parameters to control how the Z data are related to the X and Y data. Enter the number of parameters requested for the function you want to use. For example, one of the functions in USERFUNC.MAC generates bivariate normal Z data. For the bivariate normal function, you have the option of entering the means and standard deviations of the X and Y variables, as well as the correlation coefficient between X and Y, a total of five parameters. If you do not enter these parameters, the function uses defaults.

For a list of the optional parameters you can use with the example functions included in the USERFUNC.MAC, as well as the equations used to generate the example functions, see Help.

Creating your own functions

You can create your own custom functions by adding them to the MINITAB macro USERFUNC.MAC. When you add a custom function to the macro, you assign your function a number between 1 and 1,000. You will access your function in the Make Mesh dialog box using this function number (see *To execute your custom function* below).

You can allow for optional parameters in the functions you create. Values for these parameters can be set in the Make Mesh dialog box when you create the data. However, you should create reasonable defaults when creating the parameters, in case parameter settings are not entered in the Make Mesh dialog box.

▶ **To add your own functions**

1 Start a word processor or text editor, such as Notepad.

2 Open the file USERFUNC.MAC. The file is in the Macros folder of your main MINITAB directory.

3 Back up the file by saving it as a different name, such as USERFUNC.BAK. Save the file as a plain text (ASCII) file.

4 In USERFUNC.MAC, add you own function by following the instructions at the top of the file. In the macro you will assign your function a number between 1 and 1,000.

5 Save USERFUNC.MAC as a plain text file.

▶ **To execute your custom function**

1 Choose **Calc ➤ Make Mesh Data**.

2 Under **Store in X** and **Store in Y**, enter variables.

3 In **Use function number**, enter the number of your function.

4 If you have parameters in your function, you can enter values for them in the **Function Parameters** text box. Values should be entered in order, separated by a space. Click **OK**.

Lists of Symbols, Colors, Lines, and Fills

Symbol types

Applies to markers.

Code	Type	Name	Code	Type	Name
0		None			
1	○	Circle	16	◆	Solid Diamond
2	+	Plus	17	◇	Dot Diamond
3	×	Cross	18	◈	Plus Diamond
4	✳	Asterisk	19	△	Triangle
5	·	Dot	20	▲	Solid Triangle
6	●	Solid Circle	21	△	Dot Triangle
7	⊙	Dot Circle	22	▷	Triangle Right
8	⊕	Plus Circle	23	▶	Solid Triangle Right
9	⊗	Cross Circle	24	▷	Dot Triangle Right
10	◎	Circle Circle	25	◁	Triangle Left
11	□	Square	26	◀	Solid Triangle Left
12	■	Solid Square	27	◁	Dot Triangle Left
13	⊡	Dot Square	28	▽	Triangle Down
14	⊠	Cross Square	29	▼	Solid Triangle Down
15	◇	Diamond	30	▽	Dot Triangle Down

Colors

Applies to:

- titles and footnotes
- text
- lines
- markers
- polygon fore colors and back colors

Code	Color	Code	Color	Code	Color
0	White				
1	Black	6	Magenta	11	Dark Cyan
2	Red	7	Yellow	12	Dark Magenta
3	Green	8	Dark Red	13	Dark Yellow
4	Blue	9	Dark Green	14	Dark Gray
5	Cyan	10	Dark Blue	15	Light Gray

Note | In polygons, the fore color is the color of the edge line *and* the foreground color of any fill pattern.

Line and edge types

Applies to:

- line types
- polygon edge types

Code	Line type	Name	Code	Line type	Name
0		None	4	—— - —— - —— -	Dash 1-Dot
1	——————————	Solid	5	—— -- —— -- —— --	Dash 2-Dot
2	— — — — — —	Dash	6	—------—------—------	Dash 3-Dot
3	- - - - - - - - - - -	Dot	7	—— —— ——	Long Dash

Fill types

Applies to polygon fills.

Code	Fill type	Name	Code	Fill type	Name
0		None	5		Horizontal line
1		Solid (background is white)	6		Vertical line
2		Right slant	7		Cross line
3		Left slant	8		Dots
4		Cross slant	9		Squares

21

3D Graphs: Viewing Tools

Viewing Tools Overview

You can use MINITAB's viewing tools to adjust the display of three-dimensional plots. The viewing tools all operate in the same manner, whether you are working with a 3D scatter plot, a 3D wireframe plot, or a 3D surface plot.

▶ **To access the viewing tools**

1 Choose **3D Effects ➤ View** from any 3D graph dialog box.

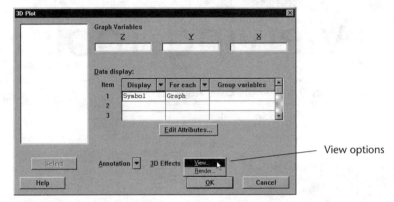

View options

2 In the **View** subdialog box, change a number of options.

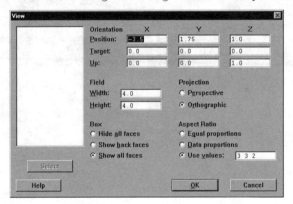

Orientation

These tools allow you to view a three-dimensional plot from different positions and angles.

Field

These tools allow you to zoom in and out from a three-dimensional plot.

Projection

These tools allow you to view a three-dimensional plot from perspective or orthographic projections.

Box

These tools allow you to adjust the box display surrounding a three-dimensional plot.

Aspect ratio

Adjusting the aspect ratio of a plot changes the relationship between the units of each axis direction.

Orientation

With the orientation tools, you can define the viewing location for a three-dimensional graph. You can see the different sides of a graph by changing the orientation. The movement allows you to see the graph as if you were viewing it from the rear (if we call the initial position the front of the graph).

You achieve these changes in orientation by setting coordinates for three points: the view position, the view target, and the view up direction. These points exist in *object space*.

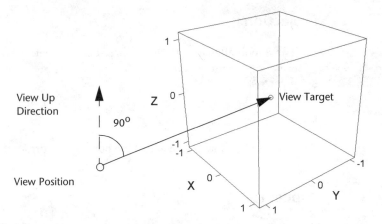

View Position

The view position is the point from which you look at an object. For simple movement around a three-dimensional graph, these are the only values you will need to adjust.

Tip | To view a 3D plot from the same orientation as the default orientation for a contour plot, change the view position of the 3D plot to -5, -4 and 3 for X, Y, and Z respectively. Also, switch the axis order.

View Target

The view target is the point in object space at which you look, usually located at the center of an object. The default target is in the center of the box. You generally change the view target only when you want to move the center of the box from the center of the figure region.

View Up

The view-up direction defines how the graph is turned or rotated for your view. The effective view-up direction in a graph is perpendicular to the line of sight (that is, the vector between the view position and the view target). If you give a vector that is not perpendicular to the line of sight, MINITAB calculates a perpendicular vector from the values that you give. Varying the view-up direction is useful for things such as rotating a graph or perhaps turning a graph upside down without changing the target.

The coordinates of the points for view up orientation are given in *object units*. Generally, you can think of the object units as running from −1 to 1 in each direction. A coordinate of −1 in a direction corresponds to the minimum data value on the axis for that direction. A coordinate of 1 in a direction corresponds to the maximum data value on the axis for that direction. A coordinate of 0 is the (maximum − minimum) / 2. The center of the box that displays is (0, 0, 0).

▶ **To change orientation**

1 In the 3D graph dialog box, choose **3D Effects ➤ View**.

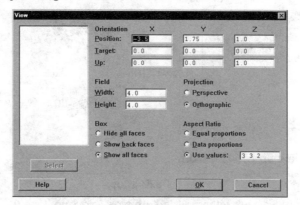

2 Under **Orientation**, do one or more of the following:

- To change the view position, enter x-, y-, and z-coordinates in **Position**

- To change the view target, enter x-, y-, and z-coordinates in **Target**

- To change the view up direction, enter x-, y-, and z-coordinates in **Up**

3 Click **OK**.

> **Examples of orientation**

   1 Open the worksheet PULSE.MTW.

   2 Choose **Graph ➤ 3D Plot**.

   3 Type *Pulse1* in **Z**, *Weight* in **Y**, and *Height* in **X**.

   4 Choose **3D Effects ➤ View**.

   5 Do one of the following and click **OK**.

Change position to view from

the front:	above:	below:
Do nothing (the default settings will be used).	In **Z position**, type *4*.	In **Z position**, type *-4*.

Change view up to view from

Z axis as up:	X axis as up:	Y axis as up:
Do nothing (the default settings of Z up = 1, X up = 0, Y up = 0 will be used).	In **X up** type *1*, in **Y up**, type *0*, and in **Z up**, type *0*.	In **X up** type *0*, in **Y up**, type *1*, and in **Z up**, type *0*.

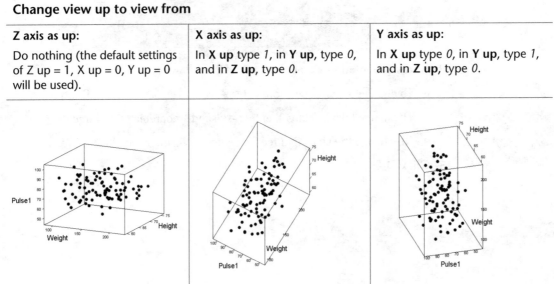

Field

The field of view is the rectangle in object space centered on the target which defines the portion of object space to be displayed in a figure region. You can define the width and the height of the view field in object space units.

▶ To change the field of view

1 In the 3D graph dialog box, choose **3D Effects ➤ View**.

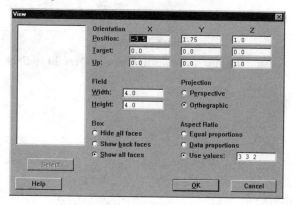

2 Under **Field**, do one or more of the following:

- To change the width of the field size, enter a new value in **Width**

- To change the height of the field size, enter a new value in **Height**

3 Click **OK**.

> **Examples of changing the field of view**

1 Open the worksheet PULSE.MTW.

2 Choose **Graph ➤ 3D Plot**.

3 Type *Pulse1* in **Z**, *Weight* in **Y**, and *Height* in **X**.

4 Choose **3D Effects ➤ View**.

5 Set the field, according to the outline below. Click **OK**.

Set field size to

default:	enlarged view:	reduced view:
Do nothing (the default settings will be used).	In **Width**, type *3*. In **Height**, type *3*.	In **Width**, type *5.5*. In **Height**, type *5.5*.

Projection

You can choose either an orthographic or perspective method for projecting the 3D object space into the 2D view space. The default view projection is perspective. The following table compares the two projections:

Orthographic	Perspective
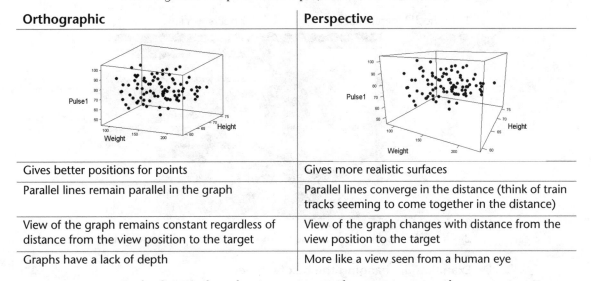	
Gives better positions for points	Gives more realistic surfaces
Parallel lines remain parallel in the graph	Parallel lines converge in the distance (think of train tracks seeming to come together in the distance)
View of the graph remains constant regardless of distance from the view position to the target	View of the graph changes with distance from the view position to the target
Graphs have a lack of depth	More like a view seen from a human eye

As the distance from the view position to the target increases, the perspective view approaches that of the orthographic view.

Box

You can choose how the box surrounding the data is displayed.

▶ **To change the Box face view**

1 In the 3D graph dialog box, choose **3D Effects ➤ View**.

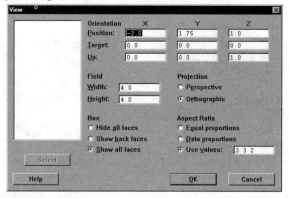

2 Under **Box**, select **Hide all faces**, **Show back faces**, or **Show all faces**. Click **OK**.

⮞ **Examples of changing the box face view**

1 Open the worksheet PULSE.MTW.

2 Choose **Graph ➤ 3D Plot**.

3 Type *Pulse1* in **Z**, *Weight* in **Y**, and *Height* in **X**.

4 Choose **3D Effects ➤ View**.

5 Set the box face view, according to the outline below. Click **OK**.

Change box face settings to

show all faces (default):	show back faces:	hide all faces:
Do nothing (the default setting **Show all faces** will be used).	Under **Box**, click **Show back faces**.	Under **Box**, click **Hide all faces**.

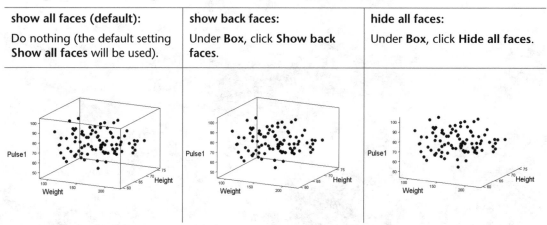

Aspect Ratio

The aspect ratio of the box (data area) is the relative proportion of the x-axis to the y-axis to the z-axis. You can use the default ratio (3:3:2) or set your own custom ratio, You can also choose for the aspect ratio to be set by data proportions or to use equal proportions. Data proportions are the range (that is the maximum – minimum) of the x-variable, the range of the y-variable, and the range of the z-variable. Equal proportions make all axis have the same proportions, the equivalent of setting a ratio of 1:1:1. The following are some common reasons for changing aspect ratios.

- **To make the graph a certain shape** - For example, values of 3:3:2 (the default) give a pleasing aspect ratio, often known as a golden rectangle. By making the graph a different shape, you can do things such as visually emphasizing changes in one variable (say, a variable with a large range) over the other variables (which might have ranges and variation that you can show on a shorter axis).

- **To make similar units be the same length on different axes** - For example, if you have a range of 50 cm on the x-axis, 30 cm on the y-axis, and the z-axis has different units, and you want one centimeter to be the same length on both the x- and y-axis, you can set the aspect ratio to 50 for the x-value, 30 for the y-value, and anything that makes the graph look good for the z-value.

▶ **To change the aspect ratio**

1 In the 3D graph dialog box, choose **3D Effects ➤ View**.

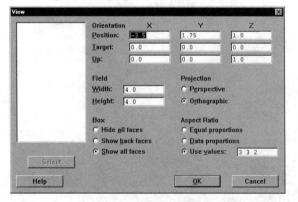

2 Under **Aspect Ratio**, do one or more of the following:
   - To use your own custom ratio, click on **Use values** and enter three new values
   - To use data proportions, click on **Data proportions**
   - To use equal proportions, click on **Equal proportions**

3 Click **OK**.

> **Examples of changing the aspect ratio**

1 Open the worksheet PULSE.MTW.

2 Choose **Graph ➤ 3D Plot**.

3 Type *Pulse1* in **Z**, *Weight* in **Y**, and *Height* in **X**.

4 Choose **3D Effects ➤ View**.

5 Change the aspect ratio, according to the outline below. Click **OK**.

Change aspect ratio to

from a ratio of 3:3:2 (default):	from data proportions:	from equal proportions:
Do nothing (the default settings will be used).	Under **Aspect Ratio**, click **Data proportions**.	Under **Aspect Ratio**, click **Equal proportions**.

22

3D Graphs: Lighting and Rendering Tools

Lighting and Rendering Tools Overview

You can use a variety of tools to adjust the lighting and rendering of 3D surface and wireframe plots. These tools are available under the **3D Effects** menu in the surface and wireframe plot dialog boxes. Lighting and rendering tools have different effects depending on whether you are working with a surface or wireframe plot.

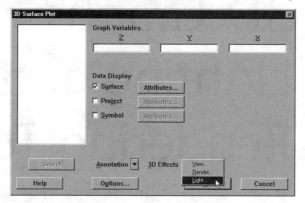

Lighting

You can add or delete lights, as well as adjust the light angle, color, and brightness.

Rendering

You can select the hidden surface removal algorithm, and choose the light shading method used for the graph.

Lighting

You can add or delete lights that shine towards the view target from the positions specified. You can have up to 100 lights, each with a defined color. The direction from which the light originates is determined by the values of the x-, y-, and z-coordinates of the light in object units. For more information on object units, see *Orientation* on page 21-4.

The direction is defined as the vector between the light position you give and the view target. The light that emanates from the coordinates you specify illuminates the graph in the same manner (at the same angle) as it would if the light were placed an infinite distance away in the same direction. This means that all rays of light from the specified light are parallel and strike flat surfaces at the same angle.

The default number and type of lights vary depending on the type of graph and how it is specified as follows:

Type of Graph	Number of Lights	Position(s) of Lights			Color	Visibility
		X	Y	Z		
3D Surface Plot	2	0	0	1	Red	On
		0	0	−1	Blue	On
3D Wireframe Plot	1	0	0	1	Black	On

Lighting effects differ depending on whether you are using a surface or wireframe plot. If you are creating a surface plot, lighting adjustments affect the surfaces of the plot. If you are creating a wireframe plot, lighting adjustments affect the edges of the plot.

▶ **To adjust the lighting**

1 Choose **Graph ➤ 3D Surface Plot** or **Graph ➤ 3D Wireframe Plot**.

2 Choose **3D Effects ➤ Light**.

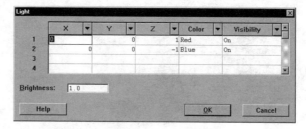

3 Do one or more of the following:

- Adjust the position of individual lights. In **X**, **Y**, and **Z**, enter new values in object units for the x-, y-, and z-coordinates. For more information on object units, see *Orientation* on page 21-4.

- Adjust the color of individual lights. Click the arrow next to **Color** and choose the color for each light.

- Turn lights on or off. Click the arrow next to **Visibility** and choose **On** or **Off**. In most cases, you will want to have lights turned on.

- To add new lights, enter the x-, y-, z-coordinates of the new light.

- Adjust the total brightness of all lights in the graph. In **Brightness:**, enter a value between 0.2 (darkest) and 5.0 (almost white). The default brightness is 1.0. The actual brightness is proportional to the number of lights you have in the graph.

⊳ **Example of lighting**

1 Choose **Calc** ➤ **Make Mesh Data**.

2 Under **Store in X**, type X. Under **Store in Y**, type Y. Under **Store Z variable in**, type Z.

3 Select **Use function example** and choose **Bivariate Normal**. Click **OK**.

4 Choose **Graph** ➤ **3D Surface Plot**.

5 Under **Graph Variables**, enter Z in **Z**, Y in **Y**, and X in **X**.

6 To produce the graph on the left (default lighting), click **OK**. To produce the graph on the right, choose **3D Effects** ➤ **Light**.

7 For light 1, under **X**, type *1*. Under **Y**, type *1*. Under **Color**, choose **Yellow**.

8 For light 2, under **X**, type *-1*. Under **Y**, type *-1*.

9 Click **OK** in each dialog box.

Surface plot with default light positions and colors　　　　**Surface plot with adjusted light positions and colors**

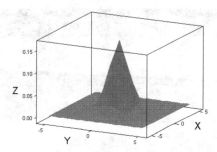
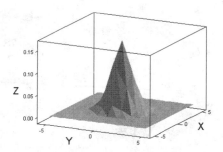

Rendering

Two rendering options are available to improve the rendering speed or accuracy of 3D graphs. These are **Hidden Line and Surface Removal** and **Light Shading**. If you are using a three-dimensional scatter plot, only **Hidden Line and Surface Removal** is available.

▶ **To select a method for hidden line and surface removal, and light shading**

1 Choose a 3D graph from the **Graph** menu.

2 Choose **3D Effects ➤ Render**.

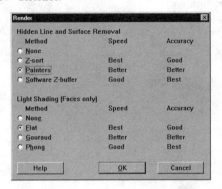

3 Select a method for **Hidden Line and Surface Removal** and for **Light Shading**.

For explanations of the available methods of hidden line and surface removal and light shading, see *Hidden line and surface removal* on page 22-6 and *Light shading* on page 22-7.

4 Click **OK**.

Hidden line and surface removal

Hidden surface and line removal algorithms suppress the display of surfaces and lines that are covered by other surfaces. The exact lines and surfaces that are removed vary when you change the viewing position. The basic trade-offs you face when choosing a hidden surface removal method are as follows:

Method	Speed	Accuracy	Remarks
None (no hidden surface removal)	fastest	highly variable	■ acceptable for some scatter plots and surface plots with few hidden surfaces ■ all surfaces shown, even surfaces behind other surfaces, regardless of position in graph
Z-sort (default)	very good	good	■ generally good quality with default lights ■ with no lights, quality can degrade substantially; with default lights, very good ■ fairly prevalent edge stitching (incomplete surface or edges) inaccuracies ■ occasional front/back inversions of objects
Painters	good (can depend on view position)	better	■ few edge stitching inaccuracies ■ fairly good with no lights, very good with default lights ■ few front/back inversions of objects
Software Z-buffer	moderate	best	■ nearly perfect edge stitching ■ lights not generally needed to improve overall surface quality ■ nearly perfect front/back display of objects

In general, you do not need to know much about the methods themselves to use them. You can regenerate the same graph using several different methods. For example, for a quick investigation consisting of many graphs, you may want to use the Z-sort method. Then, when you find a graph that you wish to use in a presentation, you can regenerate the graph using the Software Z-buffer method for greater accuracy.

Speed varies across different machines and different configurations, and depends on how many applications you are running. Refer to the *Enhancing Performance* section in Help for suggestions on how to improve performance.

Light shading

MINITAB provides several methods for shading of faces (surface plots) and edges
(wireframe plots) when lights are used. The different methods affect the rendering
speed or the accuracy of the plot. The basic trade-offs you face when choosing a light
shading method are as follows:

Method	Relative speed	Accuracy	Remarks
None (no shading)	fastest	often unacceptable	surface or face coloration not affected by lights
Flat	very good	good	shades uniform for entire faces or entire edges
Gouraud	good	better	shades for groups of pixels on each face or edge calculated together
Phong	moderate	best	shades for each pixel on an edge or face calculated individually

The light shading methods you can use vary depending on the type of graph and how it
is specified as follows:

Type of Graph	Defaults	
	Faces	Edges
3D Wireframe Plot	No Light Shading (for 3D surface plot only)	Flat
3D Surface Plot	Flat	No Shading (for wireframe plot only)

Speed varies across different machines and different configurations, and depends on
how many applications you are running. Refer to the *Enhancing Performance* topic in
Help for suggestions on how to improve performance.

23

Specialty Graphs

Specialty Graphs Overview

Using the core graph commands, you could create an incredible variety of two-dimensional graphs. The drawback is that for a complex graph, you might have to follow a large number of steps. With specialty graphs, the work is already done for you. The specialty graph commands let you specify just a few options to create useful, complex graphs.

The specialty graphs described in this chapter are useful across many statistical disciplines, though they have a common purpose: you can use them to examine the distribution of your data. All of these graphs appear in the **Graph** menu. They include:

- **Dotplot** for viewing individual points along a number line
- **Pie Chart** for viewing the distribution of categorical data
- **Marginal Plot** for viewing a scatterplot along with plots of the y and x variables in the margins
- **Probability Plot** for assessing the fit of different distributions to your data
- **Stem-and-Leaf** for viewing individual points in a stem-and-leaf display

Other specialty graphs that are more narrowly focused can be found in the documentation for the appropriate statistical area. You can access these graphs in two ways:

- as stand-alone commands in the menus for that area. For example, to create a Run Chart, you would choose the menu command **Stat ➤ Quality Tools ➤ Run Chart**.
- through the **Graphs** subdialog box for the appropriate analysis command. For example, to create a normal plot of residuals for a regression analysis, you would choose the menu command **Stat ➤ Regression ➤ Regression**, click **Graphs**, and check **Normal plot of residuals**. Specialty graphs of this type are described in the in the documentation as options under the main analysis command.

Tip | **For macro writers:** Specialty graphs that are stand-alone commands look and work like core graph commands, but they are actually macros that combine core graph commands in sophisticated ways. You can look at the code of these macros to get ideas for your own macros. Using a text editor, open any of the files in the Macros subdirectory of your main MINITAB directory. Stem-and-Leaf is an exception as it is not produced by a macro.

Dotplots

A dotplot displays a dot for each observation along a number line. If there are multiple occurrences of an observation, or if observations are too close together, then dots will be stacked vertically. If there are too many points to fit vertically in the graph, then each dot may represent more than one point. In this case, a message will be displayed on the graph denoting the maximum number of observations that the dots represent. When dots represent multiple points, dotplots cannot be brushed. Other dotplots can be brushed.

The Dotplot command allows you to generate dotplots for several variables at once, and to create dotplots for each group within variables. You can create:

- a dotplot for each variable you specify, with each dotplot appearing in its own Graph window, using its own scale.

- a dotplot for each group in a variable. The groups are determined by the grouping variable (or "By" variable) you specify. The dotplots for each group appear in the same Graph window, stacked on top of each other, using the same scale.

  For example, here is a graph of the variable Pulse1 with a By variable of Sex. MINITAB creates one dotplot for males and one dotplot for females. Both dotplots appear in the same Graph window.

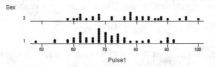

- a dotplot for each variable you specify, with all dotplots appearing in the same Graph window, stacked on top of each other, using the same scale. For example, here is a graph of Pulse1 and Pulse2.

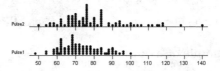

Data

You can arrange your data in your worksheet in one of two ways: 1) in a separate column for each sample or data group; or 2) in a single column for each variable with a separate By column that contains the group labels. If you measure different variables, you can enter more than one data column when you use a By variable.

Your main variables must be numeric, but the By variable can be numeric, text, or date/time. If you wish to change the order in which text categories are processed from their default alphabetical order, you can define your own order. See *Ordering Text Categories* on page 6-19.

An unlimited number of groups is allowed. If all the dotplots cannot fit on one graph page, then they will be displayed over multiple pages. Grouped dotplots share a common scale.

▶ **To create a dotplot**

1 Choose **Graph ➤ Dotplot**.

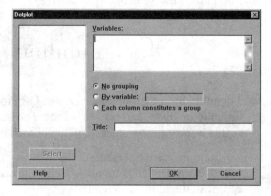

2 In **Variables**, enter the column(s) containing the data.

3 Select one of the following:

   ■ To obtain a separate graph window for each dotplot, click **No grouping**.

   ■ To obtain dotplots for each value of a group variable, click **By variable** and enter the group variable.

   ■ To obtain dotplots with each column constituting a group, click **Each column constitutes a group**.

4 If you like, replace the default graph title with your own title, then click **OK**.

▷ **Example of a dotplot**

You conduct a study to see how ozone affects azalea plants. During each of five weeks, you subject each of ten different azalea plants of certain varieties to ozone. Several days later you rate the leaves for ozone damage. At the end of your five week study you wish to compare the ozone damage from the five different weeks for all variety A plants.

1 Open the worksheet AZALEA.MTW.

2 Choose **Graph ➤ Dotplot**.

3 In **Variables**, enter *A-WEEK-1* through *A-WEEK-5*.

4 Click **Each column constitutes a group**. Click **OK**.

Graph
window
output

Dotplot for A-WEEK-1-A-WEEK-5

Interpreting the results

Because you requested grouping, the Dotplot command creates a graph window with five dotplots, each corresponding to a different week of the study. The bottom dotplot corresponds to the first entered column, or the week 1 data, while the top dotplot corresponds to the last entered column, or the week 5 data. These dotplots show that the highest ozone damage to azalea variety A occurred in weeks 1 and 4.

Pie Charts

You can generate a single pie chart or two pie charts within the same Graph window. Pie charts can be calculated using raw data or summary data. You can have up to 50 categories in your data, for a maximum of 50 slices on the chart.

By default, slices start at the 3 o'clock position and go counter-clockwise. For numeric and date/time data, by default, slices are placed in increasing order. For text data, by default, slices are placed in alphabetical order. Each slice is labeled with the category name. You can override all of these defaults and control slice position, category order, labeling, and colors. You can even "explode" specific slices, pulling them away from the graph to emphasize those categories.

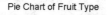

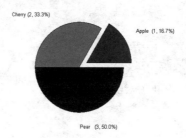

Data

You can enter the data in your worksheet in one of two ways: *raw form* or *summary form*.

Raw form

If your data are in raw form, you can have a classification column with each row representing one observation. In this form, the pie chart contains a slice that corresponds to the number of occurrences of each unique value in the column. The data represent categories and may be numeric, text, or date/time.

Data in raw form	Pie chart
Fruit	Pie Chart of Fruit
Cherry	
Cherry	
Pear	Cherry (2, 33.3%)
Pear	Apple (1, 16.7%)
Pear	
Apple	Pear (3, 50.0%)

Summary form

If your data are in summary form, you must have a column containing category names and a second column with numerical summary data for each category. These are commonly frequencies of occurrences, but can also be sums or percentages. If you have missing summary data, you must omit these data before creating the pie chart.

Data in summary form		Pie chart

Fruit Type	Number Picked
Cherry	2
Pear	3
Apple	1

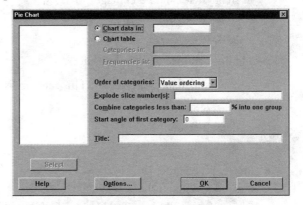

Pie Chart of Fruit Type

Cherry (2, 33.3%)

Apple (1, 16.7%)

Pear (3, 50.0%)

Categories and order

You can have up to 50 categories for a pie chart. If you have many small categories, they can be combined into an "other" slice—see *Combining small categories into an Others group* on page 23-10.

If you wish to change the order in which text categories are processed from their default alphabetical order you can define your own order. See *Choosing an order for pie slices* on page 23-9.

Sometimes your data includes missing values (* for numeric data, blanks for text data). These categories are included in the pie chart by default, although you can elect to omit them.

▶ To create a pie chart

1 Choose **Graph ➤ Pie Chart**.

2 Enter your data.

- If you have raw data, click **Chart data in** and enter one or two columns containing the raw data. Entering two columns will give you side-by-side pie charts in the same graph window.

- If you have summary data, click **Chart table**. In **Categories in** , enter one or two category columns. In **Frequencies in**, enter one or two summary columns that correspond to the category columns. A separate pie chart will be produced for each set of columns, but within a single graph window.

3 If you like, use one or more of the options described below, then click **OK**.

Options

Pie chart dialog box

- select an order for the pie slices. See *Choosing an order for pie slices* on page 23-9.

- select pie slices to "explode," moving them away from the center of the pie. See *Exploding pie slices* on page 23-10.

- combine categories less than a certain percentage into a single category labeled as "Others", which is placed last. See *Combining small categories into an Others group* on page 23-10.

- specify the angle of the first slice. The default is 0 degrees (the 3 o'clock position). See *Specify a starting angle* on page 23-10.

- replace the default graph title with your own title.

Options subdialog box

- select labeling options for slices. You can choose:
  - no labels
  - frequencies and percentages
  - frequencies only
  - percentages only

- add lines connecting labels to slices.

- omit missing data as a category. This category is included by default.

- specify colors for the pie slices:
  - default colors
  - specify the color for each slice—see *Color and fill type choices* on page 23-11

- specify fill types for the pie slices:
  - solid fills for all slices
  - specify the fill for each slice—see *Color and fill type choices* on page 23-11

Choosing an order for pie slices

You can place the slices of a pie chart in one of several orders.

▶ **To change the order of slices**

1 In the Pie chart dialog box, in **Order of Categories**, pick an order from the list. The order choices and their effects are shown in the following table:

Order choice	Places numeric and date/ time categories like this	Places text categories like this
Value ordering (default)	in increasing order	in alphabetical order, unless column has value order applied in the worksheet—see the first item under *Notes* below
Worksheet	in increasing order	in the order in which categories appear in the worksheet
Increasing	in increasing order by slice size	in increasing order by slice size
Decreasing	in decreasing order by slice size	in decreasing order by slice size

Notes

- When you choose value ordering for text categories, categories will appear on the graph in the order in which categories appear in the worksheet, unless you have applied a value order to that text column using the command **Editor ➤ Set Column ➤ Value Order** (see *Ordering Text Categories* on page 6-19). A typical value order is "Monday, Tuesday, Wednesday, etc."

- If you want slices in worksheet order for numeric categories, convert the data to text using **Manip ➤ Change Data Type ➤ Numeric to Text**, then use the converted data with worksheet order.

- Changing the order changes the assignment of slice numbers. Slice numbers are used to designate particular slices when you choose to explode pie slices (*Exploding pie slices* on page 23-10) or specify colors or fill types (see *Color and fill type choices* on page 23-11).

Exploding pie slices

Exploding a pie slice means that it is moved away from the center of the pie. This is useful for emphasizing particular categories.

▶ **To explode one or more slices**

1 In the Pie chart dialog box, click in **Explode slice number(s)**.

2 Enter the slice number(s) from 1, 2, …, s (where s is the number of slices or categories).

   Slices are numbered in the order that they appear on the graph, beginning from the start position and going counterclockwise. You can change the order in which they are drawn—see *Choosing an order for pie slices* on page 23-9.

Combining small categories into an Others group

You can combine slices whose individual percentages are less than a certain amount into a category named Others. The Others category will always be placed last regardless of the specified order (see *Choosing an order for pie slices* on page 23-9).

▶ **To combine categories**

1 In the Pie chart dialog box, click in **Combine categories less than**.

2 Enter a value from 1 to 99.

Combining categories changes the assignment of slice numbers. Slice numbers are used to designate particular slices when you choose to explode pie slices (*Exploding pie slices* on page 23-10) or specify colors or fill types (see *Color and fill type choices* on page 23-11).

Specify a starting angle

You can specify a starting angle, in degrees, for the slices. By default, the starting angle is 0 degrees, and slices start at the 3 o'clock position and go counterclockwise. If you specify a start angle of 90 degrees, slices start at the 12 o'clock position.

▶ **To specify a starting angle**

1 In the Pie chart dialog box, click in **Start angle of first category**.

2 Enter a value.

Color and fill type choices

You can control the appearance of slices. Slices can appear with a default set of colors, no colors, or a set of colors you specify. Slice can have a solid fill pattern (the default) or a set of pattern types you specify. When you specify a set of colors or fill patterns, the attribute for each slice is set by codes that you place in columns in the Data window.

▶ To specify a set of colors or fill types

1   In the Data window, enter codes in one or two columns: one column for color codes, and one column for fill type codes. The codes are integers that define the attributes of the slices (see *Fill types* on page 23-12 and *Colors* on page 23-12).

2   In the Pie chart dialog box, click **Options**.

3   Do one or both of the following, and click **OK**.

   ■ Under **Colors**, select **Use colors in** and enter the column name or number of the colors column you created.

   ■ Under **Fill types**, select **Use colors in**, and enter the column name or number of the types column you created.

Attributes are designated in the order in which the codes appear in the column, and are assigned to slices in the order in which slices are displayed. The code in row 1 of the code column is applied to the first slice, the code in row 2 is applied to the second slice, and so on.

Slices are numbered in the order that they appear on the graph, beginning from the start position and going counterclockwise. You can change the order of slices (see *Choosing an order for pie slices* on page 23-9).

When you specify a column that contains fewer rows than the number of slices in the pie chart, the arguments cycle until all slices get an attribute. When you specify a column with more arguments than slices, the extra rows are ignored. You may want to adjust colors and fill patterns using graph editing after the graph displays.

When you do not specify colors, the slices cycle through colors 2–15.

Fill types

Code	Fill type	Name	Code	Fill type	Name
0		None	5		Horizontal line
1		Solid (background is white)	6		Vertical line
2		Right slant	7		Cross line
3		Left slant	8		Dots
4		Cross slant	9		Squares

Colors

Code	Color	Code	Color	Code	Color
0	White				
1	Black	6	Magenta	11	Dark Cyan
2	Red	7	Yellow	12	Dark Magenta
3	Green	8	Dark Red	13	Dark Yellow
4	Blue	9	Dark Green	14	Dark Gray
5	Cyan	10	Dark Blue	15	Light Gray

To obtain a solid colored slice, use 1 as the fill type attribute. To obtain slices with foreground patterns over solid-colored backgrounds, use values from 2 to 9 in the fill type column with use values from 1 to 15 in the colors column.

▷ Example of pie chart

You, as an engineer, wish to examine the distribution of defects in parts that your company produces. You have data from all the different plants that produce parts. You use pie chart to view this distribution for one month of production.

1 Open the worksheet DEFECTS.MTW.

2 Choose **Graph ➤ Pie Chart**.

3 Check **Chart table**. In **Categories**, enter *Describe*. In **Frequencies in**, enter *Defects*.

4   In **Order of categories**, choose *Decreasing*.

5 In **Title**, enter *Defects at all Plants, June*. Click **OK**.

*Graph
window
output*

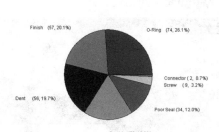

Interpreting the results

The pie chart shows the distribution of all defects in parts produced in June. By choosing decreasing order, you see the categories arranged from largest to smallest.

Marginal Plots

A marginal plot is a scatter plot with graphs in the margins of the x- and/or y-axes that show the distribution of the points in each direction, or the sample marginal distributions. You can choose to have histograms, boxplots, or dotplots as the marginal plots. Here is an example:

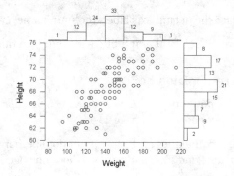

Data

To create a marginal plot, you need a numeric y-variable and a numeric x-variable.

▶ **To create a marginal plot**

1 Choose **Graph ➤ Marginal Plot**.

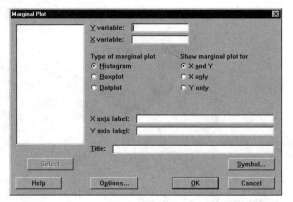

2 In **Y variable**, enter the column containing your y variable. In **X variable**, enter the column containing your x variable.

3 If you like, use one or more of the options described below, then click **OK**.

Options

Marginal plot dialog box

- choose histograms (default), boxplots, or dotplots as the plot type for the y and x distributions

- choose to display marginal plots for y and x (default), x only, or y only

- replace the default axis labels (column names) with your own labels

- replace the default graph title with your own title

Options subdialog box

- set tick positions for the y and/or x axes. See *Specifying tick, bin boundary, and scale endpoint positions* on page 23-15.

- set bin boundaries for histogram or dotplot marginal plots. See *Specifying tick, bin boundary, and scale endpoint positions* on page 23-15.

- specify the scale minima or maxima for the y and/or x axes. See *Specifying tick, bin boundary, and scale endpoint positions* on page 23-15.

- set the tick label angle for the x axis. See *Labeling options for the x-axis* on page 23-16.

- set the vertical offset for the x axis label. *Labeling options for the x-axis* on page 23-16.

Symbol subdialog box

- change the symbol type by selecting from a list of 31 types. See *Symbol types and colors* on page 23-16.

- change the symbol color by selecting from a list of 16 colors. See *Symbol types and colors* on page 23-16.

- change the symbol size by entering a value (default is 1.0).

Specifying tick, bin boundary, and scale endpoint positions

You can specify scatterplot tick positions that are different from the default ones. Histogram or dotplot bins are not affected if you change tick positions. However, if the tick positions that you specify extend outside the data scale, they may not show unless you specify new minimum and maximum scale endpoint positions that include your tick positions.

You can specify bin boundaries for y or x marginal histograms or dotplots. The default histogram bins are the default tick intervals for the scatter plot. The default number of dotplot bins is three times the square root of the sample size, up to a maximum of 30 bins. However, if the bin positions that you specify extend outside the data scale, they may not show unless you specify new scale minima or maxima to include your bin positions.

▶ **To specify tick positions, bin boundaries, and scale endpoint positions**

1 In the Marginal Plot dialog box, click **Options**.

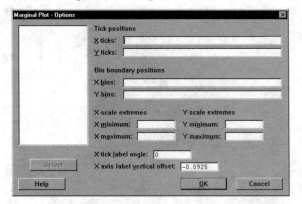

2 Do one or more of the following, and click **OK**.

- Under **Tick positions**, in **X ticks** and **Y ticks**, enter each tick position. You can enter positions for the x-axis, the y-axis, or both.

- Under **Bin boundary positions**, in **X bins** and **Y bins**, enter data values that are the cutpoints for the bins. You can enter positions for the X bins, the Y bins, or both.

- Under **X scale extremes** and **Y scale extremes**, enter minimums and maximums for each axis.

Labeling options for the x-axis

Sometimes x tick labels overwrite each other. If this happens you can work around this problem by using two labeling options. First, try changing the angle of the x tick labels. If the offset tick labels overlap the x axis label, then change the vertical offset of the x-axis label to move it down.

▶ **To change labels so that they do not overlap**

1 In the Marginal Plot dialog box, click **Options**.

2 In **X tick label angle**, specify an angle of rotation between 0 and 360 (0 is the default).

3 If tick labels overlap the x-axis label, in **X axis label vertical offset**, enter a value smaller than the default of −0.0925, for example −0.13. Click **OK**.

Symbol types and colors

Symbol types:

Code	Type	Name	Code	Type	Name
0		None			
1	○	Circle	16	◆	Solid Diamond
2	+	Plus	17	◇	Dot Diamond
3	×	Cross	18	⬦	Plus Diamond
4	✳	Asterisk	19	△	Triangle
5	·	Dot	20	▲	Solid Triangle
6	●	Solid Circle	21	△	Dot Triangle

Code	Type	Name	Code	Type	Name
7	⊙	Dot Circle	22	▷	Triangle Right
8	⊕	Plus Circle	23	▶	Solid Triangle Right
9	⊗	Cross Circle	24	▷	Dot Triangle Right
10	◎	Circle Circle	25	◁	Triangle Left
11	□	Square	26	◀	Solid Triangle Left
12	■	Solid Square	27	◁	Dot Triangle Left
13	⊡	Dot Square	28	▽	Triangle Down
14	⊠	Cross Square	29	▼	Solid Triangle Down
15	◇	Diamond	30	▽	Dot Triangle Down

Colors

Code	Color	Code	Color	Code	Color
0	White				
1	Black	6	Magenta	11	Dark Cyan
2	Red	7	Yellow	12	Dark Magenta
3	Green	8	Dark Red	13	Dark Yellow
4	Blue	9	Dark Green	14	Dark Gray
5	Cyan	10	Dark Blue	15	Light Gray

▷ **Example of a marginal plot**

As part of a study, you measure the resting pulse rates and weight of 92 subjects. Because you wish to examine a bivariate scatterplot along with the distribution of each variable (the marginal distributions), you use a marginal plot.

1 Open the worksheet PULSE.MTW.

2 Choose **Graph ➤ Marginal Plot**.

3 In **Y Variable**, enter *Pulse1*. In **X Variable**, enter *Weight*. Click **OK**.

Graph window output

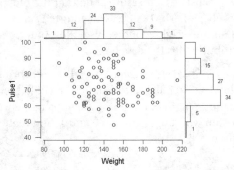

Interpreting the results

The bivariate scatterplot allows you to examine the joint distribution of the data. You can also examine the distributions for the y-variable and x-variable at the same time. This may help you in your investigation of these data.

Probability Plots

Use the probability plot to assess whether a particular distribution fits your data. The plot consists of:

- *plot points*, which represent the proportion of failures up to a certain time. The plot points are calculated using a nonparametric method, which assumes no parametric distribution. The proportions are transformed and used as the y variable, while their corresponding values may be transformed and used as the x variable.

- the *fitted line*, which is a graphical representation of the percentiles. To make the fitted line, MINITAB first calculates the percentiles for the various percents, based on the chosen distribution. The associated probabilities are then transformed and used as the y variables. The percentiles may be transformed, depending on the distribution, and are used as the x variables. The transformed scales, chosen to linearize the fitted line, differ depending on the distribution used.

- a set of approximately 95.0% *confidence intervals* for the fitted line.

Because the plot points do not depend on any distribution, they would be the same (before being transformed) for any probability plot made. The fitted line, however, differs depending on the parametric distribution chosen. So you can use the probability plot to assess whether a particular distribution fits your data. In general, the closer the points fall to the fitted line, the better the fit.

MINITAB provides two goodness-of-fit measures to help assess how the distribution fits your data: the Anderson-Darling statistic for both the maximum likelihood and the least squares methods and the Pearson correlation coefficient for the least squares method.

The Anderson-Darling statistic is a measure of how far the plot points fall from the fitted line in a probability plot. MINITAB uses an adjusted Anderson-Darling statistic, in which points in the tails are weighted more. A smaller Anderson-Darling statistic indicates that the distribution fits the data better.

For least squares estimation, MINITAB calculates a Pearson correlation coefficient. If the distribution fits the data well, then the plot points will fall on a straight line. The correlation measures the strength of the linear relationship between the X and Y variables. The correlation will range between 0 and 1, and higher values indicate a better fitting distribution.

Use the Anderson-Darling statistic and Pearson correlation coefficient to compare the fit of different distributions.

You can enter up to 10 samples per analysis. MINITAB estimates the probabilities independently for each sample. All of the samples display on a single plot, in different colors and symbols, which helps you to compare their distributions.

Graphical output consists of a single probability plot. If you have more than one sample, each sample is represented on the plot, using different symbols and colors. If the points in a probability plot are within the confidence intervals, you can judge that the fit of that distribution is a good one. Usually, points outside the confidence limits occur mostly in the tails. For small probabilities, points above the upper confidence limit indicate that there are more data in the left tail than one would expect. For large probabilities, points below the lower limit indicate that there are more data in the right tail than one would expect. The opposite conditions imply less data than expected.

Data

You can arrange your data in your worksheet by one of four arrangement combinations. First, the numbers in your data columns can be in one of two data forms:

- Your data can be in *raw form*, with each observation in its own cell in the worksheet.

- Your data can be in *frequency* form, with a column containing unique observed values and a second column containing frequencies for those values.

Second, your samples can be arranged in your worksheet in one of two ways:

- Your can enter data from a sample into its own column, with from 1 to 10 samples, either in raw form or in frequency form. If your data are in frequency form, you will have a second column for each sample that contains the frequencies.

- You can enter data from multiple samples into a single column, with up to 10 samples. The By column may contain from 1 to 10 unique numeric, text, or date/time values that define the samples.

If you choose lognormal, Weibull, exponential, or loglogistic distributions, your data must be positive. Missing data are automatically omitted from the calculations.

▶ **To create a probability plot**

1 Choose **Graph ➤ Probability Plot**.

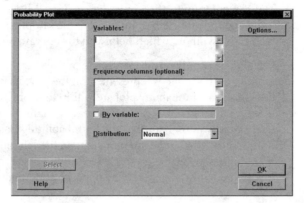

2 In **Variables**, enter the column(s) of data. You can enter from 1–10 columns (each contains a different sample). Enter only one column if you have a By variable.

3 If you have frequency data, in **Frequency columns** enter the columns containing the frequencies. These columns must correspond to the columns in **Variables**. Enter only one column if you have a By variable.

4 If all of the samples are in one column, check **By variable**, and enter a column of grouping indicators in the box.

5 If you like, use any of the options listed below, then click **OK**.

Options

Probability Plot dialog box

■ choose one of seven distributions for the data—normal (default), lognormal base$_e$, Weibull, extreme value, exponential, logistic, or loglogistic

Options subdialog box

■ estimate parameters using the maximum likelihood (default) or least squares methods.

■ specify the method for obtaining plot points—the default, Herd-Johnson, Kaplan-Meier, or a modified Kaplan-Meier method. See *Method of obtaining plot points* below.

■ handle ties by plotting all of the points (default), the maximum of the tied points, or the average (median) of the tied points.

- specify percentiles to estimate in addition to the default percentiles (expressed in percentages) of 1, ... , 5, ... , 9, 10, 20, 30, ... , 90, 91, 92, 93, ... , 99. The values that you enter should be percentages between 0 and 100. The estimates will be displayed in the session window if the following option is selected.

- display in the session window a table of maximum likelihood percentile estimates for each sample (to display is the default). This table includes confidence intervals for the percentiles.

- specify the confidence level for the percentile confidence intervals (95% is the default) that are displayed in the session window and the plot.

- include percentile confidence intervals on the probability plot (the default).

- replace the default graph title with your own title.

Method of obtaining plot points

The probability plot is a plot of estimated cumulative probabilities versus the data, though both variables may be transformed to induce linearity. You can use the degree of linear fit to help you in assessing the fit of the distribution.

For each column, MINITAB estimates the cumulative distribution function by one of four methods: default, Herd-Johnson, Kaplan-Meier, or modified Kaplan-Meier. For large samples, the differences between the methods are minimal. For very small samples, the differences may be more noticeable.

The default bases its estimates on $\frac{rank - 3/8}{n + 1/4}$. When the distribution is normal, these are the normal scores.

The estimators for the Herd-Johnson, Kaplan-Meier, and modified Kaplan-Meier methods are $\frac{rank}{n + 1}$, $\frac{rank}{n}$, and $\frac{rank - 0.5}{n}$, respectively.

Probability Plot also performs an analysis based on a selected probability distribution. You may choose from among normal (default), lognormal base$_e$, Weibull, extreme value, exponential, logistic, or loglogistic distributions. This analysis, which is done independently for each sample, produces maximum likelihood parameter estimates for the selected distribution, and a table displaying maximum likelihood estimates of percentiles (with confidence intervals) of the distribution. The maximum likelihood percentile estimates are the basis for the y coordinates of the straight lines drawn on the plot.

> ▷ **Example of a probability plot**

You, as a wildlife biologist, measure the size of black bears. You want to know if the weight of the bears follows a lognormal distribution, so you use probability plot.

1 Open the worksheet BEARS.MTW.

2 Choose **Graph** ➤ **Probability Plot**.

3 In **Variables**, type *Weight*.

4 From **Distribution**, choose *Lognormal base e*. Click **OK**.

Session window output

Lognormal Dist. Parameter Estimates (ML)

Data: Weight
Location: 5.09006
Scale: 0.602525

Percentile Estimates

Percent	Percentile	95% CI Approximate Lower Limit	95% CI Approximate Upper Limit
0.1	25.23	19.902	31.99
1.0	39.98	33.058	48.35
2.0	47.12	39.587	56.08
3.0	52.29	44.368	61.63
4.0	56.56	48.331	66.18
5.0	60.28	51.807	70.14
6.0	63.64	54.955	73.70
7.0	66.74	57.866	76.98
8.0	69.65	60.598	80.05
9.0	72.40	63.190	82.96
10.0	75.03	65.669	85.73
20.0	97.80	87.186	109.71
30.0	118.40	106.567	131.55
40.0	139.41	126.101	154.12
50.0	162.40	147.128	179.26
60.0	189.18	171.123	209.15
70.0	222.74	200.477	247.48
80.0	269.66	240.384	302.50
90.0	351.51	307.648	401.62
91.0	364.27	317.926	417.37
92.0	378.66	329.456	435.22
93.0	395.15	342.588	455.77
94.0	414.41	357.840	479.92
95.0	437.52	376.022	509.08
96.0	466.33	398.512	545.69
97.0	504.36	427.932	594.43
98.0	559.75	470.299	666.22
99.0	659.67	545.461	797.80
99.9	1045.24	824.426	1325.19

Graph window output

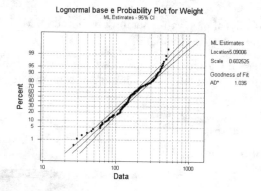

Lognormal base e Probability Plot for Weight
ML Estimates - 95% CI

Interpreting the results

The probability plot for the black bear weight data does not exhibit a simple pattern. Many of the points fall within the confidence intervals, but there are some that do not. For example, there are more bears in the 300–400 lb range than you would expect for a lognormal distribution. This can be diagnosed from the probability plot as points with x-values of 300–400 dipping slightly below the confidence limits with the percentile being above 50. There also tends to be too few bears of slightly greater than 100 lb, as these points dip slightly below the confidence limits with the percentile being below 50. There are too many points in the left tail (points above the limits) and too few points in the right tail (points above the limits) compared to what is expected in a lognormal distribution. For some purposes, assuming a lognormal distribution for these data would be acceptable, however.

Printed output consists of two tables. The first table displays maximum likelihood estimates of the population parameters for each sample. The second table displays maximum likelihood estimates and approximate confidence limits of the percentiles of the distribution. A default set of percentiles is always estimated though you can request estimates for additional percentiles.

Stem-and-Leaf Plots

A stem-and-leaf display is similar to a dotplot in that it displays individual data along a number line, but it is different in that it uses the actual numbers to create the display. See [1] for more details.

Data

To create a stem-and-leaf plot, your data must be numeric. Missing data are automatically omitted by the command.

You can also enter a By variable to produces a separate stem-and-leaf display for each unique value in the By column. This column can contain integers from −10,000 to +10,000 or the missing value code (*).

▶ **To create a stem-and-leaf plot**

1 Choose **Graph ➤ Stem-and-Leaf**.

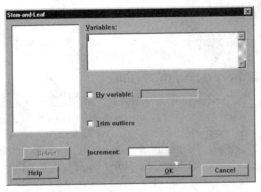

2 In **Variables**, enter the column(s) containing your variables.

3 If you like, use one or more of the options described below, then click **OK**.

Options

- enter a By variable to give stem-and-leaf displays for groups of data. All displays for one column are put on the same scale.

- trim outliers beyond the inner fences. You cannot use this option if you enter a BY variable. See *Trimming outliers* on page 23-24.

- specify the increment between lines of the stem-and-leaf display. See *Choosing an increment* on page 23-25.

Trimming outliers

If you have outliers in your data, the portion of the stem-and-leaf that corresponds to the center of the distribution may be compacted. By trimming outliers, you can expand the display of this central portion of data.

Outliers are defined as those observations beyond the "inner fences" and these are shown on special lines labeled LO and HI. The inner fences are calculated relative to the "hinges." The hinges are data values calculated by their depths, or their position from either end of the ordered data. This depth hinge is ([d(M)]+1)/2, where d(M) is the depth of the median, (n+1)/2. The lower and upper hinges are calculated by counting in from the lower and upper ends, respectively, of the ordered data. The inner fences are 1.5 hinge spreads (difference between upper hinge and lower hinge) above the upper hinge and below the lower hinge.

Choosing an increment

You can control the scaling of a stem-and-leaf display by specifying an increment. The increment is the distance in data units between two lines of the display (i.e., the distance between the smallest possible number on one line and the smallest possible number on the next). An increment of 5 is used in the below *Example of a stem-and-leaf plot*. In that example, you can see that values between 60 and 70 are split into two lines, those 60 to 64 and those 65 to 69. If you were to redo the display with an increment of 10, there will be only seven total lines, including only one for the 60's.

▷ Example of a stem-and-leaf plot

In order to study resting pulse rates, you would like to see a display of the distribution that shows the actual numbers. Therefore, you use stem-and-leaf.

1 Open the worksheet PULSE.MTW.

2 Choose **Graph ➤ Stem-and-Leaf**.

3 In **Variables**, enter *Pulse1*. Click **OK**.

Session window output

Character Stem-and-Leaf Display

```
Stem-and-leaf of Pulse1     N  = 92
Leaf Unit = 1.0

     1     4 8
     3     5 44
     6     5 888
    24     6 000012222222224444
    40     6 6666688888888888
   (17)    7 00000022222244444
    35     7 6666688888
    25     8 0002224444
    15     8 67888
    10     9 0000224
     3     9 66
     1    10 0
```

Interpreting the results

The stem-and-leaf displays pulse rates for 92 people. There are three parts to the display. The first column holds the depths, the second column holds the stems, and the rest of the display holds the leaves. Each leaf digit represents one observation.

The first stem is 4 and the first leaf is 8. The corresponding observation is 48. The second stem is 5 and has two leaves, both 4. The corresponding observations are 54 and 54. The last stem is 10 and has just one leaf, 0. The corresponding observation is 100.

Leaf Unit, at the top of the display, tells us where to put the decimal point. In the exhibit, Leaf Unit = 1.0, so the decimal point goes at the end. Thus the first observation is 48.0. If Leaf Unit were 0.10, the first number would be 4.8; if Leaf Unit were 10, the first number would be 480.

Now let's return to the first column, the depths. Each depth says how many observations are on its line or beyond. For example, the number 6 on the third line from the top says there are 6 observations on that line and the two lines above. They are 58, 58, 58, 54, 54, 48. The number 10 on the third line from the bottom says there are 10 observations on that line and below. There is one special line, the line that contains the median. Its value is enclosed in parentheses and says how many observations are on just that line. (Note, if the number of observations is even and the two middle numbers are on two different lines, then the parentheses are not used.)

References

[1] P.F. Velleman and D.C. Hoaglin (1981). *ABC's of EDA*, Duxbury Press.

24

Editing Graphs

Editing Graphs Overview

Graph editing is useful for putting text, lines, marker symbols, and polygons anywhere on an existing Graph. You can also edit and change the attributes of objects generated with the existing graph.

Graph editing affects the current graph. If you create the graph again, the new graph will not contain your editing changes.

If you want graph items to appear on a graph each time that you regenerate it in a different window, you should use graphics options available from the graph's dialog box. For a list of graphics options for each graph, see the description of that graph command in the user's guides and Help.

If you are using core graphs (plots, time series plots, charts, and other graphs described in Chapter 14, *Core Graphs*) you have available an extensive set of graphics options. For an overview of these options, see *Common Core Graph Graphics Options* on page 14-2.

After you finish editing, keep the graph in your project, or save it to a separate file using **File ➤ Save Graph As**. If you save the graph in a MINITAB Graphics Format (MGF) file, you can reopen the graph later in MINITAB using **File ➤ Open Graph**, then edit the graph some more. See Chapter 26, *Saving and Printing Graphs*.

3D graph editing limitations

You cannot move, cut, or copy three-dimensional graph objects, but you can delete them. You can add additional objects with the Tool palette as with other graphs.

Starting Graph Editing

Beginning graph editing is easy. Once the graph is in edit mode, the Tool and Attribute palettes automatically appear by default.

▶ **To enter edit mode**

Do one of the following:

- double-click on a Graph window
- from an active Graph window, choose **Editor ➤ Edit**

▶ **To display the Tool and Attribute palettes**

If the palettes do not automatically display when you begin editing, you can make them appear.

■ Choose **Editor** ➤ **Show Tool Palette** and/or **Editor** ➤ **Show Attribute Palette**.

The Tool palette and Attribute palette are shown below:

This is the Tool palette. It is explained in the next section, *Meet the Tool Palette*, on page 24-4.

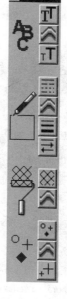

This is the Attribute palette. It determines the attributes of the selected object(s) and is explained in the section *Meet the Attribute Palette* on page 24-5.

▶ **To save your palette layout**

1 Choose **Edit** ➤ **Preferences** and select **Graphics Editing**.

2 Check **Save current palette layout**. Clicking **OK**, then click **Save**.

Meet the Tool Palette

Here is the Tool palette, along with a description of each of the tools:

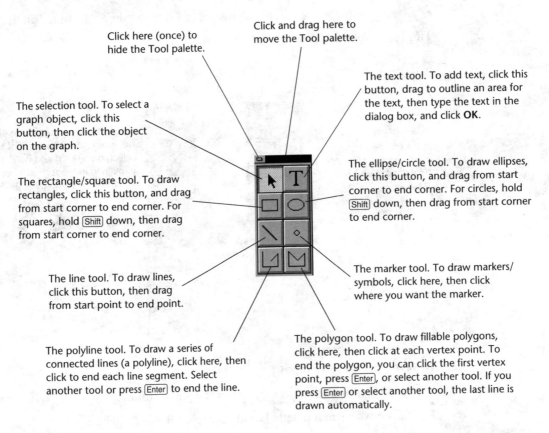

Click here (once) to hide the Tool palette.

Click and drag here to move the Tool palette.

The text tool. To add text, click this button, drag to outline an area for the text, then type the text in the dialog box, and click **OK**.

The selection tool. To select a graph object, click this button, then click the object on the graph.

The ellipse/circle tool. To draw ellipses, click this button, and drag from start corner to end corner. For circles, hold (Shift) down, then drag from start corner to end corner.

The rectangle/square tool. To draw rectangles, click this button, and drag from start corner to end corner. For squares, hold (Shift) down, then drag from start corner to end corner.

The line tool. To draw lines, click this button, then drag from start point to end point.

The marker tool. To draw markers/symbols, click here, then click where you want the marker.

The polyline tool. To draw a series of connected lines (a polyline), click here, then click to end each line segment. Select another tool or press (Enter) to end the line.

The polygon tool. To draw fillable polygons, click here, then click at each vertex point. To end the polygon, you can click the first vertex point, press (Enter), or select another tool. If you press (Enter) or select another tool, the last line is drawn automatically.

If you press (Shift) *after* you depress the mouse button, you can draw lines, polylines, or polygon lines or move objects along the nearest 45-degree line. This is especially helpful when you want to draw or move an object only horizontally, only vertically, or an equal distance horizontally and vertically.

Meet the Attribute Palette

You can change object attributes (or properties) using the Attribute palette. Here is the Attribute palette, along with a description of each of the tools:

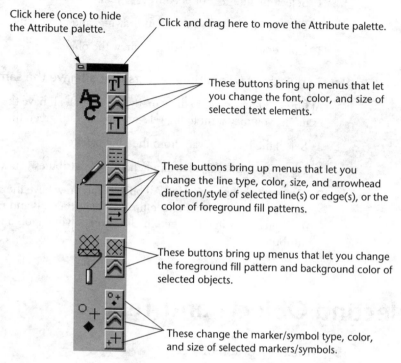

Click here (once) to hide the Attribute palette.

Click and drag here to move the Attribute palette.

These buttons bring up menus that let you change the font, color, and size of selected text elements.

These buttons bring up menus that let you change the line type, color, size, and arrowhead direction/style of selected line(s) or edge(s), or the color of foreground fill patterns.

These buttons bring up menus that let you change the foreground fill pattern and background color of selected objects.

These change the marker/symbol type, color, and size of selected markers/symbols.

▶ **To change the attributes of a graph item**

1 In the Tool palette, with ![cursor] , the selection tool, and select objects on the graph.

2 In the Attribute palette, click on an Attribute palette button, and choose a setting from the menu that appears for each button.

When button faces are dimmed, they are inactive (not available). When buttons are black or colored, they are active (available for use).

Drawing Objects and Adding Text on a Graph

You draw objects, or add text to a graph, by selecting the tool you want from the Tool palette, then drawing on the graph. See *Meet the Tool Palette* on page 24-4 for a description of all the tools and how to use them.

▶ **To draw lines or polylines along the nearest 45-degree angle**

This is especially helpful when you want to draw (or move) an object only horizontally, only vertically, or an equal distance horizontally and vertically.

1 Select the line ◥ or polyline ◳ tool.

2 Point to where you want to start drawing, and depress the mouse button.

3 Hold down the [Shift] key drag to draw the object.

▶ **To quickly draw multiple objects that all have the same attributes**

At times you may need to draw many objects that all have the same attributes. For example, you may want to draw 12 rectangles with green fills and blue edges.

1 Select the tool you want from the Tool palette.

2 Go to the Attribute palette and choose the attributes you want for the objects.

3 Draw the objects you want. All objects you draw have the same attributes. You can switch among the rectangle, ellipse, or polygon tools and retain the same attributes. You can also switch between the line and polyline tools and retain the same attributes.

Selecting Objects and Text

▶ **To select a graph object**

1 Click �R, the selection tool on the Tool palette.

2 Click the object on the graph.

To select hollow polygons (polygons that have no fill), click on the edge line. Note that when you draw objects, the default fill is solid white.

Selected objects have handles that appear as follows:

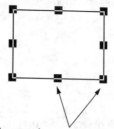

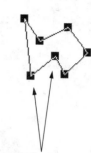

When you select symbols, they display two handles.

Text strings have handles at vertices (corners) and at line midpoints of a rectangle that surrounds them.

Unrotated rectangles, squares, ellipses, and circles have handles at vertices (corners) and at line midpoints. For circles and ellipses, the vertices and endpoints are located on a rectangle that surrounds the object.

Selected polygons have handles at each vertex.

You can select objects even if you make them invisible.

Tip | If you cannot select an object you can see, it may be because another object is in front of it. Select the object in front, choose **Editor ➤ Send to Back**, then select the first object. See *Bringing to Front and Sending to Back* on page 24-14.

Selecting multiple objects

You can select and deselect multiple objects as follows. All of the following start with ⬆, the selection tool, active:

To...	Do this
Select items one at a time, object by object	While holding down [Shift], click on each item you wish to select.
Add an item to a current selection	While holding down [Shift], click on each item you wish to add to the current selection.
Select all objects in a rectangular area—including all objects that extend even *partially* into the rectangular area	1 Move the mouse to an empty place on the graph. 2 Outline the area by dragging diagonally from corner to corner. When you begin to drag, the cursor turns into a ➥ and a dashed rectangle indicates the extent of the selection area while you are dragging.
Deselect objects in a current selection	While holding down [Shift], click on each item you wish to deselect. (This may take a moment or two.)

To...	Do this
Add all objects in another rectangular area to a current selection	1 While holding down (Shift), go to an empty place on the graph. 2 Outline the area by dragging from corner to corner diagonally. When you begin to drag, the cursor turns into a ⇨ and a dashed rectangle indicates the extent of the selection area while you are dragging.
Select all objects on a graph	Choose **Edit ➤ Select All**.

When you have multiple objects selected, you can

■ change their text, line, fill, or marker attributes all at once. For example, if you have several text strings and several symbols selected, you can change the color of all of the text by choosing the text color button. You can also change the color of the selected symbols by choosing the symbol color button on the Attribute palette.

■ move them all at the same time by dragging one of the selected objects where you want it. The other selected objects move along with the selection.

Adjusting mouse sensitivity

Depending on how you edit and use MINITAB graphics and the resolution of your display screen, you may want more or less sensitivity when moving and selecting objects in MINITAB. You can adjust this sensitivity of your mouse by changing the *selection proximity* and *movement threshold*.

Selection proximity refers to how close you need to be to an object in order to select the object when you click. Movement threshold refers to the amount of space you need to move in order for the object to change its location.

The default settings should provide more than reasonable performance under most circumstances. If you have no problems with selecting or moving objects, you never need to adjust these settings.

▶ **To change your mouse sensitivity**

1 Choose **Edit ➤ Preferences** and select **Graphics Editing**.

2 In **Selection proximity**, enter a value from 0.05 to 1.0. The default is 0.1. Smaller values mean that you need to be closer to the object, larger values let you select with less precision.

3 In **Movement threshold**, enter a value from 0.05 to 1.0. The default is 0.0125. Smaller values result in movement starting immediately, larger ones keep the object more stable before movement begins.

4 Click **OK**, then in the Preferences dialog box, click **Save**.

Copying and Pasting

You can cut, copy, or paste any graph element from the active Graph window to the same Graph window or to any other active Graph window. You can also *duplicate* items, which is like copying and pasting in one step. Finally, you can copy and paste an entire graph and paste it into another application.

Copying and pasting graph items

You can copy graphical elements (such as lines, markers, polygons, and text) and paste them into the same MINITAB Graph window or another MINITAB Graph window.

With text items, you can copy text from other applications and MINITAB windows and paste the text directly into a Graph window.

When you paste objects into a Graph window, the objects are placed in the center of the window.

When you cut, copy, or paste data display objects, the duplicated objects retain data display editing restrictions, such as clipping attributes, and alignment restrictions.

▶ **To copy and paste graph items within MINITAB**

1 Using ![selection tool], the selection tool, select the object(s) you want to copy.

2 Choose **Edit ➤ Copy**.

3 In any MINITAB Graph window, and in Edit mode, choose **Edit ➤ Paste**.

Duplicating graph items

Duplicating is like copying and pasting in one step. You can only duplicate within a Graph window.

Centers of duplicated items are placed 20 pixels down and 20 pixels to the right of the current selection.

You can duplicate all objects in a selection at once.

When you duplicate data display objects, the duplicated objects retain data display editing restrictions, such as clipping attributes, and alignment restrictions.

▶ **To duplicate**

1 Using ![selection tool], the selection tool, select the object(s) you want to affect.

2 Choose **Editor ➤ Duplicate** or press F3 .

Copying and pasting an entire graph

You can copy and paste an entire graph. The graph can be pasted into another application as an OLE object, as a bitmap, or as a Windows metafile drawing. For details, see *Copying and Pasting Graphs* on page 26-6.

▶ **To copy and paste an entire graph**

1 With the Graph window active, choose **Editor ➤ View**.

2 Choose **Edit ➤ Copy Graph**.

When you copy certain 3D graphs, including 3D wireframe plots, MINITAB will display a dialog box with this message: "I can only copy a bitmap of this graph. Proceed?" To copy the graph, just click **OK**.

3 In the other application, choose the paste command.

Moving Objects and Text Strings

You can move objects and text strings using either the mouse or the keyboard.

Note | With 3D graphs, you cannot move objects created in the 3D graph dialog boxes, such as surfaces, symbols, or projection lines. You can move any object you have added to the graph using the graph editing tools.

▶ **To move objects and text**

1 Click ![selection tool], the selection tool.

2 Do one of the following:

- With your mouse, drag the object or text string to where you want it. Do *not* drag a handle—dragging a handle resizes an object.

- With the keyboard do the following:

To move	Do this
one pixel in any direction:	use any arrow key
five pixels in any direction:	Shift + any arrow key
ten pixels in any direction:	Ctrl + any arrow key
fifty pixels in any direction:	Shift + Ctrl + any arrow key

Tip | Press Shift before you drag the objects to move objects along the nearest 45-degree line. This is especially helpful when you want to move an object only horizontally, only vertically, or an equal distance horizontally and vertically.

Resizing and Reshaping Objects

▶ **To resize symbols**

1 Select one or more symbols.

2 On the Attribute palette, click the marker size button ⊞ and choose a new size from the menu.

▶ **To resize squares or circles**

You can resize a selected square or circle without changing the shape of the object.

1 With ▣, the selection tool, click and hold one of the corner handles.

2 While holding down (Shift), drag the handle until the object reaches the size you desire.

If you do not hold down (Shift), the square or circle turns into a rectangle or ellipse. In this case, turn the rectangle or ellipse back into a square or circle by holding down (Shift) and dragging a vertex (corner) handle.

▶ **To reshape rectangles or ellipses**

1 With ▣, the selection tool, do one of the following:

- drag a handle at a midpoint. This adjusts either the width or the height of the object, but not both at once.

- drag a corner handle. This allows you to adjust both the width and the height of the object at the same time.

Some rotated ellipses cannot be reshaped

Ellipses rotated to angles other than 0, 90, 180, or 270 cannot be reshaped in rotated form. Unrotate the ellipse, reshape it, then rotate it again.

Some rotated rectangles become polygons

Rectangles rotated to angles other than 0, 90, 180, or 270 become polygons. Polygons do not have midpoint handles. If you want to reshape the rotated rectangle using midpoint handles, rotate the rectangle to an angle of 0, 90, 180, or 270, reshape the rectangle with the midpoints, and rotate it again. If you reshape the rotated polygon without rotating it back to 0, 90, 280, or 270, the shape will not become a rectangle again at any rotation angle.

▶ **To reshape polygons, polylines, and lines**

1 With ![selection tool], the selection tool, select the polygon, polyline, or line.

2 Drag one of the handles to the desired location.

Resizing, Reshaping, and Editing Text

You can resize or reshape any text string by changing the font size and/or changing the size of the text area. You can also edit the text.

Resizing text

▶ **To resize text**

1 With ![selection tool], the selection tool, select the text.

2 On the Attribute palette, click ![text size tool], the text size tool, and choose a size from the menu.

When you enlarge or shrink the text, the *width* of the text area stays constant, but the height of the area grows or shrinks accordingly. Here is an example that resizes a selected text string from size 1 to size 1.5:

Here is some text. ⟶ Click ![TT], then select 1.5 from the menu. ⟶ Here is some text.

Reshaping text

▶ **To reshape a text area**

1 With ![selection tool], the selection tool, select the text.

2 Drag a handle to where you want the text area to end.

Here is an example:

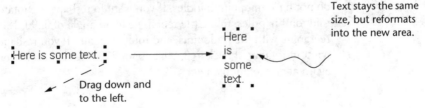

Here is some text. ⟶ Here is some text.   Text stays the same size, but reformats into the new area.

Drag down and to the left.

When you resize text areas, you really only resize the width of the text area. The text fills as many lines as necessary in the given width. (If you grab the top handles, the text area may *move* up or down, but the size of the text area is still determined by the width.)

The minimum width of a text area is the length of the smallest word in the area.

Editing text

▶ **To edit text**

1   Using ▨, the selection tool, double-click on the text area. Or, click once on the text and press ⟨Enter⟩. A dialog box appears.

2   Edit the text in the dialog box.

Add line breaks in a text string by pressing ⟨Ctrl⟩+⟨Enter⟩. When you add a line break in a text string, lines separated by line breaks stay separated even when you resize the text.

3   Click **OK**.

Unlocking Data Display Objects

By default, data on a graph are fixed in place. This is a check against moving or deleting a data object by accident. When you want to move data objects, you can unlock the data display, move the data, then lock it again.

▶ **To unlock and relock data display objects**

1   Choose **Editor ➤ Unlock Data Display**.

2   Move, change, or delete data.

3   Choose **Editor ➤ Lock Data Display**.

Clipping—Disappearing Objects

Clipping is an option that by default is turned on when you create a graph. When clipping is on, any data display elements that would fall outside the data region are not drawn, or clipped. Some annotation items that would fall outside the figure region will also be clipped. Clipping is turned on to make it convenient to restrict the scale of axes without showing all the data that is outside the maximum and minimum values.

When you edit a graph that has been created with clipping turned on, some objects will disappear when you move them outside of the appropriate region.

When you drag data display objects (such as symbols, connect lines, areas, projection lines, and so on) out of the data region, the data display objects disappear. Other objects, such as those generated using the Annotation options (titles, footnotes, extra text, lines, marker symbols, and polygons) are not clipped when moved out of the data region, but are clipped when moved out of the figure region. Objects that you draw are never clipped.

In a layout (that is, a Graph window generated with **Graph ➤ Layout**), you can have many graphs on a single page. Each graph in a layout is contained in a separate figure region. If you drag any object that was generated with a graph out of its figure region, it will disappear if clipping was turned on for that figure region.

More | For more information on clipping in different regions, see Chapter 19, *Core Graphs: Controlling Regions.*

▶ To turn off clipping

By default, clipping is turned on in all graphs. You can override the default and turn off clipping for any graph that has a **Regions** drop-down menu in the graph dialog box. All core graph dialog boxes and many control chart dialog boxes have this drop-down menu.

1   In the graph dialog box, choose **Regions ➤ Data** or **Regions ➤ Figure**.

2   Uncheck **Clip data elements** or **Clip figure elements**.

▶ To restore objects that are clipped

1   Before doing anything else, choose **Edit ➤ Undo**.

Bringing to Front and Sending to Back

Objects can overlap or completely cover each other. You can move most objects to the back of all other objects, or to the front of all other objects.

This feature works with all objects that you draw, but not between most objects generated with the graph (items created by choosing options in the graph dialog boxes). You can, however, bring to front or send to back annotation items generated with the **Graph ➤ Layout** dialog box.

▶ To bring to front or send to back

1   Using ▣, the selection tool, select the object(s) you want to affect.

2   Choose **Editor ➤ Bring to Front** or **Editor ➤ Send to back**.

You can see the effect of these commands on a selected object from the following illustrations:

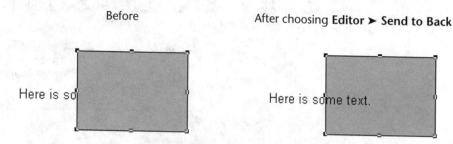

Before

After choosing **Editor ➤ Send to Back**

Here is so...

Here is some text.

In the first picture, the rectangle obscures the text string. In the second, the text is in front of the rectangle. Choosing **Editor ➤ Bring to Front** restores the polygon to the way it was at left.

Tip | If you cannot select something because an object is in front, select the object in front and send it to the back, then select the first object.

Flipping and Rotating Objects

You can reverse, or show a mirror image of, an object in the horizontal or vertical directions. You can also rotate objects.

Note | With 3D graphs, you cannot flip or rotate objects created in the 3D graph dialog boxes, such as surfaces, symbols, or projection lines. You can flip or rotate any object you have added to the graph using the graph editing tools.

▶ **To flip or rotate**

1 Using ⬚, the selection tool, select the object(s) you want to affect.

2 Do one of the following:

   ■ To flip, choose **Editor ➤ Flip Horizontal** or **Editor ➤ Flip Vertical**.

   ■ To rotate, choose **Editor ➤ Rotate Left** or **Editor ➤ Rotate Right**, and choose the angle you want from the submenu. The menus have choices for 15, 30, 45, 60, and 90 degrees.

If you want to specify an angle that is not on the menu, choose **Other**, enter a value, and click **OK**.

Method of flipping and rotating

Flipping occurs according to the center lines of an object. To illustrate, the polygon below shows the horizontal and vertical flip lines.

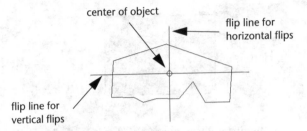

When you rotate selections comprising several objects, the objects rotate around their individual centers. When you flip selections comprising several objects, the objects flip around the center of the group.

When you flip text, the text will rotate instead of flipping. Flipping would create mirror image text that is difficult to read.

When you rotate a rectangle to certain degrees, the rectangles become polygons that will reshape differently. See *Some rotated rectangles become polygons* on page 24-11.

Examples of flipping and rotating

Here are some examples of flipping and rotating the polygon:

Example	Before	After
Flipping horizontally		
Flipping vertically		
Rotating left 60°		

Aligning Objects

You can align objects on a graph with other objects in a selection, or with the page (the page corresponds to the selectable area of the Graph window).

▶ **To align objects**

1 Using , the selection tool, select the object(s) you want to affect.

2 Choose **Editor ➤ Align**.

3 Select **Align with each other** or **Align with page**.

4 Check **Align horizontally** and/or **Align vertically**.

5 Select a horizontal location and/or a vertical location. Click **OK**.

When you align objects with the page, the *entire* selection aligns relative to the associated clipping regions. If clipping is turned off, objects align relative to the Graph window rather than the clipping region.

Examples of aligning objects

All of the examples that follow use the following arrangement of objects:

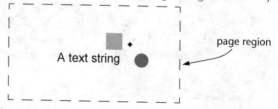

▷ **Example of aligning horizontally**

1 Using , the selection tool, select all four objects: the text, the square, the marker, and the circle.

2 Choose **Editor ➤ Align**.

3 Select **Align with each other**.

4 Check **Align horizontally** and uncheck **Align vertically**.

5 Select **Left**, **Center**, or **Right**, then click **OK**. The objects move as follows:

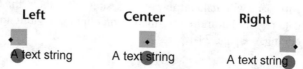

Left	Center	Right

☞ Example of aligning vertically

1 Repeat steps 1 through 3 of *Example of aligning horizontally* above.

2 Check **Align vertically** and uncheck **Align horizontally**.

3 Select **Top**, **Center**, or **Bottom**, then click **OK**. The objects move as follows:

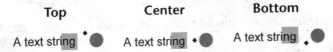

☞ Example of aligning objects with the page

1 Using 🡑 , the selection tool, select all four objects: the text, the square, the marker, and the circle.

2 Choose **Editor ➤ Align**.

3 Select **Align with page**.

4 Check **Align horizontally** and uncheck **Align vertically**.

5 Choose **Left** and click **OK**.

The selection moves on the page as follows:

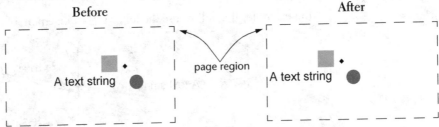

If objects move unexpectedly

If objects align in ways that you didn't expect, you can use **Edit ➤ Undo Move** to return to the initial arrangement. Here are the three most common reasons that objects may line up differently than you expected:

■ Because objects align with their associated clipping regions, you may encounter results that seem unexpected, especially when you have selections that mix items from different clipping regions. This means, for example, that when you use **Align with page** with data display objects, such as symbols, the objects align only with the data region. For more information on clipping regions and how they affect graph editing, see page 24-13.

- Symbols and text follow different alignment rules than other objects. Symbols are treated as points, and are always aligned by their centers, not their edges. Text strings are aligned by their text area extent, not by the exact space that the text appears in.

- Occasionally, an object will cover up another object after the objects are aligned because of the Bring to Front/Send to Back order.

Defining Custom Colors

When selecting a color from one of the color buttons ( ) on the Attribute palette, you have the option of defining a color that is not already present on the default palette. Custom colors are saved from project to project.

▶ **To define a custom color**

1 Choose ➤ **Custom** when a color button is active to display the following dialog box:

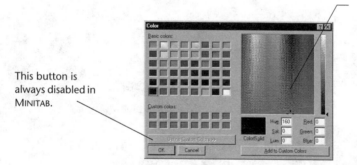

The color refiner area. You can move the cursor by either clicking anywhere in the area or dragging the cursor.

This button is always disabled in MINITAB.

2 Click on the **Custom Colors** box where you want the color to appear.

3 Define a color to the **Custom Colors** palette in one of the following ways:

- by clicking in the color refiner area, then adjusting the luminosity by dragging the luminosity selector arrow until you get a satisfactory color

- by typing values in the **Hue/Sat/Lum** or **Red/Green/Blue** boxes

- by clicking on a basic color

4 Click the **Add to Custom Colors** button to add the color in the Color rectangle. To add the Solid color, first double-click in the Solid rectangle or press [Alt]+[O], then click **Add to Custom Colors**. Click **OK** to save your changes.

Note | When editing a graph, if you choose a dithered color for edges, lines, or hollow markers that are size 1 or less, Windows substitutes the closest solid color. A dithered color is any color that changes when you double-click in the **Color** box.

25

Brushing Graphs

Brushing Graphs Overview

Graphs allow you to visually see the relationships between points. However, after you make a graph, you often want to learn more about a point, or a group of points. Brushing allows you to highlight points on a graph to learn more about them.

Initially you may find brushing to be especially good at

- showing the characteristics of outliers
- telling whether points that lie in a brushing region share other characteristics

But brushing can do much more. You may start out brushing a point or two, then make another graph to see a general relationship between other variables, brush points on that graph, then find more interesting relationships, and so on. You may come away with a much greater understanding of your data after brushing, but you may also spot critical areas in a process that need immediate attention.

Parts of brushing

- Brushing tool ➥—the special cursor that lets you create a brushing region in a graph.
- Brushing region—the highlighted data points in the graph. Brushed points are displayed in the brushing color.
- Brushing palette—a floating window which shows you the Data window row number for each point in the brushing region, as well as up to ten other column values for that row.
- Brushing markers—symbols in the Data window row headers that indicate which rows are currently being brushed.

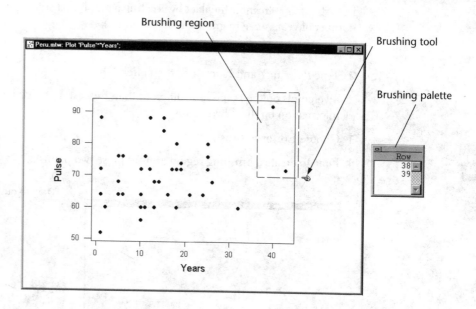

Graphs that support brushing

You can brush any graph in which a symbol represents a single value in the worksheet.

You cannot brush graphs in which graph points are

- not displayed with symbols

- based on a calculation involving more than one row, as in histograms, bar charts, boxplots, or pie charts

Starting Brushing

▶ To start brushing

1 Make the Graph window active.

2 Choose **Editor ➤ Brush**.

3 Drag the ⇒ cursor over the points in the graph.

➤ Example of exploring data with brushing

Let's look at a graph that uses the Peru data (PERU.MTW). This data was collected by anthropologists investigating the long-term effects of altitude change on human blood pressure. The subjects of the experiment were Peruvians native to the high Andes mountains who had since migrated to lower altitudes.

Let's start to get to know the data by creating a graph that shows pulse rate versus the number of years since migration to low altitudes:

1 Choose **Graph ➤ Plot**.

2 Type *Pulse* in **Y** and *Years* in **X**, then click **OK**.

Two points on the graph look different than the rest. Let's see if we can get more information on these two points.

3 Choose **Editor ➤ Brush**.

4 Drag to create a brushing region around those two points.

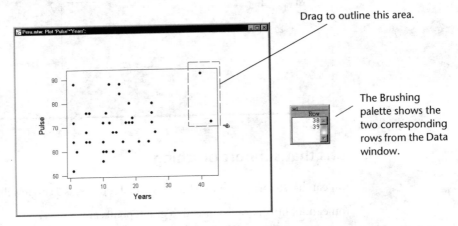

Drag to outline this area.

The Brushing palette shows the two corresponding rows from the Data window.

The Brushing palette shows that rows 38 and 39 are associated with those points. You can now look at rows 38 and 39 in the Data window to see the values of other variables for these individuals.

If you don't want to look in the Data window, you can view just the data you want by adding ID variables to the Brushing palette.

5 Choose **Editor ➤ Set ID Variables**.

6 Click **Use columns** and type *Age Weight Height Systol*, then click **OK**.

Now the Brushing palette looks like this:

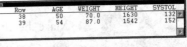

Now you can begin to see the faceless points on the graph start to come to life. You can almost visualize the two subjects, both in their early fifties, with slightly elevated systolic blood pressure.

But which data point in the graph corresponds to which subject? You can see which point is which by clicking in a row of the Brushing palette. This selects the point on the graph that corresponds to that row. For example, to select the point that corresponds to the point in row 39, click in row 39. Refer to page 25-5 for other ways to select/add rows to an existing selection.

Controlling the Brushing Region

▶ **To move the existing brushing region**

1 Move the mouse on top of the existing brushing region.

2 When the cursor turns into an open hand 🖐, drag the brushing region around, brushing whatever points fall within the region. This allows you to explore the points in an entire graph very quickly.

▶ **To add points to the brushing region**

- To add one point to the group of brushed points, hold down Shift and click the point.

- To add multiple points to the region, hold down Shift while moving the brushing region. The points you pass over will be added to the group of brushed points.

▶ **To change the brushing color**

When points are highlighted in the brushing region, they use the brushing color. The brushing color is kept from session to session.

1 Choose **Editor ➤ Set Brushing Color**.

2 Change options in the Custom Colors dialog box. For details, see *Defining Custom Colors* on page 24-19.

Controlling the Brushing Palette

▶ **To add or change identifier variables to the Brushing palette**

1 Choose **Editor ➤ Set ID Variables**.

2 Click **Use columns** and type the column names or numbers you want to see.

3 If you want to hide row numbers, uncheck **Use row numbers**.

▶ **To find graph points that correspond to palette rows**

- To find one point, click in a row in the Brushing palette. The graph point that corresponds to this row will be selected in the Graph window.

- To find multiple points, drag to highlight contiguous rows in the Brushing palette.

Viewing Brushed Data in the Data Window

When graph points are brushed, the corresponding rows are indicated in the Data window.

Brushed rows are indicated with this symbol.

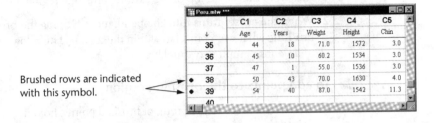

▶ To move between brushed rows

1 With brushed points in the Graph window, make the Data window active.

2 Do one of the following:

- To move to the next brushed row, press F4.

- To move to the previous brushed row, press Shift+F4.

Working with brushed data

Brushing markers are attached to the row numbers, not to the actual data in that row.

After brushing a graph, if you change the data in the Data window in any way—such as deleting rows, changing values in cells, or moving data to another row—the brushing markers stay with the original row numbers.

For example, if row 2 is marked as a brushed row, and you then delete row 2, all of the following rows move up—and row 2 retains the brushing marker.

Data window before deleting row 2

1	1	11
• 2	2	12
3	3	13
4	4	14
5	5	15

And after

1	1	11
• 2	3	13
3	4	14
4	5	15
5		

If you want to work with data from only the brushed rows, or from only the non-brushed rows, create an indicator variable (see below) and subset your data using that new variable (also described below).

Note | Although data in the Data window can be changed while using brushed values, entire rows of data should not be deleted. The values in the Indicator Variables window and the brushed values which are marked by row in the Data window will be incorrect if any rows are deleted in the Data window.

Creating an Indicator Variable

You can create a column in the Data window called an *indicator variable* that is made up of 0's and 1's. If a row is currently being brushed, the cell has a value of 1. If a row is not being brushed, the cell has a value of 0. The contents of the column change dynamically as you move the brushing region on the graph.

The indicator variable lets you explore your data in different ways. For example, you can

- subset your data based on brushed points
- calculate descriptive statistics separately for the brushed and unbrushed points
- do a regression analysis, omitting the brushed points

▶ **To create an indicator variable based on brushed points**

1 Brush points of interest on a graph.

For example, brushing this graph of data from the PULSE.MTW data set shows that the highest pulse rates are from female subjects. (In this data set, the variable Sex contains 1's for males, 2's for females.)

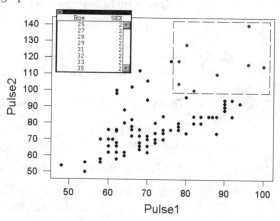

2 Choose **Editor ➤ Create Indicator Variable**.

3 In **Column**, enter a name for the indicator variable.

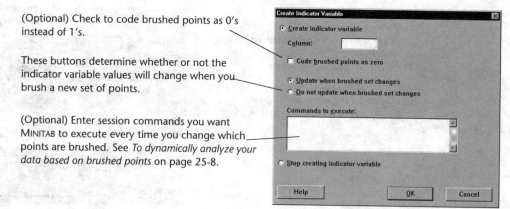

(Optional) Check to code brushed points as 0's instead of 1's.

These buttons determine whether or not the indicator variable values will change when you brush a new set of points.

(Optional) Enter session commands you want MINITAB to execute every time you change which points are brushed. See *To dynamically analyze your data based on brushed points* on page 25-8.

4 Set any options (see above). Click **OK**.

The Data window will now contain a new column with the name you specified (for example, *HighPulse)* that contains 1's in the rows corresponding to the brushed points, and 0's in the remaining rows.

Subsetting Based on Brushed Points

▶ **To subset your data based on brushed points**

1 Brush some points on the graph.

2 Choose **Manip ➤ Subset Worksheet**.

3 If you like, enter a name for the new worksheet (instead of using the default name).

4 Under **Include or Exclude**, choose **Specify which rows to include**.

5 Under **Specify Which Rows to Include/Exclude**, choose **Brushed rows**. Click **OK**.

More | For more examples of subsetting your data, see page *Subsetting: Copy Data to a New Worksheet* on page 6-9 and 6-14.

▶ **To dynamically analyze your data based on brushed points**

Every time you move the brushing region, MINITAB can execute a series of session commands.

1 Choose **Editor ➤ Create Indicator Variable**.

2 Select **Update when brushed set changes**. This means the commands will execute every time the brushing region is moved.

3 In the **Commands to execute** text box, enter commands, either by typing directly or by pasting commands copied from the History folder in the Project manager, then click **OK**.

To follow along with the example below, check the **Code brushed points as zero** box.

If you type the commands, press ⌈Ctrl⌉+⌈Enter⌉ to go to the next line.

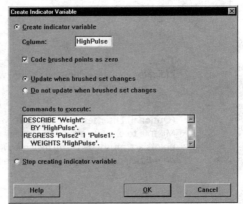

For example, here is what the session commands shown in the above dialog box will do:

- The DESCRIBE command displays a table of descriptive statistics (such as mean, median, and standard deviation) with separate statistics for the brushed points and the non-brushed points.

- The REGRESS command does a simple regression with Pulse2 as the response variable and Pulse1 as the predictor variable. Because we checked **Code brushed points as zero**, the variable HighPulse contains 0's for all brushed points, 1's for all remaining points. By specifying HighPulse as a weighting variable, we have instructed MINITAB to omit the brushed points (because they have a 0 weight) from the regression.

If you brush a new set of points—for example, the lower pulse values—MINITAB will update the contents of the HighPulse variable accordingly re-execute this same set of commands.

Brushing Across Graphs

When you brush points, MINITAB automatically highlights points from the same row that appear in other graphs. This is true whether the graphs appear in the same graph window or in other Graph windows. Brushing across graphs can help you quickly see visual relationships across many variables.

▶ **To brush across graphs**

1 Click once on the Graph window to make it active, and choose **Editor ➤ Brush**. Repeat for all the graphs you want to brush.

2 Arrange the graphs so you can see them all at once.

Tip | To quickly tile all the Graph windows, click on the Graphs folder in the Project Manager, highlight the graphs you want, and then right-click on them and select **Tile**. See *Managing, Arranging, and Naming Graph Windows* on page 13-9.

3 Brush the points you are interested in.

Note | If you open a different worksheet in the same MINITAB session, you can still brush graphs created from the first worksheet. However, the Brushing palette will show the row numbers and row values from the new worksheet. Also, any graphs created from the new worksheet will highlight points that correspond to row numbers in the new worksheet. Unless the rows are the same in the old and new worksheets, the results may be misleading.

▷ Example of brushing across graphs

Here are three graphs—two plots and one fitted line plot—based on the Peru data from page 25-3. Here we find evidence that one of the subjects (row 39) is quite overweight (which may contribute to his high pulse rate). Further exploration may reveal more about the cause of this subject's high pulse rate. The other subject (Row 38) has a more normal Height/Weight ratio.

Here is the brushing region. Points in the other graphs that have the same row number are highlighted, allowing you to compare different characteristics visually.

Although this subject's weight and height are displayed in the Brushing palette, seeing this point highlighted on the graph gives you a much better indication of how the subject compares to the rest of the participants.

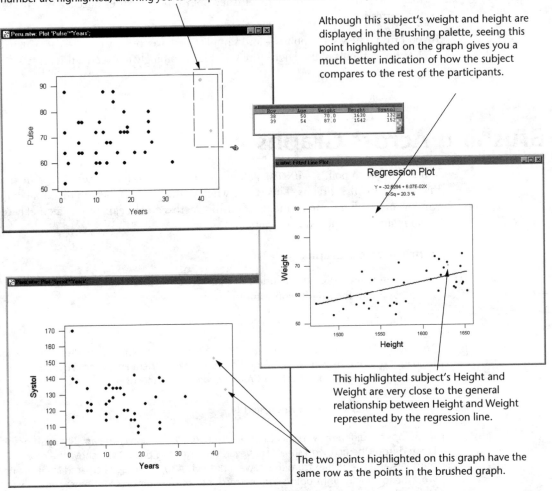

This highlighted subject's Height and Weight are very close to the general relationship between Height and Weight represented by the regression line.

The two points highlighted on this graph have the same row as the points in the brushed graph.

26

Saving and Printing Graphs

Saving and Printing Graphs Overview

You can save and print your graphs in several different ways. You can also share your graphs with other applications.

You can save your graphs in a number of file formats, and your choice should depend on where you intend on using the graph. Some file formats are better suited for importing graphs to specific applications. See *Saving, Opening, and Closing Graphs* below.

Your graph can be printed to a traditional printer. It can also be printed to an EPS file so that it will appear in a printed word processing document at the highest-possible resolution. Both methods are discussed in *Printing Graphs* on page 26-7.

You can also use MINITAB graphs in other applications by copying and pasting:

- If you want to view *and* edit that graph in other Windows applications, you can paste the graph as an OLE (pronounced "o lay") object. That object can be edited with MINITAB graph editing tools within the other application.

- If the application is not set up to handle OLE objects, you can paste the graph as a Windows Metafile drawing, or as a static bitmap. Copying and pasting is described in *Copying and Pasting Graphs* on page 26-6.

Saving, Opening, and Closing Graphs

Graphs are part of your project. When you save a project, you are also saving any open Graph windows. Those Graph windows will reappear when you reopen the project. You can open graphs that are inside other project files.

You can also save a graph into a separate file, in one of several graphics formats. The graph file can be opened in another MINITAB project or in another application.

If you want to use the graph in another application, you can also copy and paste it (see *Copying and Pasting Graphs* on page 26-6), or print the graph as an encapsulated PostScript file (see *Printing to an Encapsulated PostScript (EPS) file* on page 26-8).

File formats for saving

The table below lists the file types that the graph can be saved into, and the programs and applications where you can use that file.

File type	File extension	Use in
MINITAB Graph (MINITAB Graphics Format)	MGF	MINITAB projects, where you can edit, brush, print, and save again. MGF files cannot be opened in other applications.
JPEG (Joint Photographic Experts Group)	JPG	HTML documents on the World Wide Web. JPEG uses a "lossy" compression scheme, so the edges and color boundaries between graph items may be blurred.
TIFF (Tagged Image File Format)	TIF	Graphics and desktop publishing programs. TIFF files can be used on PCs or Macintoshes.
PNG (Portable Network Graphics)	PNG	HTML documents on the World Wide Web. PNG is a recently-adopted standard that is not yet supported by all browsers. PNG uses a lossless compression scheme, so edges and color boundaries are sharply defined.
Windows BMP (Windows Bitmap)	BMP	Graphics and word processing programs that run on the Windows family of operating systems.

Most of these graphics formats can be saved in black-and-white, color, or high color. The more colors you use, the larger the file size, so save in color only if your graph uses colors; save in high color only if your graph uses a large number of colors (as in a 3D surface graph).

Note | "Black-and-white" means there are only two colors, full black and full white, with no grays. Light colors such as yellow may translate to white. If your graph uses any colors besides black and white, save with color; on a non-color printer the colored lines will print as shades of gray.

▶ To save a graph

1 With the Graph window active, choose **File ➤ Save Graph As**.

2 In **Save as type**, choose the format that can be used by the other application. To use the graph in MINITAB, choose **Minitab Graph (*.MGF)**.

3 In **File name**, type a name and click **Save**.

Opening graphs

You can open a MINITAB Graphics Format (MGF) file that was created in Release 12 or Release 11 of MINITAB. You can also open graphs that are contained in a MINITAB Project (MPJ) file.

▶ **To open a graph**

1 Choose **File ➤ Open Graph**.

2 Under **Files of type**, select either MINITAB Graphics Format or MINITAB Project.

3 Select a directory and file name, then click **Open**.

4 If you select a MINITAB Project file, MINITAB then displays a list of the graphs in that project. Select a graph and click **OK**.

Closing graphs

You can close graphs one-by-one or all at once.

▶ **To close a Graph window**

1 Click ☒ in the corner of the window.

▶ **To close all Graph windows**

1 Choose **Window ➤ Close All Graphs**.

More | You can also close one or more graphs using the Graphs folder in the Project manager— see *Managing, Arranging, and Naming Graph Windows* on page 13-9.

MINITAB will prompt you to save graphs

You can have up to 100 Graph windows open at a time. If you create more graphs than the graphics preference indicates, MINITAB will prompt you to close one or more of the other Graph windows. When you close the window, MINITAB will ask you to save the graph. MINITAB will also ask you to save a graph when you close a Graph window.

You can choose a preference for how you wish to be prompted in these situations—or if you want to be prompted at all.

When many Graph windows are produced by a single command or a single MINITAB macro file, then by default, MINITAB pauses to allow you to view, save, print, and close Graph windows when you have too many graphs.

▶ **To change your prompt preference**

1 Choose **Edit ➤ Preferences** and select **Graphics**.

2 Select one of the following options under **Before closing a graph, Minitab should prompt you to save the graph when**:

- **The graph has not been saved since it was created or last edited** — This is the safest option, and is a good choice when
  - you want to make sure that you never accidently lose any graphs
  - you never want to lose any changes you make to a graph

- **You have edited the graph since it was created or last saved** — This is a good choice if you think that any graph you edit is generally worth more than a graph that you have not edited. MINITAB automatically closes unedited graphs and edited graphs that have already been saved.

- **Never** — This is a good choice when
  - you never want to be bothered with prompts at all
  - you don't care whether you lose an occasional graph
  - you can easily reproduce all graphs that you generate

3 Select one of the following options under **When there are too many graphs, Minitab should**:

- **Prompt you to close one or more graphs** — the default. When you choose this preference, you must close a graph before continuing with your procedure. Before closing a graph, you may view, save, and print graphs before closing at least one.

- **Close the oldest graph** — that is, the first graph generated

- **Close all graphs** — unclutters the display, may help performance if you have many complex graphs

Note | The **When there are too many graphs...** options only tell MINITAB which graphs are the *candidates* for closing. Once MINITAB makes a graph a candidate for closing, the **Before closing a graph...** preference determines if you will receive a prompt or not. Then, if no prompt is issued for the graph, and your preference is **Close the oldest graph** or **Close all graphs**, MINITAB closes the graph(s) automatically. When you receive a prompt, you can print, save, or close the graph.

Copying and Pasting Graphs

One of the easiest ways to use MINITAB graphs in another software package is to copy and paste them. The pasted graph can take one of several forms, depending on the capabilities of the application you are pasting to:

- If the application is OLE compliant, the graph will be pasted as an OLE object you can edit with the MINITAB graph editor.

- If the application is not OLE compliant, the graph will be pasted as a Windows Metafile drawing whose parts (titles, lines, symbols, etc.) can be individually edited by that application's editing tools.

- If the application has no editing tools for drawings, the graph will be pasted as a static bitmap.

Note   This section is on copying and pasting entire graphs. If you want to copy and paste portions of a graph, see *Copying and Pasting* on page 24-9.

▶ **To copy and paste a graph**

1   With the Graph window active, choose **Editor ➤ View**.

2   Choose **Edit ➤ Copy Graph**.

When you copy certain 3D graphs, including 3D wireframe plots, MINITAB will display a dialog box with this message: "I can only copy a bitmap of this graph. Proceed?" To copy the graph, just click **OK**.

3   In the other application, choose the paste command.

▶ **To edit a pasted MINITAB graph in another application**

This option is only available if the application is OLE compliant.

1   Double-click the graph. The MINITAB Graph Editor window will appear.

2   Use MINITAB's graph editing tools. See Chapter 24, *Editing Graphs*.

3   Close the window or choose **File ➤ Exit and return**. Either action will automatically update the graph in the application.

Tip   With the OLE graph editor, you can also save a copy of the graph to a file: choose **File ➤ Save Copy As**.

Printing Graphs

You can print graphs to color or black-and-white printers. MINITAB prints the contents of each Graph window on a single page. The printed graph has the same aspect ratio (ratio of width to height) as the graph has on your screen. For more information on aspect ratios, see *Changing the aspect ratio of a page* on page 19-7.

▶ To print a graph

1 Make the Graph window active.

2 Choose **File ➤ Print Graph**. You will see the standard Windows printing dialog box, which contains printing options for your specific printer.

3 When you print certain 3D graphs, including 3D wireframe plots, MINITAB will display a dialog box with this message: "I can only print a bitmap of this graph. Proceed?" To print the graph, just click **OK**.

▶ To print multiple graphs

1 Click on the Graphs folder in the Project Manager.

2 Highlight the graphs you wish to print.

3 Right-click on the highlighted graphs and select **Print**.

▶ To correct color problems on black-and-white printers

If your black-and-white printer is not properly displaying color elements as scales of grey, you can force MINITAB to print parts of graphs as true black and white (no greyscales).

1 Choose **Edit ➤ Preferences** and select **Graphics**.

2 Under **Printing**, check options to print text, fills, lines, or markers as black.

More | Refer to the Help topic for the **Edit ➤ Preferences** dialog box for details.

Tip | If you notice problems with the printed copy of a graph, search in Help for the topic *troubleshooting*, and click the topic called *problems with printed graphs*. Printing errors are often due to problems with the printer drivers supplied with your operating system or printer, but the troubleshooting tips in Help list several work-arounds.

Printing to an Encapsulated PostScript (EPS) file

You can print a graph to an EPS file, then import that file in another application. EPS files are generally of higher quality than graphs copied and pasted using the Clipboard, or graphs saved as different file types.

Note | This option is not available on Windows NT.

▶ **To save a graph as an EPS file in Microsoft Windows 95/98**

1 Choose **File ➤ Print Graph**.

2 In **Name**, select a PostScript printer.

3 Click **Properties**.

4 Click the **PostScript** tab.

5 In **PostScript output format**, select **Encapsulated PostScript**.

6 Click **OK**.

7 In the Print dialog box, check **Print to File**, and click **OK**.

8 In the Print to File dialog box, type a file name (it is a good idea to use the EPS file extension).

▶ **To save a graph as a non-EPS printer file**

As well as EPS, you can save graphs in other printer file formats.

■ Follow the instructions for saving as an EPS file (above), making sure that the right printer is listed under **Name**.

part V

Using Session Commands and Macros

27

Using
Session Commands

Using Session Commands Overview

MINITAB's functions are accessible through menus, as well as through a command language called *Session commands*. You can use menu commands and session commands interchangeably, or you can use one of the two exclusively. Menu commands provide clickable options through menus and dialog boxes.

Session commands allow you to provide specific instructions, through a command language. They are a useful alternative to menu commands, especially when creating macros to automate repetitive analyses. Most session commands are simple, easy to remember words like PLOT, SAVE, or SORT. You can type commands in two places: the Session window or the Command Line Editor.

Entering Commands in the Session Window

The Session window is primarily used for displaying the results of commands, as text. However, you can also type session commands in the Session window by turning on the MTB> command prompt.

▶ **To type commands in the Session window**

1 With the Session window active, choose **Editor ➤ Enable Commands** so that **Enable Commands** is checked. For details, see *Enabling and Disabling Command Language* on page 27-4.

2 Start typing commands, which should automatically appear at an MTB> prompt in the last line of the Session window.

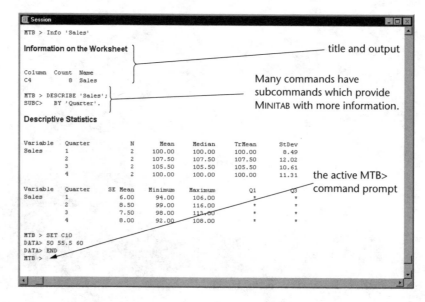

3 If the command has subcommands, end the command line with a semicolon, and press (Enter).

4 Type subcommands at the SUBC> prompt. Put a semicolon (;) after each subcommand, and press (Enter).

5 Put a period (.) after the last subcommand.

6 Press (Enter) to execute the command. Use (Ctrl)+(Enter) to insert a blank line.

Entering Commands with the Command Line Editor

The Command Line Editor is used to type, edit, and enter commands. Choose **Edit ➤ Command Line Editor** to reveal the Command Line Editor at any time, even when command language is disabled, or when the Session window is not active.

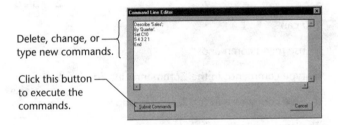

Delete, change, or type new commands.

Click this button to execute the commands.

▶ To execute commands using the Command Line Editor

1 Create the commands in the dialog box, using one of three methods:

- Type the commands and subcommands directly into the dialog box. Using the (Enter) key will insert blank lines, unless you change your preferences.

- Highlight the commands in the Session window or in the contents pane of the History folder. The highlighted commands will appear in the Command Line Editor. You can quickly re-execute commands using this method.

- Paste text from other applications, or other MINITAB windows.

2 To execute all of the commands in the Command Line Editor, click **Submit Commands**. To clear all commands in the Command Line Editor, press (F3).

▶ **To change and save your preference for the (Enter) key**

1 Choose **Edit ➤ Preferences** and select **Session Window**.

2 Under **Submitting Commands from the Command Line Editor**, click on the option you want. You can change your preferences to have (Enter) submit commands and (Ctrl)+(Enter) insert blank lines.

3 Click **OK**, then click **Save**.

Enabling and Disabling Command Language

By default, the Session window shows only the output from commands. But sometimes you may want to show the command language that generated the output, or you may want to be able to type Session commands directly in the Session window.

When command language is...

	Enabled	**Disabled** (default)
You can		
▪ use menu commands	Yes	Yes
▪ type commands in the Command Line Editor	Yes	Yes
▪ type commands in the Session window	Yes	No
The Session window displays		
▪ output from menu or session commands	Yes	Yes
▪ the commands used to generate output	Yes	No
MINITAB displays error messages in	the Session window	pop-up message boxes
The contents pane of the History folder displays session commands	Yes	Yes

▶ **To enable or disable command language**

▪ Choose **Editor ➤ Enable Commands**, so that **Enable Commands** is checked, to restore the active command prompt and to display all subsequent commands.

▪ Choose **Editor ➤ Enable Commands**, so that **Enable Commands** is unchecked, to disable the command prompt in the Session window and hide all subsequent commands.

▶ **To save your command language preference**

You can save your current setting so that it will be in effect the next time you use MINITAB. You can change your preference at any time.

1 Choose **Edit ➤ Preferences** and select **Session Window**.

2 Under **Command Language**, click **Disable** or **Enable** as you prefer.

3 Click **OK**, then click **Save**.

Meet the History Folder

The History folder in the Project Manager displays all session commands, without the output. It provides a convenient overview of the commands that you have used in your session.

History folder

Note	If you use the Data window to change a worksheet, a note is generated in the History folder.

Here are some useful things to do with the History folder:

- Highlight History text and have it automatically appear in the Command Line Editor. See *Editing and Re-Executing Commands* on page 27-8.

- Create a MINITAB macro file for a routine analysis by first working through the steps using the menus, then copying the resulting session commands from the contents pane of the History window into a text editor, tidying up, and saving the macro file. See Chapter 28, *Introducing Simple Macros*.

▶ **To print the contents of the History folder**

You can select and print a portion of the History folder contents, or print the contents in their entirety.

1 To print only a portion of the History folder contents, highlight the block of text that you wish to print by dragging with the mouse in the contents pane of the History folder.

2 Right-click on the highlighted block of text and choose **Print**.

3 To print the entire contents of the History folder, right-click on the History folder and choose **Print History**.

▶ **To copy the contents of the History folder**

You can select a block of text in the contents pane of the History folder, then copy the text block to the Clipboard:

1 Highlight the block you want to copy by dragging with the mouse.

2 To Copy the block to the Clipboard, right-click on the highlighted text and choose **Copy**.

Rules for Entering Session Commands

A session command consists of one main command, and may have one or more subcommands. Arguments and symbols may also be included in the command.

■ Subcommands, which further define how the main command should be carried out, are optional unless otherwise specified.

■ Arguments, which specify data characteristics, may be included one or more times for both the main command and subcommands.

■ Symbols, which assist in controlling the session command language, can also be included in session commands.

▶ **To execute a command**

1 Type the main command, followed by any arguments. No extra text is allowed on the command line.

2 If you are going to use subcommands, end the main command line with a semicolon. Press (Enter). Type subcommand.

3 With the last subcommand or command, end the line with a period.

4 Press (Enter).

Specifying commands and subcommands

- Commands and column names are not case-sensitive; you can type them in lowercase, uppercase, or any combination.

- You can abbreviate any session command or subcommand by using the first four letters.

- Some subcommands have their own subcommands. The order in which you give these subcommands determines what subcommand or command they modify. You can use many subcommands more than once in a command.

- Type the subcommand ABORT as the next subcommand to exit from a multi-line command without executing it.

Note | Some commands, called %macros, are macros that are invoked by typing % followed by the full macro name (you cannot abbreviate macro names). For more information, see *Invoking a Global Macro* on page 28-7.

Specifying arguments

Arguments specify data characteristics, such as location or titles. They can be variables (columns, constants, matrices) as well as text strings or numbers.

Variables

- Enclose variable names in single quotation marks (for example, HISTOGRAM 'Salary'). Certain commands, such as ANOVA, GLM, and the high-resolution graphics commands do not require quotation marks, but all commands work properly when quotes are used.

- In arguments, variable names and variable numbers can be used interchangeably. For example, the two following commands do the same thing (if C1 is named 'Sales'):

    DESCRIBE C1 C2
    DESCRIBE 'Sales' C2

- You can abbreviate a consecutive range of columns, stored constants, or matrices with a dash. For example, PRINT C2–C5 is equivalent to PRINT C2 C3 C4 C5.

- You can use a stored constant (such as K20) in place of any constant. You can even use stored constants to form a range such as K20:15, which represents all integers from the value of K20 to 15.

Text strings

- Enclose text strings, such as labels or file names, in double quotes (for example, TITLE "This is My Title"). In earlier versions of MINITAB, text was enclosed in single quotes. Although this still works, it is no longer recommended, and can cause a conflict with column and constant names.

Numbers

- Do not enclose numbers in quotes unless you want the numbers to appear as text.

- To specify a range of numbers, abbreviate the sequence using these conventions:

1:4	expands to 1 2 3 4
4:1	expands to 4 3 2 1
1:3/.5	expands to 1 1.5 2 2.5 3

  The session command SET includes additional abbreviation conventions. See *SET command* in Help for details.

Using symbols

- **Continuation**: Continue a command or row of data onto the next line with the continuation symbol &. For example:
  ```
  MTB > NAME C1 = 'Qtr1' C2 = 'Qtr2' C3 = 'Qtr3' &
  CONT>   C4 = 'Qtr4'
  ```

- **Comment**: Place the comment symbol # anywhere on the line to tell MINITAB to ignore the rest of the line. For example,
  ```
  MTB > DESCRIBE C1 #This is a comment
  ```

- **Missing Values**: Place the missing values symbol * anywhere a number would normally interact, to represent values that could be missing. The asterisk should be enclosed in single quotation marks ('*'). You could use the following command to copy data from one column to another, omitting rows that have missing values:
  ```
  MTB > COPY C1 C2;
  SUBC>   OMIT C1 = '*'.
  ```

Editing and Re-Executing Commands

Sometimes, it is convenient to copy a previously executed session command (or sequence of session commands) from the Session window or History folder, make minor changes if necessary, then execute the changed command(s). The Command Line Editor is a powerful tool for quickly editing and resubmitting commands. You can also copy, paste, and edit commands directly at the active prompt of the Session window. This section gives the steps for using the Command Line Editor, steps for using copy and paste at the session prompt, and an example of using the Command Line Editor to edit and re-execute a command.

▶ **To re-execute using the Command Line Editor**

1 Highlight the block you want to copy by dragging with the mouse.

2 Open the Command Line Editor by choosing **Edit ➤ Command Line Editor**. The highlighted commands will appear in the edit window. Any MTB>, SUBC>, or DATA> prompts in the highlighted Session window commands are ignored.

3 Edit the text, as necessary, in the Command Line Editor. Change highlighted command text by typing new text.

4 Execute the command(s) by clicking the **Submit Commands** button.

▶ **To re-execute using Copy and Paste at the command prompt**

You can also Copy previous commands, Paste them to the active prompt in the Session window, and edit them there.

1 Highlight a block of command text, from other MINITAB windows or another application, by dragging with the mouse.

2 Copy the block of command text by choosing **Edit ➤ Copy**.

3 Paste the block of command text into the Session window. If necessary, return to the Session window by choosing **Window ➤ Session** or clicking in the Session window. Place your cursor in the command prompt line. Choose **Edit ➤ Paste**. MINITAB ignores MTB>, SUBC>, and DATA> prompts in Session window commands when it pastes from the Clipboard.

4 Edit the text, as necessary, in the Session window. Change highlighted command text by typing new text.

5 Execute the command(s) in the block of command text by pressing ⌷Enter⌷.

Interrupting Execution of a Command

To interrupt the display of data from a command or the execution of a macro, type ⌷Ctrl⌷+⌷Break⌷. In a macro, MINITAB finishes executing the current command, then exits the macro. Display of data is halted as soon as possible.

To stop a session command when you have already begun typing it, type the subcommand ABORT. For example,

```
PLOT;
  TITLE "My Graph";
  ABORT.
```

Documentation of Session Commands

All session commands are documented in the Session Command Help file. In addition, session commands that are of particular use when creating macros are also described in the following chapters of this book.

Opening the Session Command Help file

You can open the contents page of the Session Command Help file using a menu command, or by using a session command. You can also open a command-specific Session Command Help file using a session command.

▶ **To open the Session Command Help file with a menu command**

1 Choose **Help** ➤ **Session Command Help**.

▶ **To open the Session Command Help file with a session command**

1 In the Command Line Editor, or at the active command language prompt in the Session window, type HELP.

2 Press (Enter).

▶ **To open a command-specific Session Command Help file**

1 In the Command Line Editor, or at the active command language prompt in the Session window, type HELP followed by a command or subcommand name. For example,

   HELP REGRESS   explains the REGRESS command

2 Press (Enter).

Reading a syntax description

Each session command topic in the Session Command Help file starts with a syntax description. The syntax description displays the format for typing the command.

The bold text highlights the commands, subcommands, symbols, or arguments that you may need to provide for the command. The remaining text, which is not bold, explains or emphasizes specific parts of the command. This extra text is not allowed on the command line in the Session window or Command Line Editor. Also, arguments in brackets are considered optional.

The following is an example of a syntax description:

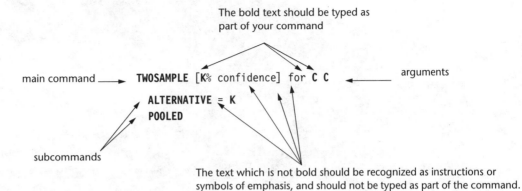

C means a column
K means a stored constant or number
M means a matrix
E means "everything": the argument can be a column, stored constant, number, or matrix.

28

Introducing Simple Macros

Macros Overview

MINITAB is usually used interactively, which means that each command carries out as soon as you click OK in a dialog box or enter it in the Session window. You can also use a MINITAB macro—a set of MINITAB commands stored in a file—to automate a repetitive task, such as generating a monthly report, or to extend MINITAB's functionality, such as computing a special test statistic. In other words, you can write macros tailored to your needs.

Once you create a macro file, you invoke it in the Session window or Command Line Editor. Type % followed by the macro file name, as in %mymacro. For details, see *Invoking a Global Macro* on page 28-7.

Terminology: three types of macros

Three types of macros have been developed in MINITAB to perform various repetitive tasks easily and effectively. In MINITAB's documentation, you may see the following terms which distinguish between the three types of MINITAB macros:

- **"Global macros,"** also referred to as simple macros, refers to the simplest form of macro—the type discussed in this chapter.

- **"Local macros,"** also referred to as advanced macros, refers to the more sophisticated form of macro discussed in Chapter 29, *Advanced Macros*.

- **"Execs"** refers to an older form of MINITAB macro, described in Chapter 33, *Using Execs*.

Similarities between global and local macros

"%macros" refers to both global and local macros. Because they share many qualities—for example, both are invoked by typing %, end in the extension MAC, and can use many of the same macro statements—the two types are often discussed together. Both global and local macros allow you to create a program of MINITAB commands, to use control statements such as DO-loops and IF statements, and to include subroutines. Both types also allow you to invoke other macros from within a macro. So how do you decide which type you want to use?

Using global macros

Global macros are usually simpler, and thus easier to write than local macros. Global macros act directly on your current worksheet. When you write a global macro, you must know which columns, constants, and matrices will be used when the macro is invoked. For example, when writing the global macro, you must know that C1 will contain the data, that K2 will contain the correct constant, and that C5 will be an empty column you can use to store the results of the macro.

Global macros, however, cannot invoke local macros, which means that some of the commands available from the menus and dialog boxes will not be available to you. In a number of MINITAB's dialog boxes, when you click **OK**, you are actually invoking a local macro. For example, the **Stat ➤ Time Series ➤ Trend Analysis** dialog box invokes the %TREND local macro.

In summary, write a global macro when

- the task is fairly simple
- you know the worksheet layout ahead of time
- the task does not require commands that are local macros

Using local macros

Local macros are more complex than global macros, and thus harder to write, but they are more powerful and flexible. Local macros can use arguments, subcommands, and "local" variables (see *Local Macro Elements* on page 29-2). If you need to write a fairly complex macro, or if you want a macro which you can execute like a MINITAB command, then you should write a local macro.

Using Execs from previous releases

If you have Execs that were written using previous releases of MINITAB, you may continue to use them with no change. If you would like to convert them to the new form, it is very easy to do; see *Converting Execs to %Macros* on page 33-3. If you are writing a new macro, we recommend you write it as a %macro, because we may phase out Execs in a future release of MINITAB and because the new macros provide much greater power and flexibility than do Execs.

Terminology: two types of worksheets

Worksheets include all of the data contained in the Session window, the Data window, and the Worksheet folder for a particular file. While most menu and session commands use only one worksheet, macros use two different kinds of worksheets. Both local and global macros work with a global worksheet, but only local macros work with both a global worksheet and a local worksheet.

- The "global worksheet" (sometimes called the "regular worksheet") is whatever worksheet is current when you invoke the global macro. The global worksheet consists of more than just the columns of data you see in the Data window—it is all the columns, constants, and matrices you see listed in the Worksheet folder for that worksheet. Global macros act directly on the global worksheet.

- The "local worksheet" is created when you invoke the macro, and is deleted from your computer's memory when the macro finishes. The local worksheet is completely separate from the global worksheet, and is not visible in a Data window.

Only the macro can "see" and manipulate the variables in that worksheet—which is why the worksheet is said to be "local" to the macro. You can write your macro to use arguments, so that you can pass variables from the global worksheet to the local worksheet when you invoke the macro, and pass variables out of the local worksheet into the global worksheet when the macro finishes.

The Structure of a Global Macro

A macro consists of lines of text, which represent command language, stored in a text file. While all macros follow a similar structure, global macros follow this specific structure:

GMACRO
template
body of the macro
ENDMACRO

GMACRO and ENDMACRO

These commands mark the beginning and end of each global macro. GMACRO must be the first line of your macro because it labels the macro type as global, not local. ENDMACRO ends the macro command. GMACRO and ENDMACRO, as well as all macro commands, cannot be abbreviated.

Template

The term "template" is used much differently when discussing global macros than when discussing local macros. Global macros simply use a "template" to name the group of commands for the macro. Local macros use a "template" to store the most repetitive commands, subcommands, and corresponding arguments. See *Invoking a Local Macro* on page 29-10.

You type the name of the template for your global macro starting with a letter. The remaining characters in the name can contain letters, numbers, or the underscore character. The template name can be upper, lower, or mixed case; MINITAB ignores case when you invoke the macro.

Using the macro file name as your template name is probably most convenient, but not required. All of the following are valid combinations of templates and file names:

Template	File name	Invoked by
MyMacro	MYMACRO.MAC	%MYMACRO
Analyze	TEST.MAC	%TEST
Analyze2	TEST2.TXT	%TEST2.TXT[a]

a. When invoking a macro, you only have to include the file name extension if it is not the default of MAC. See *Invoking a Global Macro* on page 28-7.

Body of the macro

The body of a macro consists of command language that controls the automatic data processing. The language includes:

- MINITAB commands

- Control statements (see *Adding Control Statements* on page 28-8)

- Macro statements
  (such as IF, THEN, PAUSE, CALL and GOTO - see Chapters 30 and 31)

- Invocation of other global macros
  (see *Invoking Macros from Within Macros* on page 30-7)

Example of a Global Macro

Here is a simple example of a macro file named ANALYZE.MAC. Indenting is not necessary, but may be done to improve readability, as illustrated here.

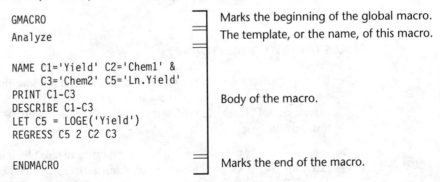

```
GMACRO                              Marks the beginning of the global macro.
Analyze                             The template, or the name, of this macro.

NAME C1='Yield' C2='Chem1' &
    C3='Chem2' C5='Ln.Yield'
PRINT C1-C3                         Body of the macro.
DESCRIBE C1-C3
LET C5 = LOGE('Yield')
REGRESS C5 2 C2 C3

ENDMACRO                            Marks the end of the macro.
```

Chapters 30 and 31 contain more examples of macros.

Tip | **Use &, the continuation symbol**
| If you want to continue a macro statement onto another line, end the first line with the symbol &, just as you do with commands in interactive MINITAB.

Creating a Global Macro

▶ **To create a global macro using a text application**

1 Write your macro using any text editor or word processor.

2 Save the updated global macro file in text-only format, with a file name and the file extension MAC, to the Macros subdirectory of your main MINITAB directory. If you want to use a different file extension, or save your file to a different directory, see *Notes on saving macro files* below.

▶ **To create a global macro using MINITAB**

1 Execute a series of commands using either menu commands or session commands.

2 Click on the History folder in the Project Manager. This folder displays the most recent commands (just commands, not output) executed in your session.

3 Highlight the commands you want to include in your macro, right-click on them and choose **Copy**.

4 Open any word processing application and choose **Edit ➤ Paste**.

5 Change any commands if you wish. Then insert three lines:

GMACRO	at the top of the file
template	a name you choose as the second line in the file.
ENDMACRO	at the bottom of the file

6 Save the updated global macro file in text-only format, with a file name and the file extension MAC, to the Macros subdirectory of your main MINITAB directory. If you want to use a different file extension, or save your file to a different directory, see *Notes on saving macro files* below.

Notes on saving macro files

- If you are using a word processor, make sure you do not save the file in that application's native format. For example, if you used Microsoft Word to write the macro, do not save the file as a Word document. Choose **File ➤ Save As** and select a text-only file type.

- You may use any file extension when you name a macro file, but MAC is the default extension MINITAB looks for when invoking a macro. A MAC extension will eventually save you time typing the extension or browsing for your files.

- You can save the file to any directory, but MINITAB looks automatically in the macros subdirectory of the main MINITAB directory. If you save the file in a different directory, you must specify the full path when you invoke the macro, as in %C:\WORK\MYMACRO.

Tip	**Edit an existing macro**

Your MINITAB Macros subdirectory, or folder, contains some example macro files. Looking at these examples may provide ideas on how to write your own macros.

If you edit these files, be sure to save your revised file with a different name. For a description of each of the MINITAB-provided macros in the directory, search for topics that begin with % in Session Command Help.

Invoking a Global Macro

To invoke, or process, a global macro from MINITAB, enter the symbol % followed by the macro file name. For example, to invoke a macro file named ANALYZE.MAC, enter the command:

```
%ANALYZE
```

Notes on invoking macros

- The default file name extension for macros is MAC. When you invoke a macro that has an extension of MAC, you only need to type the file name, as in %ANALYZE. If the extension is not MAC, you must type the file name and extension, as in %ANALYZE.TXT.

- When you invoke a macro, by default MINITAB looks for that macro file first in the current directory, then in the Macros subdirectory. If the macro is not in one of those default directories, you can specify the directory by including a path when you invoke the macro. For example, %C:\SALES\ANALYZE.

- If a files name includes spaces, put the name in single quotes, as in
  `%'a very long file name.MAC'`

☞ Example of invoking global macros

Here are some examples of the different ways to invoke a macro, with details on where MINITAB will look first for a macro file:

`%ANALYZE`	MINITAB looks for the file ANALYZE.MAC in your current directory first, then in the \MACROS subdirectory of your main MINITAB directory.
`%C:\SALES\ANALYZE`	MINITAB looks for the file ANALYZE.MAC in the \SALES subdirectory on the C drive.

%TEST.CMD	MINITAB looks for the file TEST.CMD (where CMD is an extension created by the user) in your current directory first, then in the \MACROS subdirectory of your main MINITAB directory.
%'A Very Long Macro Name'	MINITAB looks for the file A VERY LONG MACRO NAME.MAC in your current directory first, then in the \MACROS subdirectory of your main MINITAB directory.

Adding Control Statements

Control statements can make your macro flexible and powerful. For example, if you want the macro to…

- perform some action only if some condition is true or false, use an IF statement

- perform some action a set number of times, use a DO–ENDDO loop

- repeat a block of commands as long as some condition is true, use a WHILE–ENDWHILE loop.

- start another macro from within your macro, use CALL and RETURN

These control statements and others are detailed in Chapter 30, *Controlling Macro Flow*.

Adding Comments

You can annotate your macro program by using the comment symbol # and the NOTE command.

▶ **To add comments that do not display in the Session window**

1 Place the symbol # anywhere on a line to tell MINITAB to ignore the rest of the line. Text after # is not displayed in the Session window when the macro is executed (even when you use the ECHO mode described on page 32-4).

▶ **To add comments that display in the Session window**

1 Put the NOTE command at the beginning of a line. All text on that line will be ignored by the macro processor. However, text on a NOTE line (except the first five spaces—the word NOTE and a space) does display in the Session window when the macro is executed. To display a blank line, type a line containing only the word NOTE.

▷ **Example of using NOTE in a macro**

Macro code	Results in Session window

```
NOTE Here come the data
NOTE
PRINT C1-C3
```

Here come the data

Data Display

Row	Yield	Chem1	Chem2
1	11.28	87	1.83
2	8.44	61	25.42
3	13.19	59	28.64

. . .

Tip	**Increase readability by adding blank lines**
	NOTE can add blank lines to make your output more readable. But you can also make your macro file more readable by adding blank lines between the lines of macro statements and commands. The blank lines will not interfere with the execution of the macro, and will not appear in the Session window. You do not have to start a blank line with a # symbol.

Macros that Start Automatically

You can create a special file called STARTUP.MAC which executes automatically every time you start or restart MINITAB. A startup macro is a handy tool if you wish to avoid typing the same commands every time you start a MINITAB session.

STARTUP.MAC can be a global macro (the type discussed in this chapter) or local macro (discussed in Chapter 29, *Advanced Macros*). Users of earlier versions of MINITAB may have an Exec file named STARTUP.MTB which serves the same purpose and will still work (see Chapter 33, *Using Execs*).

▶ **To create a macro that starts automatically**

1 Create your macro with session commands using a text editor or MINITAB. The macro can be written as a global or a local macro.

2 Save the global macro file in text-only format, with a file name STARTUP and the file extension MAC, to the Macros subdirectory of your main MINITAB directory.

When you start or restart MINITAB, MINITAB looks for macro files in the order shown below, and executes the first one it finds, if one exists.

1 STARTUP.MAC in your current directory

2 STARTUP.MTB in your current directory

3 STARTUP.MAC in the Macros subdirectory of the main MINITAB directory

Finding Problems in Macros

If your macro produces unexpected results or generates an error message, MINITAB provides several tools to help you track down and correct the problem. Chapter 32, *Handling Errors in Macros*, describes the tools that can help you find problems, details how MINITAB responds to errors, and lists the MINITAB session commands that act differently in macros than in interactive MINITAB. However, you could easily check for, and correct, these common problems first:

■ The syntax used in the macro is not correct—for example, the macro does not begin with GMACRO or end in ENDMACRO.

■ The MINITAB commands in the macro are not correct—for example, the REGRESS command is misspelled, or a column name is provided when the command expected a constant. This kind of mistake generates the same kind of error message you would have received if you were using MINITAB in interactive mode.

■ The macro uses a MINITAB command that works differently in a macro than in interactive MINITAB—see *Commands that Work Differently for Macros* on page 32-7.

What Next?

The simple macros discussed in this chapter demonstrate only a few of the things you can do with MINITAB macros. The other chapters in this part of *MINITAB User's Guide 1* describe the rest of MINITAB's macro capabilities:

■ Chapter 29, *Advanced Macros*, shows you how to create more sophisticated local macros that act just like regular MINITAB commands, with arguments and subcommands. These advanced macros can also create temporary data that do not have to be stored in your worksheet—for example, if your macro uses a list of random numbers, you do not have to first store the data in a column, in order to complete the command.

■ Chapter 30, *Controlling Macro Flow*, describes techniques and commands you can use to control which commands are executed, and when.

■ Chapter 31, *Managing Input and Output*, shows you how to make a macro interactive, label output, save data, and more.

■ Chapter 32, *Handling Errors in Macros*, discusses how to interpret error messages, which MINITAB commands behave differently in macros, and tools you can use to track down and correct problems.

■ Chapter 33, *Using Execs*, discusses MINITAB's older macro functionality.

29

Advanced Macros

Advanced Macros Overview

Local macros are more complex than global macros, and thus harder to write. However, they are more powerful and flexible. If you need to write a fairly complex macro, or if you want a macro which you can execute like a MINITAB command, then you should write a local macro. If you are new to writing macros, you should read Chapter 28, *Introducing Simple Macros*.

Local macros can use temporary variables, arguments, and subcommands to enhance the processing capabilities of the macro. Local macros also have a different structure that allows you to include areas for defining the common commands and the variables.

Local Macro Elements

Local macros have the capability to handle several elements which improve the processing capabilities of your macro. These following three elements are mentioned throughout this chapter, and explained further in the next three sections:

- **Variables** - see *Using Variables* on page 29-2
- **Arguments** - see *Using Arguments* on page 29-4
- **Subcommands** - see *Using Subcommands* on page 29-6

Local Macro Structure

Template

Global macros use the template for naming purposes. Local macros use the template for naming the macro, but more importantly use the template for storing commands, subcommands and arguments. Templates for local macros are explained further in *Writing a Template* on page 29-12.

Declaration statements

The data variables that are used throughout a local macro need to be defined as columns, constants, or matrices. Declaration statements define the variable data type. See *Declaration Statements* on page 29-13.

Using Variables

A variable is an alias that can refer to some piece of data: a number, text string, column, constant, or matrix. For example, a variable named "Test1" could represent any of the following: a column of test scores, a constant that is the mean of the test scores, or a text string that is the name of the test.

Variables can be utilized in a local macro argument to allow you to enter data as the macro is invoked. They can also be used in a local macro control statement (found in the body of the macro) to enable complex calculations and data manipulations. And, all types of variables have to be declared in a declaration statement.

Variables for arguments

With global macros, you must provide the specific location, or specific value, of the data that needs to be processed from the command each time a macro is created. The data can not be changed when the global macro is invoked. A local macro can use variables to establish data unknowns that are determined when the macro is invoked. These variables are determined in the macro template, and are considered arguments. For more information on templates, see *Writing a Template* on page 29-12. For more information on arguments, see *Using Arguments* on page 29-4.

Variables for control statements

Local macros also allow you to use temporary variables that are known only to the macro and that are stored in the local worksheet. These temporary variables exist only while the macro is running. They are defined and manipulated using control statements within the body of your macro.

The only way you can utilize results within interactive MINITAB or in a global macro is by storing them in the global worksheet as columns, stored constants, or matrices. This can clutter your worksheet, especially if you need a lot of scratch storage.

With local macros, you can store data in variables on the local worksheet and manipulate them as you wish, without affecting your regular worksheet at all. When you exit the local macro, the local variables disappear. These temporary variables are especially useful for performing calculations and using control statements. For more information on control statements, see Chapter 30, *Controlling Macro Flow*.

Declaring Variables

In order to use argument or control statement variables, you must first declare the data type of the variable. The data can be text, suffixed, or unknown (considered "free") for all variables. For more information on declaring variables see *Declaration Statements* on page 29-13.

Naming variables

You should choose a variable name that represents the value that is going to take the place of the variable when the macro is invoked. The following rules apply for naming variables:

- can be a maximum of eight characters

- may include letters, numbers, and the underscore, but they must begin with a letter

- can be in capitals, lower case, or mixed. On output, variable names appear the way they are written in declaration statements.

- cannot be the same name as a subcommand

Note   If you see the error "Missing END for READ, SET, or INSERT," it may be because you have named a local variable with the same name as a MINITAB command, and entered it after READ, SET, or INSERT. For example:

```
SET col1
   min:max/1
END
```

where min and max are local variable names. MINITAB interprets the second line as a command because MIN and MAX are also MINITAB commands. It displays the error message because it thinks you are trying to execute a command without first having entered the required END statement. You must avoid using MINITAB commands for variable names if you need to use them in this way.

▶ To add variables to a macro

1 Adding variables can be done within the macro template, or within control statements. Do either of the following:

- Write a template that includes arguments. See *Example of a template for a command with arguments* on page 29-13.

- Write the command language in the body of a macro so that includes control statement variables. See Chapter 20, *Controlling Macro Flow*.

2 If any of your arguments or control statements include variables, you must declare the variable data type in the declaration statements. See *Declaration statements* on page 29-9.

Using Arguments

Arguments are variables that are passed into and out of a macro when it is invoked. The variables are listed on the main command line and subcommand lines of the macro. If you pass a global worksheet variable (a column, constant, or matrix) to a macro and the macro changes the value of that variable, the global worksheet variable will contain that changed value after the macro executes. An argument can be a variable which represents:

- a stored column, constant, or matrix from a global worksheet: 'Sales', C1, K2, or M1

- a number such as 2.3

Suppose that you want a macro that will draw a scatter plot with a fitted regression line and 95% confidence bands. Using a global macro for this situation would require you to specify, or predetermine, which columns contain the data while creating the macro. While invoking the global macro, you would not be able to specify different columns for the command.

However, with a local macro, you could specify which columns to use either when you create the macro, or when you invoke the macro using variable arguments. The undetermined column specification variables, used when creating the local macro for this situation, are examples of arguments. They allow you to enter whatever columns you wish when you invoke the macro.

Type of macro	Invoked by	Does this
Global	%REGRPLOT	Draws 95% confidence bands. Worksheet columns to be used for the plots are predetermined in the macro—for example, the data must always be in C1, C2, and C3.
Local	%REGRPLOT C15 C22 C34	Draws 95% confidence bands using the worksheet columns you list while invoking the macro.

Arguments can also be used to tell the macro the name of a file to open, the title of a graph, or the number of times to repeat some action. In addition, arguments can tell the local macro where to store results when the macro is finished processing.

Within the macro, you can also change the name of a variable passed in as an argument, then pass the name back out to the global worksheet. For example, the variable K1 could be given the name TestMean within the macro; when the macro finished, K1 would show the name TestMean in the Constants folder in the Project manager. For details, see *Naming Arguments* on page 31-8.

▶ **To add arguments to a macro command**

1 Write a template that includes arguments. See *Example of a template for a command with arguments* on page 29-13.

2 If any of your arguments include variables, you must declare the variable data type in the declaration statements. See *Declaration statements* on page 29-9.

▷ **Example of a macro template with arguments**

The three arguments in the following template are X, XBAR, and PCT. X is a column that contains the data, XBAR is the constant where the answer will be stored, and PCT is an optional constant that affects the subcommand. All three arguments will be given specific values when the macro is invoked.

```
TRIM2 X XBAR;
  PERCENT PCT.
```

Using Subcommands

Local macros can also have subcommands that can modify the behavior of the macro—just as subcommands in interactive MINITAB can change the behavior of a command. Subcommands can have their own arguments. You can also choose to include or not include the subcommand when invoking the local macro.

For example, the scatter plot macro described above could be made more flexible by including a subcommand that lets you decide at what level the confidence bands should be drawn.

Type of macro	Invoked by	Does this
Global	%REGRPLOT	Draws 95% confidence bands on predetermined worksheet columns. No subcommands allowed.
Local	%REGRPLOT C15 C22 C34; CONFIDENCE .90.	Without the subcommand, draws 95% confidence bands using the worksheet columns you list while invoking the macro. With the subcommand, draws confidence bands at whatever level you specify.

▶ **To add subcommands to a macro**

1 Write a template that includes a subcommand. See *Example of a template for a command with a subcommand* on page 29-13.

2 If any of your subcommands include arguments, you must declare the variable data type for those arguments in the declaration statements. See *Declaration statements* on page 29-9.

3 If any of your subcommands include arguments that are constants, you can assign default statements to those arguments in the body of the macro. See *Assigning default values to subcommand arguments* on page 29-7.

Invoking macros that use subcommands

- When invoking a macro, if you type a subcommand more than once, MINITAB uses the first occurrence of the subcommand.

- Individual arguments on subcommands cannot be optional. For example, suppose a subcommand has two arguments. When you invoke the macro, you can either omit the subcommand entirely, thereby accepting the default, or use it with two arguments. You cannot use the subcommand with the data value for one argument and take a default for the other argument.

Assigning default values to subcommand arguments

The DEFAULT statement is an optional line that allows you to assign a default value to a stored constant that appears on an optional subcommand. If a subcommand is not used when a user invokes the macro, the value on the DEFAULT line is used for the subcommand argument.

You cannot use DEFAULT to assign values to arguments on the main command—only arguments that are stored constants for a subcommand. Defaults for columns and matrices must be handled within the body of the macro.

Two rules about the syntax of DEFAULT:

- The DEFAULT line must come immediately after the declaration statements, before any other commands in the macro.

- The DEFAULT command cannot be abbreviated.

▷ **Example of creating and invoking a macro with a subcommand**

Suppose we improve TRIM by adding an optional subcommand, PERCENT, that allows the user to specify the trimming percent. If the user does not specify PERCENT, we use the default value of 5%. We give this default value using the macro statement DEFAULT.

- Here what you would type for the macro:
```
MACRO
TRIM2  X  XBAR;
  PERCENT PCT.
#
# TRIM2 takes one column, X, as input. It orders the data, trims
# the percent specified by PCT from each end, calculates the
# mean of the remaining data and stores it in XBAR.
# If PCT is not given, 5% is used.
#
MCONSTANT  N  T1  T2  XBAR  PCT
MCOLUMN    X  XSORT  XTRIM
DEFAULT    PCT = 5
#You can find the complete version of this macro in the file TRIM2.MAC.
```

Then suppose, in your global worksheet, you have data in a column named Score and you want to calculate the 4% trimmed mean and store it in a constant named Sbar. When you invoke a macro, you must use single-quotes around variable names, as with most other MINITAB commands. It is only in the macro text that quotes are not used.

- Here is what you would type for invoking the macro:

```
%TRIM2  'Score' 'Sbar';
   PERCENT  4.
```

Determining whether or not the subcommand invokes

As with regular MINITAB commands, subcommands of macros are optional—when invoking the macro, you can choose whether or not to type the subcommand. You can structure your macro to respond differently depending on whether or not a subcommand was used.

Each subcommand listed on the template is an *implicit constant*, which means that it is automatically created and does not have to be declared. This is why there is a rule against declaring a variable with the same name as a subcommand.

If the macro is invoked using the optional subcommand, MINITAB sets the subcommand constant to 1; if the subcommand was not used, MINITAB sets the subcommand constant to 0.

If you type the PERCENT subcommand while invoking the macro below, MINITAB sets the variable subcommand constant equal to 1, thereby leaving the percent value up to you. If you do not type PERCENT, the variable subcommand constant defaults to 0, thereby accepting the percent value. The NOTE command after the "IF PERCENT = 0" statement tells the user when the macro is using the default trim size of 5 percent.

```
MACRO
TRIM2  X  XBAR;
   PERCENT PCT;
MCONSTANT  N  T1  T2  XBAR  PCT
MCOLUMN    X  XSORT  XTRIM
DEFAULT    PCT = 5
body of the macro
IF PERCENT = 0
   NOTE Trimming 5 percent from each end
ENDIF
ENDMACRO
```

The Structure of a Local Macro

Local macros are created in the same way as global macros, using a text editor or various features of MINITAB (see *Creating a Global Macro* on page 28-6). However, the structure and the contents of a local macro can differ significantly.

The structure of a local macro is similar to that of a global macro, but it includes additional elements that allow you to define the syntax of the user command, and to declare variables for the local worksheet. The contents of a local macro follow this structure:

MACRO
template
declaration statements
body of the macro
ENDMACRO

MACRO and ENDMACRO

MACRO and ENDMACRO mark the beginning and end of each macro. You can have more than one macro within a local macro file—see *Invoking Macros from Within Macros* on page 30-7. MACRO must be the first line of your macro because it labels the macro type as local, not global. MACRO and ENDMACRO can not be abbreviated.

Template

The template gives the macro command name and any subcommands, as well as any undetermined arguments. See *Invoking a Local Macro* on page 29-10.

Declaration statements

Each variable that will be used in the macro must be "declared" with a declaration statement. Declaring a variable tells the local macro what type of variable to expect when the macro is invoked: a column, constant, or matrix. See *Declaration Statements* on page 29-13.

Body of the macro

The body of a macro consists of command language that controls the automatic data processing. The language includes:

- MINITAB commands

- Control statements (see *Adding Control Statements* on page 28-8)

- Macro statements
  (such as IF, THEN, PAUSE, CALL and GOTO—see Chapters 30 and 31)

- Invocation of other global macros
  (see *Invoking Macros from Within Macros* on page 30-7)

Invoking a Local Macro

1 From a command prompt in the session window, enter the percentage symbol %
  followed by the macro file name, as in %TRIM. Also consider the following issues:

  - The default file name extension for local macros is MAC. When you invoke a
    macro that has an extension of MAC, you only need to type the file name, as in
    %TRIM. If the extension is not MAC, you must type the file name and extension,
    as in %TRIM.TXT.

  - When you invoke a local macro, by default MINITAB looks for that macro file first
    in the current directory, then in the \MACROS subdirectory. If the macro is not
    in one of those default directories, you can specify the directory by including a
    path when you invoke the macro. For example, %C:\SALES\TRIM.

  - If a local macro file name includes spaces, put the name in single quotes, as in
    %'a very long file name.MAC'

2 After the file name, type any undetermined arguments which belong with the main
  command:

  - Unnamed columns, constants, and matrices are not surrounded by quotes, as in
    %TRIM C1 K2

  - Named columns, constants, and matrices are surrounded by single quotes, as in
    %TRIM 'Sales' 'NewMean'

  - Text strings, such as titles or file names, are surrounded by double quotes, as in
    %TRIM C1 K2;
       TITLE "Results";
       STOREIN "OUTPUT.TXT".

3 If the macro has optional subcommands, consider typing them as in interactive
  MINITAB, ending each line with a semicolon or a period, as in
  %TRIM C1 K2;
     PERCENT 4.

Example of a Local Macro

The macro TRIM calculates a 10% trimmed mean for a column of data from the global worksheet and stores it in a constant in the global worksheet. Remember, all macro lines beginning with the comment symbol # are comments, which are ignored by MINITAB when you invoke a macro. See *Adding Comments* on page 28-8.

	Macro Language	Explanation
(1)	`MACRO`	MACRO marks the beginning of a local macro.

(2)	`TRIM  X  XBAR`
	`#`
	`# TRIM takes one column, X, as`
	`input. It orders the data, trims 5%`
	`# from each end, calculates the`
	`mean of the remaining data, and`
	`# stores it in the constant XBAR.`
		Template. Says to invoke this macro with two arguments: argument 1 is the column of data to be trimmed, and argument 2 is the constant where the trimmed mean is to be stored. See *Invoking a Local Macro* on page 29-10.

(3)	`MCONSTANT N T1 T2 XBAR` `MCOLUMN X XSORT XTRIM`	**Declaration statements.** MCONSTANT declares four constants (N, T1, T2, and XBAR) to be used as variables by the local macro. One of these constants, XBAR, is an argument that corresponds to the constant that is passed into the macro when the user invokes the macro. MCOLUMN declares three columns (X, XSORT, and XTRIM) to be used as variables by the local macro. One of these columns, X, is an argument that corresponds to the column that is passed into the macro when the user invokes the macro. See *Declaration Statements* on page 29-13.

(4)	`# first we calculate the trimming`
	`points T1 and T2`
	`LET N = COUNT(X)`
	`LET T1 = ROUND(N*0.05)`
	`LET T2 = N-T1+1`
	`# next we check for the case when`
	`T1 = 0 and nothing is trimmed`
	`IF T1 = 0`
	`   LET XTRIM = X`
	`# otherwise, we sort X, trim the`
	`ends and calculate the mean`
	`ELSE`
	`   LET XSORT = SORT(X)`
	`   COPY XSORT XTRIM;`
	`     OMIT 1:T1  T2:N.`
	`ENDIF`
	`LET XBAR = MEAN(XTRIM)`
		Body of the macro.
		
		The body is mostly comprised of control statements and macro statements that are explained in Chapter 30, *Controlling Macro Flow* and Chapter 31, *Managing Input and Output.*

(5)	`ENDMACRO`	ENDMACRO marks the end of the macro.

Invoking TRIM

Suppose you save these lines in a text file called TRIM.MAC stored in your current directory. Now suppose you have data in C5, and you want to calculate the trimmed mean and store it in K1. To invoke the macro, you type,

```
%TRIM C5 K1
```

Writing a Template

A global macro template simply names the group of macro commands, whereas a local macro template lists the name and the macro command language. While the local macro template does not include macro statements or control statements, it does contain the command, its subcommands and any associated arguments.

Syntax

```
commandname [argument1] [argument2][...]
    [subcommandname1 [argument1] [argument2][...] ]
    [subcommandname2 [argument1] [argument2][...] ]
    ...
```

Template Requirements

- The only lines that can appear between the word MACRO and the template are comment lines that begin with #.

- The first line of the template contains the macro name. You should use the same name for the template as the file name, unless you intend on using the template for multiple macro files. The file name is used when you invoke a macro, whereas the template name is used in constructing a macro file.

- Command and subcommand names can contain letters, numbers, and the underscore character, up to a maximum of eight characters. They must start with a letter. Only the first four letters of macro subcommands are used by MINITAB.

- Command and subcommand arguments must have legal variable names. See *Naming variables* on page 29-4.

- You may have two or more macros in one file. Each macro must follow the structure shown in *The Structure of a Local Macro* on page 29-9, and each must have a unique template name. When you invoke the macro containing multiple macros, MINITAB executes the first macro in the file. You can invoke subsequent macros within the file by using a CALL statement with each template name (see *Invoking Macros from Within Macros* on page 30-7).

- If the command has subcommands, use punctuation just as in interactive MINITAB: end each line with a semi-colon, and put a period after the last subcommand.

▷ Example of a template for a command with arguments

Template: `Trim X Xbar`, **Invoked by:** `%TRIM C5 K1`

In the template, Trim is the command (and name of the macro), X is the first argument, and Xbar is the second argument. The X variable is the column (to be specified when the macro is invoked) where the macro should look for data. Xbar is the constant where the macro should store the result. For more information on arguments, see *Using Arguments* on page 29-4.

▷ Example of a template for a command with a subcommand

Template: `TRIM X Xbar;Percent Pct.`, **Invoked by:** `%TRIM C1 C5;PERCENT 5.`

In the template, the TRIM command has its arguments X and Xbar. The subcommand is Percent. Percent has an argument, Pct, that can contain a constant. For information on subcommands, see *Using Subcommands* on page 29-6.

Declaration Statements

All variables used in a local macro (with the exception of subcommand constants, as noted in *Variable types* on page 29-15) must be declared. Declaring a variable tells the local macro what type of variable to expect from the user, or the macro, while invoking. For more information on using variables, see *Using Variables* on page 29-2.

Syntax

```
MCOLUMN     variable1 variable2 … (where each variable is a column)
MCONSTANT   variable1 variable2 … (where each variable is a constant)
MMATRIX     variable1 variable2 … (where each variable is a matrix)
MFREE       variable1 variable2 … (where each variable is undetermined
                                   until macro is invoked)
```

Declaration Requirements

- Declare variables that are constants with MCONSTANT, variables that are columns with MCOLUMN, and variables that are matrices with MMATRIX. (You may also use the plural synonyms MCONSTANTS, MCOLUMNS, and MMATRICES.) After the M- command, list all the variables that are of that type, separated by a space.

- An argument, which is a variable in the template, may be given the declaration MFREE. The variable data type—column, constant, or matrix—is determined by the type of the variable that is given when the macro is invoked. The macro statement MTYPE (page 29-20) allows you to determine whether a variable declared with MFREE is a column, constant, or matrix. For more information, see *Using Free Variables* on page 29-20.

- You may use a declaration statement several times, but only for different variables and only between the template and the body of the macro. Once a variable is declared, it cannot be redeclared. Variable declarations can only be made between the template and the body of the macro.

- The declaration commands (MCOLUMN, MCONSTANT, etc.) cannot be abbreviated.

- The declared variable must have a legal name. See *Naming variables* on page 29-4.

☞ Example of declaring variables

For example, suppose the template is

```
TRIM X Xbar
```

TRIM is the name of the macro and X and Xbar are variables that will be passed into the macro. The macro would need declaration statements that define whether X and Xbar are constants, columns, matrices, or "free" variables (defined below). Let's say X is a column in the global worksheet and Xbar is a constant in the global worksheet. The user would invoke the macro by typing, say, %TRIM C5 K1. The first few lines of the local macro file would then be

```
MACRO
TRIM X Xbar
MCOLUMN X
MCONSTANT Xbar
```

Variable types

There are four special-purpose variables, which are each declared differently. They are explained in the following sections, with the exception of a subcommand that was explained earlier in *Determining whether or not the subcommand invokes* on page 29-8:

Variable type	Declare with	Contents	For more information see
Subcommand	Do not declare	An *implicit constant* that has a value of either 1 (if the subcommand was invoked) or 0 (if the subcommand was not invoked)	*Determining whether or not the subcommand invokes* on page 29-8
Text	MCONSTANT	A text constant that contains a text string	*Using Text Data* on page 29-15
Suffixed	MCOLUMN MCONSTAN	A range of columns or constants	*Using Suffixed Variables* on page 29-17
Free	MFREE	Column, constant, or matrix whose type is undetermined until the macro is invoked	*Using Free Variables* on page 29-20

Using Text Data

You can use text data in columns, in stored constants, and as text strings in all three types of macros. In addition, you can pass a text string into a macro by enclosing the string in double quotes when invoking the macro. The passed string can then be assigned to a constant in your macro. Constants that hold text data are useful for specifying graph titles, file names, and names for variables that could be created in a local macro.

▷ **Example of a macro using text strings**

The following local macro provides an example of using text data.

```
MACRO
REVERSE file1 file2
#
# REVERSE reads the first 3 columns of the input file, file1.
#
MCONSTANT file1 file2
MCOLUMN X Y Z
PRINT file1 file2
READ X Y Z;
  FILE file1.
WRITE file2 Z Y X
#
# REVERSE now stores the 3 columns from file1 in reverse order as the
output file, file2.
#
ENDMACRO
```

▷ **Example of invoking a macro using text strings**

We could use this macro to reverse the columns in the file called INPUT.DAT and store the reversed data in the file called OUTPUT.DAT by using

```
%REVERSE "INPUT" "OUTPUT"
```

Note | In older versions of MINITAB, single quotes were used instead of double quotes. Single quotes still work but are not recommended and can result in ambiguities concerning variable names and the contents of constants.

Commands for storing text in constants

```
KKNAME K C, ... , K C
KKSET K "text", ... , K "text"
KKCAT K K K
```

Three macro commands allow you to store text in a constant. They are especially useful for displaying titles and other annotation on macro output. The following text commands are used in the body of %macros, which means the commands can only be used in global or local macros:

- **KKNAME** stores the name of column C in the constant K.

- **KKSET** stores the text within the double quotes in the constant K. You can also use the regular MINITAB command LET to store text in constants. KKSET, however, can store several text strings in several constants at once, whereas LET stores one text string in one constant. (Note, in older versions of MINITAB, you used single quotes around the text in KKSET. You can still use single quotes, but they are not recommended).

- **KKCAT** concatenates, or combines, the text in the first constant K with the text in the second constant K, and stores the combined string of text in the third constant K. For example, if the constant X contained "Mr." and the text constant Y contained "Jones", the following command KKCAT X Y Z would put the string "Mr.Jones" in the constant Z.

Note | The macro command KKCAT combines constants containing text data, whereas the MINITAB command CONCATENATE combines columns containing text data.

Using Suffixed Variables

A suffixed variable is a variable that represents a range of values. The range can include columns and constants. They are most useful when:

- you want to abbreviate a list of known variables—this is a *defined range*. For example, if a command in a macro acts on five columns, it is easier to write C1-C5 than C1, C2, C3, C4, C5.

- you do not know until the macro is invoked how long a list will be—this is an *undetermined range*. For example, the user may want the macro to act on C1-C3, C1-C5, or C1-100, depending on what data is applicable.

Suffixed Variable Syntax

A suffixed variable is a variable name followed by a period, followed by the suffix. The suffix can either be an integer or a stored constant. The range of suffixed variables can be abbreviated using a dash.

Variable name	Period	Suffix	Suffixed variable	Range of suffixed variables
X	.	1	X.1	X.1-X.5
My_Data	.	1	My_Data.1	My_Data.1-My_Data.5
Test	.	1	Test.1	Test.1-Test.num
Test	.	num	Test.num	

The variable name and the suffix can each have up to eight characters. However, only the last eight characters of a suffixed variable, including the period, are shown when a suffixed variable is printed. So if you plan to print out suffixed variables, you should probably keep them short, as in Col.1-Col.5 or X.1-X.N.

Using suffixed variables in the template and declarations

Within the body of a macro, suffixed variables can be used in any order, alone or in groups. But when they appear on the template or in declaration statements, they must follow these rules:

- In the template and declarations, you must give a list of suffixed variables as one complete list, in order, and using a dash. All variables in the list must be of the same variable type.

	Templates **(Command: TRIM)**	**Declarations**
Legal:	TRIM X.1-X.5	MCOLUMN X.1-X.5
	TRIM X.1-X.5 Y.1-Y.8	MCONSTANT X.1-X.5 Y.1-Y.8
	TRIM Z X.3-X.20 W1 W2	MCOLUMN Z X.3-X.20 W1 W2
Illegal:	TRIM X.1-X.3 X.4-X.5	MCOLUMN X.1-X.3 X.4-X.5
	TRIM X.1-X.2 Y X.3-X.5	MCONSTANT X.1-X.2 Y X.3-X.5
	TRIM X.5-X.1	MCOLUMN X.5-X.1

- In the template, each command and subcommand can have as many regular arguments and as many defined-range arguments as you wish. However, the command or subcommand can have only one undetermined-range argument.

Legal template statements: MYPROG1 X.1-X.10 Y.1-Y.N

MYPROG2 X.1-X.10 Y.4-Y.20

MYPROG3 X.1-X.M;
  SUB1 Y.1-Y.N;
    SUB2 Z.5-Z.P W.1-W.10.

Illegal template statement: MYPROG4 X.1-X.M Y.1-Y.N

- Once you have declared a suffixed variable, you cannot declare another variable with the same prefix, even one of the same type. The following two declarations cannot be used in the same program. Because the prefix "X" is used with MCOLUMN, it cannot be used again—either for additional columns or for any other type of variable.

Legal first declaration: MCOLUMN   X.1-X.5
Illegal second declaration: MCOLUMN   X.6-X.10

- Do not declare the suffix of a suffixed variable. For example, suppose you have the range X.1-X.N. You do not give N a value; MINITAB applies a value to N automatically when you invoke the command.

▷ Example of suffixed variables with a defined range

The macro GENMEDIANS generates five columns of random data, then stores the median of each row in another column. There is one list of 5 columns, X.1, X.2, X.3, X.4, X.5, and a single column, MEDIANS. The variables in a list are always stored together in the worksheet. Notice that a dash abbreviates this list.

```
MACRO
GENMEDIANS MEDIANS
#
MCOLUMN X.1-X.5 MEDIANS
#
RANDOM 100 X.1-X.5
RMEDIAN X.1-X.5 MEDIANS
ENDMACRO
```

Suppose you stored this macro in a file called GEN2.MAC, and invoke it with `%GENMEDIANS C10`. After the macro finishes, the medians would appear in C10.

▷ Example of using a constant to define a range of columns

The following modification, called GEN2, allows the user to use the subcommand OBS to specify the number of observations in each sample (M).

```
MACRO
GEN2 MEDIANS;
  OBS M.
#
MCOLUMN   X.1-X.M MEDIANS
MCONSTANT M
DEFAULT   M = 5
#
RANDOM 100   X.1-X.M
RMEDIAN X.1-X.M MEDIANS
ENDMACRO
```

Suppose you stored this macro in a file called GEN2.MAC, and invoke it with

```
%GEN2 C1;
  OBS 10.
```

This generates 100 rows in the local worksheet, each containing 10 observations stored in X.1-X.10. The median of each row is calculated and stored in the macro variable MEDIANS. When the macro finishes, the medians appear in the column C1.

> **Example of suffixed variables with an undetermined range**

The following macro, ORSTATS, takes a list of columns and calculates three rowwise order statistics, the minimum, median, and maximum.

```
MACRO
ORSTATS X.1-X.N MIN MED MAX
#
# Input consists of a list of columns X.1-X.N.
# The rowwise minimums, medians, and maximums are calculated and
# stored in MIN, MED, and MAX respectively.
#
MCOLUMN X.1-X.N MIN MED MAX
#
RMIN X.1-X.N MIN
RMED X.1-X.N MED
RMAX X.1-X.N MAX
ENDMACRO
```

Suppose we want to calculate the same statistics for eight columns, C5–C12, and store them in C21, C22, and C23. When invoking the macro, we would type

```
%ORSTATS C5-C12 C21-C23
```

By matching arguments on this line with the template in the macro program, MINITAB determines that N = 8. Then MINITAB matches C5 to X.1, C6 to X.2, …, C12 to X.8 and C21 to MIN, C22 to MED, and C23 to MAX.

Using Free Variables

You may want a local macro to operate with a column, constant, *or* matrix—whatever the user decides to use when he or she invokes the macro. The local macro can then take appropriate action, depending on the type of variable used when invoking the macro. A *free variable* is an argument variable whose type—column, constant, or matrix—is not determined until the macro is invoked.

▶ **To use a free variable in a macro**

You must do five things in the local macro code to make free variables work:

1 List the free variable as an argument on the template. For example, here is a template for the macro TELLME that has X as an argument:
```
TELLME X
```

2 Declare the free variable with the declaration statement MFREE. For example:
```
MFREE X
```

3 Declare an additional variable as a constant:
```
MCONSTANT Vartype
```

4 Use the macro statement MTYPE to analyze the free variable and store its variable type number in the constant declared in step 3. If the variable is a constant, then

Vartype is set to 1; if it is a column, Vartype is set to 2; and if it is a matrix, Vartype is set to 3. You can include an MTYPE statement anywhere within the body of a local macro. For example, the command MTYPE X Vartype looks at the free variable X and stores its variable type (1, 2, or 3) in the constant Vartype.

5 Write code that can respond to the variable type that was used. In the following example, the IF statements make the macro perform different actions depending on what type of variable X is:

```
IF Vartype = 1
  NOTE X is a constant!
ELSEIF Vartype = 2
  NOTE X is a column!
ELSE
  NOTE X is a matrix!
ENDIF.
```

Note | There is one case when the macro processor cannot determine the type of a variable. This happens when a variable that appears on an optional subcommand is declared as MFREE, and a user invokes the macro without using the subcommand. In this case, the macro processor assumes the variable is a column.

▷ **Example of a macro that uses free variables**

The local macro TELLME tells the user what kind of variable was used when the variable was invoked. Here is the complete code:

```
MACRO
TELLME X
MFREE X
MCONSTANT Vartype
MTYPE X Vartype
IF Vartype = 1
  NOTE X is a constant!
ELSEIF Vartype = 2
  NOTE X is a column!
ELSE
  NOTE X is a matrix!
ENDIF
ENDMACRO
```

TELLME can be invoked in all of the following ways, and will produce the following output in the Session window:

Invoked like this	Produces this
%TELLME C1	X is a column!
%TELLME K1	X is a constant!
%TELLME M1	X is a matrix!

▷ **Example of a more complex macro that uses free variables**

In the following local macro, BETWEEN.MAC, the arguments LOW and HI can be either columns or constants.

```
MACRO
BETWEEN   X.1-X.N   LOW   HI   ANS;
    STRICT.
MCOLUMN   X.1-X.N   L   H   ANS
MFREE        LOW   HI
#
# X.1-X.N is a list of columns. LOW and HI can each be either
# a column or a constant.
#
# BETWEEN checks to see if the values in one row of X.1-X.N are
# all greater than or equal to LOW and all less than or equal
# to HI. If they are, the corresponding row of ANS is set 1.
# If not then ANS is set to 0. If the STRICT subcommand is used
# then BETWEEN checks for < and > rather than <= and >=.
#
RMINIMUM   X.1-X.N   L
RMAXIMUN   X.1-X.N   H
# Case where subcommand is not used
IF STRICT = 0
   LET ANS = ( L >= LOW )   AND   ( H <= HI )
# Case where subcommand is used
ELSE
   LET ANS = ( L > LOW )   AND   ( H < HI )
ENDIF
ENDMACRO
```

We can invoke BETWEEN in any of the following ways:

```
%BETWEEN   C1-C3   .25   .35   C10
%BETWEEN   C1-C3   C4    .35   C10
%BETWEEN   C1-C3   .25   C5    C10
%BETWEEN   C1-C3   C4    C5    C10
```

You may write a macro where a suffixed list of variables is declared as MFREE. But recall that all variables in a suffixed list must be of one type. Thus, in any one invocation of this macro, all the variables in the list must be of the same type. If you need to know what type of variable was passed in, use MTYPE, described in the section *Using Free Variables* on page 29-20.

More | If you need to find out the data type of a column or constant—whether it contains text, numeric, or date/time data—use the command DTYPE.

Finding the Variable Data Type

Use DTYPE if you need to find out the data type of a column or constant. You can find out if the column or constant contains text, numeric, or date/time data, or whether the column or constant contains no data at all. If the data are numeric, DTYPE can also tell you if the data are real numbers or integers.

DTYPE is often used with free variables (and the MFREE and MTYPE commands) in cases where the macro must be flexible enough to respond to a variety of possible inputs.

DTYPE is very useful when parts of your macro only work on some types of data. For example, you may have a subcommand of your local macro that lets the user specify a title for a graph; DTYPE can tell you if the user specified a text string or a number. Or, perhaps a part of your macro requires an integer; DTYPE could tell you if a variable was not an integer, allowing your macro to convert the real number to an integer. The syntax for DTYPE is as follows, where **Variablename** is the name of a constant or column, and **K** is the constant where you want the DTYPE code to be stored:

```
DTYPE of variablename is stored in K
```

The possible DTYPE codes are as follows:

DTYPE code	Means column or constant is
0	Text
1	Real number
2	Integer
3	Date/time
10	Empty

> **Example of a macro that uses DTYPE**

The macro TELLDATA is a variation of the TELLME macro listed under *Example of a macro that uses free variables* on page 29-21. TELLDATA tells a user the data type of the variable specified when the macro is invoked. Here is the complete code:

```
MACRO
TELLDATA X
MFREE X
MCONSTANT Vartype
DTYPE X Vartype
IF Vartype = 0
 NOTE Variable is text
ELSEIF Vartype = 1
  NOTE Variable is real number
ELSEIF Vartype = 2
  NOTE Variable is integer
ELSEIF Vartype = 3
 NOTE Variable is date/time
ELSEIF Vartype = 10
  NOTE Variable is empty
ENDIF
ENDMACRO
```

Say that you have a worksheet that contains the following variables:

```
C1     C2      C3      K1
 1   John    1.5     Hello
 2   Mary    2.5
 3   Sally   3.5
```

TELLDATA can be invoked in all of the following ways, and will produce the following output in the Session window:

Invoked like this	Produces this
%TELLDATA C1	Variable is integer
%TELLDATA "Hello"	Variable is text
%TELLDATA K1	Variable is text
%TELLDATA C2	Variable is text
%TELLDATA C3	Variable is real number

What Next?

Look in these chapters for more information on writing macros:

- Chapter 30, *Controlling Macro Flow*, describes techniques and commands you can use to control which commands are executed, and when.

- Chapter 31, *Managing Input and Output*, shows you how to make a macro interactive, label output, save data, and more.

- Chapter 32, *Handling Errors in Macros*, discusses how to interpret error messages, which MINITAB commands behave differently in macros, and tools you can use to track down and correct problems in macros.

- Chapter 33, *Using Execs*, discusses MINITAB's older macro functionality, called Execs.

30

Controlling Macro Flow

Control Statement Overview

Control statements can make your macro more flexible and powerful because they allow you to control the sequence in which commands in the macro are executed. They can perform some action given a condition using an IF statement. They can perform some action repeatedly using a DO-ENDDO LOOP statement. They can start other macros from within a macro using a CALL and RETURN statement. The following pages document these control statements, and more.

You can also nest control statements. For example, one control statement, such as an IF statement, can contain several other control statements, such as additional IF statements or a DO statement.

IF, ELSEIF, ELSE, ENDIF

```
IF      logical expression
  (a block of MINITAB and macro commands)

ELSEIF logical expression
  (a block of MINITAB commands and macro statements)

ELSE
  (a block of MINITAB commands and macro statements)

ENDIF
```

You can make your macro conditionally execute commands with the IF control statements—IF, ELSEIF, ELSE, and ENDIF. The IF control statements can evaluate a logical expression using comparison operators (such as > for "greater than" and = for "equals") and Boolean operators (such as AND, OR, and NOT). A logical expression is any expression from the LET command. The comparison and Boolean operators listed below are the features of LET that are most often used in IF statement.

=	or	EQ	equal to	&	or	AND
~=	or	NE	not equal to	|	or	OR
<	or	LT	less than	~	or	NOT
>	or	GT	greater than			
<=	or	LE	less than or equal to			
>=	or	GE	greater than or equal to			

In most cases the logical expression evaluates to a single number. If the number is 0 (false), the block of statements is skipped; if it is not 0 (true), the block is executed. If the logical expression evaluates to a column, then if all entries in the column are 0, the expression is considered false, otherwise it is considered true. You can use up to 50 ELSEIF statements within the IF-ENDIF block.

▷ Example of using IF in a macro

In the example below, the macro only executes the REGRESS command if there are more than three observations in the column Yield. If there are less than three or exactly three observations, the macro prints a message in the Session window using the NOTE command (described on page 28-8).

```
LET K1 = COUNT('Yield')
IF K1 < 3
NOTE Not enough observations
ELSEIF K1 = 3
NOTE Add one observation
ELSE
   REGRESS C5 2 C1 C2
ENDIF
```

DO, ENDDO

```
DO      K = list of numbers
   (a block of MINITAB commands and macro statements)
ENDDO
```

Allows you to loop through a block of commands. K is set equal to the first number in the list, then the block of commands is executed. When MINITAB reaches the ENDDO, K is set equal to the next number in the list and the block is executed again. This continues until all numbers in the list are used, or until you branch out of the DO-loop with a BREAK, GOTO, RETURN, or EXIT command.

The list of numbers can be an explicit list of any numbers or stored constants. A patterned list can be abbreviated using a colon and slash as in SET. For example, 1:10 is the list 1, 2, 3, ..., 10, and 1:1.8 /.2 is the list 1, 1.2, 1.4, 1.6, 1.8. Numbers can be increasing or decreasing order. The following DO-loop changes the values in rows 1 through 10 and row 50 of columns C1 and C2 to the missing value code:

```
DO  K1 = 1:10 50
   LET C1(K1) = '*'
   LET C2(K1) = '*'
ENDDO
```

Here is a local macro that calculates a moving average of length three. It shows how to loop through the values in a column.

```
MACRO
MOVAVE  X   Y
#
# Calculates the simple moving average of the data in X and
# stores the answer in Y.
#
MCONSTANT N   I
MCOLUMN    X   Y
LET N = COUNT(X)
LET Y(1) = '*'
LET Y(2) = '*'
DO I = 3 : N
   LET Y(I) = (X(I) + X(I-1) + X(I-2))/3
ENDDO
ENDMACRO
```

WHILE, ENDWHILE

```
WHILE      logical expression
   (a block of MINITAB commands and macro statements)
ENDWHILE
```

Repeats a block of commands as long as the logical expression is true. The logical expression follows the same rules as in the IF statement.

Suppose we want to find the root of the equation, $y = -1 + x + x^3$. We know this equation has just one real root and that it is between 0 and 1. The following global macro allows us to find, approximately, what the root is.

```
GMACRO
ROOT
#
# Finds the root of a specific polynomial. The result is
# within .01 of the exact answer.
# K90-K93 are used for scratch work
#
NAME  K90 = 'X'   K91 = 'Y'   K92 = 'Xlow'   K93 = 'Ylow'
LET 'X' = 0
LET 'Y' = -1
WHILE 'Y' < 0
   LET 'X' = 'X' + .01
   LET 'Y' = -1 + 'X' + 'X'**3
ENDWHILE
LET 'Xlow' = 'X' - .01
LET 'Ylow' = -1 + 'Xlow' + 'Xlow'**3
PRINT 'Xlow' 'Ylow'  'X' 'Y'
ENDMACRO
```

We first initialized the two variables, X and Y, to 0 and −1. Each time through the WHILE-loop, MINITAB first checks to see that Y is still less than zero. If it is, we increase X by .01 and calculate Y at this new value. Once the condition fails, that is, once Y is no longer less than zero, we exit the loop and go to the first statement after ENDWHILE. Then we print out the answer.

NEXT

NEXT

Transfers control from within a DO- or WHILE-loop back to the beginning of the block. For DO, the loop variable is then set to the next value in the list and the loop is executed again. Here is a simple example, using a global macro.

```
GMACRO
FIVES
#
# Takes the column named X and changes all entries
# that are greater than 5 to 5.
# Constants K90 and K91 are used for scratch work.
#
NAME K90 = 'N'  K91 = 'I'
LET 'N' = COUNT('X')
DO 'I' = 1 : 'N'
  IF  'X'('I') <= 5
    NEXT
  ELSE
    LET 'X'('I') = 5
  ENDIF
ENDDO
ENDMACRO
```

The DO-loop goes through all the values in X. If a value is less than or equal to 5, NEXT passes control to the top of the DO-loop and the value is left unchanged. If a value is greater than 5, the ELSEIF block is executed and that value is set to 5.

BREAK

BREAK

Transfers control from within a DO- or WHILE-loop to the command immediately following the end of the loop. Thus BREAK breaks out of the loop. Here is a simple example using a global macro.

```
GMACRO
NOMISS
#
# Takes data from the column named X. Finds the first missing
# observation. Then deletes all observations starting with the
# first missing to the end of the column.
# Constants K90 and K91 are used for scratch work
#
LET K90 = COUNT('X')
DO K91 = 1:K90
  IF  'X'(K91) = '*'
    BREAK
  ENDIF
ENDDO
DELETE  K91:K90 'X'
ENDMACRO
```

The program goes through the values of X until it finds a missing value. It then leaves the loop and goes to the statement following ENDDO—in this example, DELETE.

Note | This program does not handle the case when X has no missing values correctly. We will fix this when we discuss the command EXIT.

GOTO, MLABEL

```
GOTO    number
        (other MINITAB commands and macro statements)
MLABEL  number
```

Allows you to branch to any line in your macro. There can be several GOTO's in one program. A GOTO is matched to the MLABEL that has the same number. The number can be any integer from 1 to 8 digits long. It cannot be a variable.

Here is the program we used to illustrate BREAK above, but now coded with a GOTO.

```
LET K90 = COUNT('X')
DO K91 = 1 : K90
  IF  'X'(K91) = '*'
    GOTO 5
  ENDIF
ENDDO
MLABEL 5
DELETE K91:K90 'X'
```

Invoking Macros from Within Macros

You may have two or more macros in one file. Each macro in the file follows the usual structure (beginning with GMACRO or MACRO, ending with ENDMACRO, etc.), and each must have a unique template name. When you invoke a macro, MINITAB executes the first macro in the file. Subsequent macros in the file are subroutines that you can invoke using a CALL statement (see *CALL, RETURN* on page 30-8).

There are some restrictions on which type of macro another macro can call:

From within this type of macro	You can invoke…		
Global	Global		Exec
Local		Local	
Exec	Global	Local	Exec

You invoke a macro from within a macro in the same way you invoke a macro from the MINITAB prompt. On a line, put the symbol % followed by the name of the macro file, as in %TRIM. You can also include a path statement, as in %C:\MYWORK\TRIM. If it is a local macro, include all appropriate arguments and subcommands.

Because the macros you execute are stored in your worksheet area, the only limitation to the number of macros you can nest is the amount of space available in your worksheet. If you run out of room, see the macro statement SWAP (page 32-6) for a way to work around that problem.

The following example improves the global macro ANALYZE, described in Chapter 28, to handle the case when a data set is too small to analyze. The main file, stored as ANALYZE2.MAC, determines how many observations are in the data set. If there are fewer than 5, it invokes the macro file TOOSMALL.MAC. TOOSMALL prints out a message then prints the data set. If the data set has at least 5 observations, ANALYZE2 invokes the macro file OK.MAC. OK is the same as the original version, ANALYZE.

ANALYZE2.MAC

```
GMACRO
ANALYZE2
#
LET K90 = COUNT(C1)
IF K90 < 5
  %TOOSMALL
ELSE
 %OK
ENDIF
ENDMACRO
```

TOOSMALL.MAC

```
GMACRO
TOOSMALL
#
NOTE Data set has fewer than 5 observations.
NOTE No analysis will be done. Here are the data.
PRINT C1 - C3
ENDMACRO
```

OK.MAC

```
GMACRO
OK
#
NAME  C1 = 'Yield'  C2 = 'Chem1'  C3 = 'Chem2'  C5 = 'Ln.Yield'
PRINT C1-C3
DESCRIBE C1-C3
LET C5 = LOGE('Yield')
REGRESS C5 2 C2 C3
ENDMACRO
```

CALL, RETURN

```
CALL template
RETURN
```

You can include several macros in one file, just as a program often includes several subroutines. CALL and RETURN let you specify when to pass control to another macro and when to return to the main macro. You can include several global macros in one file, or several local macros in one file, but you cannot mix global and local macros together in one file.

When you invoke a macro, from interactive MINITAB or from another macro, the first macro in the file is executed first. Use the macro statements CALL and RETURN to invoke a different macro within the macro file.

Recall that the second line of a macro is the template, or the macro name. When one macro in a macro file calls another macro in that file, use the command CALL, followed by the name on that macro's template. If it is a local macro, include appropriate arguments and subcommands. Any macro in a macro file can CALL any other macro in the file, any number of times.

RETURN says to leave the current macro and go back to the calling macro, to the statement just after the CALL. RETURN is optional. If RETURN is not present in the macro that was called (the subroutine), then after it has executed, control is transferred back to the calling macro.

The following example is a variation on ANALYZE2.MAC (page 30-7) named ANALYZE3.MAC. This global macro file contains three macros:

```
GMACRO
ANALYZE3
#
NOTE Would you like all data printed?
YESNO K80
# If user types "yes" K80 = 1, if "no" K80 = 0
LET K90 = COUNT(C1)
IF K90 < 5
  CALL TOOSMALL
ELSE
  CALL OK
ENDIF
#
IF K80 = 1
NOTE Here are the data.
PRINT C1-C3
ENDIF
ENDMACRO
#
#
GMACRO
TOOSMALL
NOTE Data set has fewer than 5 observations.
NOTE No analysis will be done.
ENDMACRO
#
#
GMACRO
OK
NAME  C1 = 'Yield' C2 = 'Chem1'  C3 = 'Chem2' C5 = 'Ln.Yield'
DESCRIBE C1-C3
LET C5 = LOGE('Yield')
REGRESS C5 2 C2 C3
IF K80 = 1
  RETURN
ENDIF
NOTE Analysis done, but no data printed by request
ENDMACRO
```

In this example, ANALYZE3, we use the YESNO command (see page 31-5) to see if the user wants to print all the data. If the response is "Yes," YESNO sets K80 to 1; if the answer is "No," K80 is set to 0.

The OK subroutine checks the value of K80 with an IF statement. If K80 equals 1, the RETURN statement sends control back to the main macro. If K80 is anything else, the macro prints one more note.

When the ENDMACRO statement is encountered in either the TOOSMALL or OK subroutine, control is transferred back to the calling macro.

EXIT

EXIT

Stops the macro and transfers control back to interactive MINITAB.

Here is a modification of the macro NOMISS, that correctly handles the case when X contains no missing values.

```
LET K90 = COUNT('X')
DO K91 = 1:K90
  IF 'X'(K91) = '*'
    BREAK
  ENDIF
  IF K91 = K90
    NOTE Note: There are no missing observations in X.
    EXIT
  ENDIF
ENDDO
DELETE  K91:K90 'X'
```

PAUSE, RESUME

PAUSE
RESUME

When MINITAB encounters a PAUSE in a macro, control is shifted from the macro to the keyboard. You can then type any MINITAB command. When you want to return control to the macro, type RESUME (or just R). PAUSE can help you debug a macro you are developing. It can also allow you to get input from the macro user.

If you are in PAUSE mode from within a local macro, you have access to the local worksheet and only the local worksheet. You can also declare new local variables and use them. They will be stored at the end of the local worksheet.

When you are in PAUSE mode, you can type any MINITAB command. You cannot CALL other macros in the same file, invoke a macro from another macro file, or use control statements.

Using DOS Commands

Change and show directories

```
CD  [path]
DIR [path]
```

CD without a path displays your current directory. CD with a path changes from your current directory to the specified directory.

DIR lists the names of all the files in your current or the specified directory.

Here are some examples:

CD   displays your current directory

CD \SUE\SALES91   changes to the \SUE\SALES91 directory

DIR   lists the names of files in your current directory

Show a text file

```
TYPE "[path]filename.ext"
```

Lists the specified text (ASCII) file in the Session window.

The file must be a standard text file in order for this to work. Include the full file name and file extension within single quotation marks. If the file is not in your default directory, include the path within single quotation marks as well. For example, to list the contents of the macro file SALES.MAC on your screen, enter:

TYPE 'SALES.MAC'

31

Managing Input and Output

Managing Input and Output Overview

You can pass information through a macro using arguments, or you can pass information through macros by providing user interaction. Arguments can only be used in local macros and they are often not very user friendly. Instead, you can provide questions or messages that interact with the user of the macro. MINITAB provides several communication aids that are compatible with global macros and that provide user friendliness: the command NOTE, a special "TERMINAL" option on WRITE, READ, SET, and INSERT, the command YESNO, and the statement PAUSE.

You can also manipulate the macro output using several MINITAB commands. You can suppress your output using BRIEF. You can control graph output using command such as NOFRAME, GPRINT, GSAVE, GSCALE, GPAUSE, or NO BRUSH. You can also change or add an argument name or title.

Displaying Messages

To display a simple message, use the NOTE command. To display a message that can change depending on a variable's value, use the WRITE command with the special argument "TERMINAL."

Using NOTE

```
NOTE [comment]
```

Use NOTE to display messages to the user on the screen during execution of a macro. The text on a NOTE line, except for the first five spaces including the word NOTE and a space, is displayed.

For example, this line of code in the macro

```
NOTE This is a note
```

displays this in the Session window:

```
This is a note
```

To display a blank line, include a line containing only the word NOTE at the beginning.

Using WRITE

```
WRITE "TERMINAL" columnname
```

WRITE usually writes columns of data to a file. WRITE with the special file name TERMINAL can print the contents of columns in the Session window. WRITE "TERMINAL" is useful for displaying messages that can tell the user the result of an action. For example, the following macro, COUNTER, creates a sentence out of values in three columns.

```
GMACRO
COUNTER
NOECHO
LET C100 = "Column has"
LET C101 = COUNT(C1)
LET C102 = "observations."
WRITE 'TERMINAL' C100-C102
ENDMACRO
```

If you invoke this macro and C1 contains five values, the Session window will display

```
Column has  5  observations.
```

If you want to create a sentence from variables that are stored constants, you must copy the constants into a column with the COPY command, as in COPY K1 C100.

More | You can concatenate text columns with the CONCATENATE command (see session command Help). Convert numeric columns to text using the TEXT command. You can concatenate text constants in a macro using the KKCAT macro command (see *Commands for storing text in constants* on page 29-16).

Prompting a User for Information

READ, SET, and INSERT have a special feature that allows you to ask users questions and then use their answers in the macro. A macro will pause for user input if you use READ, SET, or INSERT with the subcommand FILE with the special file name TERMINAL. TERMINAL tells MINITAB to wait for input from the keyboard. READ, SET, and INSERT also have other subcommands—see Help.

Syntax

```
READ C...C
  FILE "TERMINAL"

                or

SET C
  FILE "TERMINAL"

                or

INSERT data [between K and K] of C...C
  FILE "TERMINAL"
```

Note | If you use READ, SET, or INSERT with the subcommand FILE "TERMINAL" while command language is turned off in the Session window (**Editor ➤ Disable Command Language**), an error message will be displayed and the macro will stop.

▷ Example of prompting a user with SET

```
GMACRO
ANALYZE4
#
NOTE How many observations do you have this month?
SET C90;
  FILE "TERMINAL";
  NOBS 1.
COPY C90 K90
IF K90 < 5
  NOTE Data set has fewer than 5 observations.
  NOTE No analysis will be done. Here are the data.
  PRINT C1-C3
ELSE
  LET C5 = LOGE(C1)
  REGRESS C5 2 C2 C3
ENDIF
ENDMACRO
```

When you type %ANALYZE4, MINITAB displays the note, "How many observations do you have this month?" and pauses, waiting for a user response. After the user types a number and presses Return, that number is entered into C90.

The subcommand NOBS tells MINITAB the number of values to expect from the user. If you omit NOBS, the user will have to type END to signal the end of data input before the macro will continue to execute. If you include NOBS, the macro will resume execution after the user has entered the expected number of observations (in our example, one number).

The macro continues executing, using the value for C90 supplied by the user. This is how it looks on the screen:

```
Executing from file: ANALYZE4.MAC
How many observations do you have this month?
```

```
DATA>   4
Data set has fewer than 5 observations.
No analysis will be done. Here are the data.

Data Display

ROW    C1   C2   C3
  1   44.0   5    8
  2   43.5   5    8
  3   46.0   5    8
  4   39.0   5   12
```

Since you can only use this feature to READ, SET, or INSERT data into columns, in our example we first put our constant into C90, then copied it into K90. The rest of the macro is the same as before.

Getting Yes or No Answers from a User

YESNO Prompts the user for a decision to execute or skip a block of commands. It reads a "Yes" or "No" response from the terminal and changes the value of its argument, K, accordingly. YESNO sets K = 1 when the user responds "Yes" and K = 0 when the user responds "No." YESNO takes only one argument, and it must be a stored constant.

Any response beginning with an upper or lower case Y is interpreted as a "Yes"; any response beginning with an upper or lower case N is interpreted as "No." With any other answer, the user receives the message "Please answer Yes or No" and is given another opportunity to enter an acceptable answer. If a valid response is not obtained after five tries, a "No" answer is assumed.

YESNO does not issue a prompt; it only reads a response. The macro writer must use the NOTE command to prompt the user for a response.

Here is a version of the macro ANALYZE4 (on page 31-4), using YESNO.

```
GMACRO
ANALYZE5
#
NOTE Do you have at least 5 observations this month?
YESNO K90
IF K90 = 0
NOTE Data set has fewer than 5 observations.
NOTE No analysis will be done. Here are the data.
  PRINT C1-C3
ELSE
  LET C5 = LOGE(C1)
```

```
    REGRESS C5 2 C2 C3
  ENDIF
  ENDMACRO
```

Note | If you use YESNO while command language is turned off in the Session window (with the menu command **Editor ➤ Disable Command Language**), an error message will be displayed and the macro will stop.

Using PAUSE and RESUME

```
PAUSE
RESUME
```

PAUSE transfers control from the macro to the keyboard. You could include NOTE lines in your macro with instructions to the user on what to do during PAUSE mode or a reminder to type RESUME to transfer control back to the macro. For more information, see *PAUSE, RESUME* on page 30-10.

Saving the Local Worksheet

Because of potential conflicts with the global worksheet, the commands SAVE, RETRIEVE, WSAVE, and WOPEN do not work in a local macro. Global worksheet variables that have been passed into the macro as arguments assume any new values given to them during the course of the macro execution. You can always save those variables after the macro executes. But you may also want to save local worksheet variables that are not passed as arguments.

To save local worksheet variables, use the WRITE command within your macro.

Syntax

```
WRITE ["filename"] C...C
```

WRITE stores the designated columns in a text file with the file name you specify and the default file extension DAT. WRITE has other subcommands—see Help for details.

▶ **Example of WRITE**

Suppose you have three column variables in the local worksheet named X, Y, and Z. The command

```
WRITE "MYWORK" X Y Z
```

saves those three columns in a text file named MYWORK.DAT.

WRITE only works with columns. If you want to save data in constants or matrices, you must copy constants and matrices into columns before using WRITE.

Labeling Output in Local Macros

There are two types of variables used in a local macro. Local variables are known only to the macro and used with control statements in the body of the macro. Arguments, the second type of variable, are passed in from the global worksheet and used to establish data unknowns. For more information on either variable type, see *Using Variables* on page 29-2. A printed macro variable label will appear differently depending on whether the variable is an argument or a local variable. The following table outlines the variable type descriptions and the associated labels:

Variable type	Description	Output displays
Local Variables	any internal variable used within the body of a macro, such as X1	X1
Arguments	Named column, constant, or matrix from within a global worksheet, such as Sales	Sales
	Unnamed column, constant, or matrix from within a global worksheet such as C1	C1

Suppressing Output

BRIEF 0	suppresses all command output
BRIEF	resumes normal output
BRIEF [integer]	suppresses partial output for some commands

BRIEF controls the amount of output commands produce in the Session window. BRIEF 0 suppresses all normal output from appearing in the Session window. BRIEF with no argument restores normal output from commands. For example, this code suppresses notes and restores them:

```
GMACRO
MYTEMPLATE
BRIEF 0
NOTE This text will not display in the Session window
BRIEF
NOTE This text will appear.
ENDMACRO
```

Most commands are affected by BRIEF only when the macro uses BRIEF 0 or BRIEF with no arguments. Some commands, however, can have their output partially limited by BRIEF followed by an integer, as in BRIEF 2. The affected commands are: ARIMA, BBDESIGN, CCDESIGN, CLUOBS, CLUVARS, DISCRIMINANT, FACTOR, FFDESIGN, GLM, KMEANS, MIXREG, REGRESS, RLINE, RSREG, SCDESIGN, and SLDESIGN. For details, see the session command Help topic for each command.

Note | WRITE "TERMINAL" is not affected by BRIEF 0. Messages created this way will always display. See *Using WRITE* on page 31-3.

Naming Arguments

In a local macro, you can use the NAME command to name arguments. For example, you could pass in an unnamed argument, such as C1, and assign it a name within your macro. Or, you could pass in a named argument, say a column named 'March,' and you could assign that column a new name in the macro. After the macro executes, that global worksheet variable will have the name assigned to it by the macro, and output will display the new name.

Limitations to NAME in a local macro

There are two limitations with using NAME in a local macro:

1 If a variable in a local macro was given a name with NAME, that name cannot be used in the code as an "alias" for the variable the way it can in a global macro in interactive MINITAB. For example,

```
NAME X 'Factor' Y 'Response'        will not work inside a local macro
REGRESS 'Response' 1 'Factor'
```

```
NAME X 'Factor' Y 'Response'        will work, and the output will be labeled
REGRESS Y 1 X                       'Response' and 'Factor'
```

2 The macro will give an error message if you assign a NAME in a macro that is the same as the name of any variable in the global worksheet. This could be a problem since you may not always know what names a user will have assigned to variables in the global worksheet.

▷ **Example of using NAME in a local macro**

Here is a macro named TEST that accepts three columns as arguments:

```
MACRO
TEST X1 X2 X3
#
MCOLUMN  X1 X2 X3 Y Z
#
SET Y
  1 2 3 4 5
END
LET Z = 2*Y
NAME X3 = 'Weight'
PRINT X1 X2 X3 Y Z
ENDMACRO
```

Then the macro is invoked on a data set in which C1 is named Height:

```
%TEST C1 C2 C3
```

The macro prints five columns: X1, X2, X3, Y, and Z.

- X1 is an argument with the global worksheet name Height, so it is labeled in the output as Height.

- X2 is an argument without a global worksheet name, so it is labeled with its column number, C2.

- X3 is an argument which was given the global worksheet name Weight in the macro, so it is labeled Weight. In addition, this name is passed back to the global worksheet as the name for C3.

- Y and Z are local variables without global worksheet names, so they are labeled Y and Z.

If an unnamed local variable is a suffixed variable (which can be as long as 17 characters), only the last eight characters are printed.

Note | You can also control the labeling of other macro output, such as titles that appear above the Session window and in the titles of Graph windows. See *Changing Titles of Output and Graphs* on page 31-10.

Changing Titles of Output and Graphs

```
MTITLE "title"

TITLE        (default)
NOTITLE
```

Use the MTITLE command to add a customized title in the Session window above the output produced by the macro. By default, TITLE creates a standard title which precedes the output whenever a command generates output in the Session window. Use NOTITLE to suppress titles.

```
WTITLE "title"
```

You can use WTITLE as a subcommand with LAYOUT and all high-resolution graphics. The title you specify becomes the *window* title of the resulting Graph window.

Commands that Affect Graph Output

All of the following commands affect graph output and are fully documented in Help—search on the command name to find the correct topic.

NOFRAME

NOFRAME with no arguments suppresses all graph frame elements: axis lines and labels, tick lines and labels, references lines, and grid lines. However, if you use a frame element subcommand (such as AXIS), the frame element you specified will be created (and all other frame elements will remain suppressed).

NOFRAME 1 suppresses all frame elements, even those specifically requested in other subcommand lines. This is the default generated by the graph dialog boxes.

GPRINT

GPRINT with no arguments prints the newest Graph window, if there is one. If there are no Graph windows, GPRINT does nothing (no error message, no error flag).

GSAVE

GSAVE saves one or more graphs from a command in a MINITAB Graphics Format (MGF) file. The first graph file for the command can be named using an argument. Each consecutive graph for the command is automatically given the same name with a three digit number attached at the end of the filename. You may specify the filename as either the name of the file in double quotes, or as a stored text constant.

GPAUSE

GPAUSE controls how long MINITAB pauses between graphs when multiple graphs are generated. Tip: In a macro that generates multiple graphs, MINITAB will interrupt the macro to ask you to save the 15th graph. Use GPAUSE 1 to suppress prompt; overflow graphs will be discarded.

GSCALE

GSCALE generates tick and scaling information about the graph MINITAB would produce given a column of data. You specify the minimum and maximum values in the column, and GSCALE stores in constants information like the number of ticks, the space between ticks, and the minimum and maximum scale. GSALE is useful primarily when you are writing a macro that produces graphs, and you need to know information before you produce the graphs to ensure that the scaling on the graphs will look right. For example, you might want to generate two or more graphs that use the same scale, but you want some control over what that scaling will be. You can use the data stored by GSCALE to specify scaling options in subsequent graph commands.

NOBRUSH

NOBRUSH can be used as a subcommand of any graphics command to disable brushing on the resulting graph. Why disable brushing? Brushing can only highlight rows of data in the global worksheet. But graphs created in local macros are sometimes based on data in the local worksheet that have no relationship to corresponding rows of data in the global worksheet.

32

Handling Errors
in Macros

Interpreting Error Messages

MINITAB has an internal program called a macro processor that handles all the work that is specific to macros. The macro processor monitors which macro file you are currently using and what macros are in the file, and it processes all macro statements.

Error messages can be sent from the macro processor to the MINITAB program. When the macro processor encounters a MINITAB command, the processor checks the command briefly and then gives the command to the MINITAB program to fully check and execute. Knowing where a message came from can help you troubleshoot:

| ** ERROR ** | (two asterisks) | means an error was found by the macro processor |
| * ERROR * | (one asterisk) | means an error was found by regular MINITAB |

Controlling How Macros Respond to Errors

Stopping or continuing on errors

```
PLUG
NOPLUG        (default)
```

There are two modes for responding to errors that the macro processor finds, PLUG and NOPLUG. You can use PLUG or NOPLUG before you invoke a macro or anywhere within the body of a macro.

- In the NOPLUG mode, the macro processor stops when it encounters an error.

- If you use PLUG, then the macro processor "plugs away" the best it can even when an error is encountered. In general, the macro routines that have errors will terminate but execute routines that are okay. PLUG can produce strange results, but at times PLUG can help you debug your program.

Resetting the environment

> **MRESET**

Several MINITAB commands can change default environment settings. These include BRIEF, which controls the amount of output produced in the Session window, and OH and OW, which control output height and width in the Session window. Other environment commands are IW, CONSTANT, and NOCONSTANT. See Help for details on all of these commands.

Use MRESET as the first line in the macro after the template to ensure that MINITAB restores environment settings to their pre-macro conditions after the macro is finished. This occurs whether or not the macro executes completely.

Interrupting a Macro

To interrupt a macro while it is running, press Ctrl + Break. The macro will finish whatever command is executing and then stop, returning you to normal interactive MINITAB.

Getting Local Worksheet Information

> **INFO**

Within a global macro, INFO gives the same output as it does in interactive MINITAB; it displays a summary of the global worksheet. Within a local macro, INFO gives information about the variables in the local worksheet in the order in which they are stored. For debugging purposes, use INFO to check that your local worksheet contains the variables that you think it should.

The INFO output in the example below shows that the local worksheet has three declared constants: Min, Max, and Range. They do not have labels (column, matrix, or constant numbers from the global worksheet, such as C2 or K5), suffix values, or a numeric value assigned to them at this point. The local worksheet also has a column which is an argument, its local worksheet name is X.* where * ranges from 1 to 5, its label is C1, and it has 10 rows. Last, the local worksheet contains a matrix named design which is currently empty.

▷ **Example of INFO output within a local macro**

Session
window
output

Information on the Local Worksheet

```
    CONSTANT Declaration
                              suffix range constant
    type      name    label   from   to    no.    value
    LOCAL     Min              -      -     1      -
    LOCAL     Max              -      -     2      -
    LOCAL     Range            -      -     3      -
        COLUMN Declaration
                              suffix range column
    type      name    label   from   to    no.    length
    ARGUMENT  X.*     C1       1      5     1      10
        MATRIX Declaration
                              suffix range matrix
    type      name    label   from   to    no.    rows cols
    LOCAL     Design           -      -     1        0    0
```

Debugging Tools

"Debugging" is the art of finding problems—"bugs"—in a computer program. You can use several techniques and commands to display information about the macro. You can also pause the macro so you can investigate problem areas.

Displaying macro commands

"Echoing" is when the commands in the body of a macro display in the Session window as they are run. ECHO and NOECHO turn echoing on and off.

ECHO
NOECHO   (default)

By default, MINITAB is set to NOECHO. In this mode, no MINITAB commands or macro statements are displayed in the Session window—only the output of MINITAB commands is shown. However, when you are first developing a macro, it is often helpful to see the commands so you can find errors more easily. Use ECHO to display the commands.

You can type ECHO and NOECHO in the session window before you invoke a macro or place them anywhere within the body of a macro. You can use ECHO and NOECHO several times in a macro to turn echo display on and off.

In ECHO mode, only commands in the body of the macro (that is, MINITAB commands, macro statements, and invocations of macros in other files) are echoed. The template and declarations (declarations are used in local macros) are not. Text after a # is not echoed.

Text after a NOTE command is always displayed, in both ECHO and NOECHO mode—see *Managing Input and Output Overview* on page 31-2.

Displaying processing status

```
DEBUG
NODEBUG        (default)
```

Use DEBUG to display information on how the macro processor is proceeding. The default is NODEBUG. In this mode no information is displayed.

You can type DEBUG or NODEBUG in the Session window before you invoke a macro or place them anywhere within the body of a macro.

Pausing in problem areas

```
PAUSE
RESUME
```

For debugging purposes, you can put PAUSE statements in various parts of your macro. When the macro pauses, you can type any MINITAB command, such as INFO to see if you have the right variables, PRINT to display various quantities to see if they are correct, and so on. Type RESUME (or just R) to return control back to the macro.

If you are in PAUSE mode from within a local macro, you have access to the local worksheet and only the local worksheet. You can declare new local variables while in PAUSE mode and use them. They will be stored at the end of the local worksheet.

While you are in PAUSE mode, you cannot CALL other macros in the same file, invoke macros in another file, or use control statements.

Displaying the macro file

```
TYPE "filename"
```

Sometimes when you are debugging a macro, it is helpful to see it on the screen. You can use TYPE to display a macro file on your screen. For example, to view a macro file named MEDIAN.MAC, enter:

```
TYPE "MEDIAN.MAC"
```

Managing Very Large Macros

```
SWAP
NOSWAP        (default)
```

Because the lines of code in your macro are stored in the MINITAB worksheet, you might run out of worksheet space and get an error message. In this event, the macro statements SWAP and NOSWAP can help.

NOSWAP, by default, stores the lines of code from your macro, and all of the nested macros, in the worksheet at the same time.

SWAP, stores only one macro file in the worksheet at a time. Macro files are swapped in and out as needed. If your entire macro and all its submacros are in one file, SWAP will not help you. But if your macro invokes macros in other files, SWAP can make a big difference. You can rewrite a large macro as several submacros and put the submacros in different files to take advantage of SWAP. Macros will run slower when SWAP is turned on and you are frequently switching between macro files.

Type SWAP in the Session window before you invoke your macro. It is a switch and will stay on until you use NOSWAP.

Commands that Work Differently for Macros

Commands that work differently in all %macros

- READ, SET, and INSERT:
  - If your macro includes data after these commands, you must use the command END on the next line following the data.
  - If you use the FORMAT subcommand with these commands, the END command must be at the beginning of the next line following the data. If you indent the END command at all, MINITAB will not recognize it and you will get an error message.
  - If you use READ, SET, or INSERT to input data from a file, you must specify the file name on the FILE subcommand. You cannot specify the file name on the main command as you can in interactive MINITAB.
  - **In local macros:** If you see the error "Missing END for READ, SET, or INSERT," it may be because you have named a local variable with the same name as a MINITAB command, and entered it after SET or INSERT.

- Commands that change output settings—OW, IW, OH, BRIEF, CONSTANT, and NOCONSTANT. If you assign a setting with any of these commands, that setting stays in effect until you change it, restart MINITAB, or use MRESET (see page 32-3).

Commands that work differently in local macros

- LET. You cannot use a MINITAB function or column statistic as a variable name in a LET command. Thus

  ```
  LET Mean = X1 + X2 + X3
  ```

  is illegal because there is a MINITAB function called MEAN. In general, it is better not to use MINITAB command names as variable names in a macro.

- ERASE. Erases local worksheet variables, but it does not erase the declaration of a variable. That is, you cannot declare the same variable twice in one macro.

- EXECUTE. You cannot invoke EXECUTE from within a local macro. You can, however, invoke a local macro from within an Exec macro.

- INFO. In a local macro, INFO displays information on the local worksheet. See INFO on page *Getting Local Worksheet Information* on page 32-3.

- SAVE and RETRIEVE. You cannot use either of these commands in a local macro. To save data in the local worksheet, use the command WRITE. See *Saving the Local Worksheet* on page 31-6 for more information.

33

Using Execs

What Is an Exec?

Execs are stored commands that you will use over and over, so you do not have to retype them each time. You can even write an interactive Exec, which pauses during execution, prompts the user for information, then continues with execution. Execs are useful for many things:

- repeating a block of commands many times—useful for simulations

- looping through columns of the worksheet, doing the same analysis on each block of columns

- looping through rows of the worksheet, doing the same analysis on each block of rows

- performing complex operations not provided as stand-alone commands

How Execs are different from global and local macros

Earlier releases of MINITAB supported only Execs. MINITAB now has a more robust programming language that allows you to create global and local macros, sometimes grouped under the term *%macros*. %Macros are more powerful and flexible than Execs. Here are some of the other differences:

Type	Have a default file extension of...	Invoked by...	Documented in...
Exec	MTB	Typing the command EXECUTE or by choosing **Files ➤ Other Files ➤ Run an Exec**	This chapter
%Macro	MAC	Entering the symbol % followed by the macro file name: for example, %SALES invokes the macro SALES.MAC	Chapters 28–32

If you have Execs that were written using previous releases of MINITAB, you may continue to use them with no change—unless, of course, the Execs use obsolete commands (see the note below). If you are writing a new macro, we recommend you write it as a %macro, because we may phase out Execs in a future release of MINITAB and because the new macros provide much greater power and flexibility than do Execs.

If you would like to convert your Execs to global or local macros, it is very easy to do; see *Converting Execs to %Macros* on page 33-3.

Note | MINITAB no longer supports the old high-resolution graph commands such as GPLOT and GHISTOGRAM. If your macros include these commands, you need to delete them or replace them with the new versions of those commands (for example, PLOT and HISTOGRAM) in order for your macros to work.

Converting Execs to %Macros

▶ **To convert your Exec to a global macro**

1 Add three lines to your Exec file: GMACRO as the first line, ENDMACRO as the last line, and the template (the macro name) as the second line of the file. See *Creating a Global Macro* on page 28-6 for details.

2 Check for MINITAB commands that work differently in %macros (below).

3 Save the macro as a text file, with the extension MAC.

Once you have converted your Exec to a global macro, you can incorporate any of the features documented in the chapters for global macros such as DO-loops and IF statements. You can also include several global macros within one global macro file.

Converting your Exec to a local macro

Local macros do not support the CK capability, which is a specialized looping feature exclusive to Execs (for information that capability, see *Using Conditional Execution and Nesting* on page 33-7). If your Exec uses the CK syntax, replace the syntax with the appropriate control statement from Chapter 30.

Commands that work differently in %macros

■ Execs allow a repeat factor, such as "3" in the command EXECUTE "MYMACRO" 3. Global macros do not allow a repeat factor because they allow control statements such as DO-loops and WHILE statements which work much more efficiently. If your Exec requires such a repeat factor, you will need to incorporate that operation within the body of the global macro.

■ In earlier releases of MINITAB, the default was ECHO. Now the default is NOECHO, which means that commands are not normally displayed while the macro executes. If your Exec contains NOECHO commands, there is no harm in leaving them there, but they may not be necessary anymore.

■ READ, SET, and INSERT commands should follow these conventions:
  – If the command reads data from a file, you must modify the command so that the file name is listed with a FILE subcommand, rather than being listed on the main command line.
  – If the command is followed by data, you must include the statement END at the end of the data, on its own line.
  – If the command is followed by a FORMAT subcommand followed by data, the END statement must begin at the beginning of the line. If END is indented at all, MINITAB will not recognize it and you will get an error message.

How to Create an Exec

There are two ways to create Execs:

1 With a text editor or word processor. If you use an editor, store the file in a text format. If you use a word processor, make sure you save the file as a text file—not the native format of the word processor. For example, if you are using Microsoft Word, do not save as a Word file, but choose **File ➤ Save As** and select a file type of Text only. Save the file with the extension MTB; that way, when you use the EXECUTE command, you will not have to type the extension because MINITAB will assume the file has the default extension of MTB.

2 With the command JOURNAL, described in Help. JOURNAL stores a copy of all commands used in a MINITAB session in a file with the extension MTJ. Note that when you EXECUTE the file, you must use the extension MTJ.

Simple Example of an Exec

Each month, a laboratory sends you data on three chemical measurements: Yield, Chem1, and Chem2. You always do the same analysis: descriptive statistics, plots of Yield versus the two other measures, a regression, and a residual plot. Suppose you use your computer's editor to create the following file called ANALYSIS.MTB:

```
NAME C1='Yield' C2='Chem1' C3='Chem2'
DESCRIBE C1-C3
PLOT C1*C2
PLOT C1*C3
REGRESS C1 2 C2 C3 C10 C11
NAME C10 = 'Resids' C11 = 'Fits'
PLOT C10 C11
```

Then, if you put the data for January in the file JAN.MTW, you can perform your analysis by doing the following:

1 Choose **File ➤ Open Worksheet** and select JAN.MTW.

2 Choose **File ➤ Other Files ➤ Run an Exec**. Click **Select File**.

3 Select ANALYSIS.MTB. Click **Open**.

Running an Exec

File ➤ Other Files ➤ Run an Exec

```
EXECUTE ["filename"] [K times]
```

Executes commands that have been stored in a file. These command files are called Execs.

The default file extension for Execs is MTB. When using EXECUTE, you do not need to type the file extension if it is MTB. The default file name is MINITAB.MTB—if you do not specify a file name with EXECUTE, MINITAB looks for the file MINITAB.MTB and runs the file if it exists.

The optional argument K lets you specify how many times to run the Exec. K can be any integer. The default value is one, which means that the macro will be executed one time. If $K > 1$, the macro is executed K times. If $K \leq 0$, the macro is not executed.

To interrupt the execution of an Exec, press [Ctrl]+[Break]. MINITAB will finish executing the command in process before it stops the macro.

Creating Loops

Looping through commands

Suppose you want to train your eye to judge normal probability plots. So you decide to generate 20 plots for data from a normal distribution. First store the following commands in a file called NPLOT.MTB:

```
RANDOM 50 C1
NSCORES C1 C2
NAME C1='Data' C2='Nscores'
PLOT C1*C2
```

To execute this file 20 times, to get 20 different normal probability plots, type

```
EXECUTE "NPLOT" 20
```

You can also loop through rows of data. Suppose we have a full year of the laboratory data from our first example, one month stacked on top of another, in a file called LAB.DAT. There are now four variables, Yield, Chem1, Chem2, and Month. To do the same analysis as before, separately for each month, we store the following commands in the file YEAR.MTB:

```
NAME C11='Yield' C12='Chem1' C13='Chem2' C20='Resids' C21='Fits'
```

```
COPY C1-C3 C11-C13;
  USE C4 = K1.
PRINT K1
DESCRIBE C11-C13
PLOT C11*C12
PLOT C11*C13
REGRESS C11 2 C12 C13 C20 C21
PLOT C20*C21
ADD K1 1 K1
```

Then, to analyze the file LAB, we type

```
LET K1 = 1
READ "LAB" C1-C4
EXECUTE "YEAR" 12
```

Looping through columns and matrices

A special feature, sometimes called the CK capability, allows you to loop through columns of the worksheet. Suppose you have a file, MYDATA.DAT, containing 21 variables and you want to plot the last variable versus each of the first twenty variables. That's twenty separate plots. First store the following commands in a file called PLOTS.MTB:

```
PLOT C21*CK1
ADD K1 1 K1
```

Then type

```
READ "MYDATA" C1-C21
LET K1 = 1
EXECUTE "PLOTS" 20
```

The first time through the loop, K1 = 1. This value is substituted for the K1 in the PLOT command, giving PLOT C21*C1. The next time through the loop, K1 = 2, giving PLOT C21*C2, and so on.

Matrices also have this capability, using MK1. Stored constants do not.

The next example shows how to accumulate column statistics in one column. Suppose you have data in C1 through C30 and you want to compute the mean of each column and store those means in C40. Store the following commands in the file MEAN.MTB:

```
LET C40(K1) = MEAN (CK1)
ADD K1 1 K1
```

Then type

```
LET K1 = 1
EXECUTE "MEAN" 30
```

The first time through the loop K1 = 1, so row 1 of C40 will equal the mean of C1. The next time through the loop K1 = 2, so row 2 of C40 will equal the mean of C2, and so on.

Note | The CK capability works in global macros, documented in Chapter 28, but not in local macros, documented in Chapter 29. In global and local macros, the macro statements such as DO and WHILE, documented in Chapter 30, are more powerful than the CK capability.

Using Conditional Execution and Nesting

If the argument K on EXECUTE is zero or negative, the Exec is not executed. This feature allows you to do conditional execution. As an example, we will modify the Exec MEAN.MTB so that it accumulates means for just those columns that have more than 9 observations. We need two files. MEAN10.MTB contains:

```
LET K3 = (COUNT(CK1) > 9)
EXECUTE "OVER9" K3
ADD K1 1 K1
```

and OVER9.MTB contains

```
LET C40(K2) = MEAN(CK1)
ADD K2 1 K2
```

To use this macro, we type

```
LET K1 = 1
LET K2 = 1
EXECUTE "MEAN10" 30
```

First, notice that we have nested two Execs, that is, MEAN10 calls (or executes) OVER9. Nesting helps you write fairly sophisticated Execs. You can nest up to five deep on most computers.

To see how this macro works, we will look at the first three columns. Suppose C1 has 23 observations, C2 has 7, and C3 has 35. When we first execute MEAN10, K1 = K2 = 1. Then K3 = 1 since COUNT (C1) > 9. Since K3 = 1, OVER9 is executed once, MEAN (C1) is stored in row 1 of C40, and K2 = 2.

For the second time through the loop, K2 = 2 and K1 = 2. This time K3 = 0 since COUNT (C2) < 9, and OVER9 is not executed. For the third time through the loop, K1 = 3 and K2 = 2. Then K3 = 1 since COUNT (C3) > 9, OVER9 is executed, and MEAN (C3) is stored in row 2 of C40.

Handling a Variable Number of Arguments

Sometimes you do not know how many columns of data will be used in each analysis; one time you may need the exec to operate on 10 columns, and the next time on 12 columns. The CK capability, described on page 33-6, also allows you to write an exec that can operate on a variable number of columns.

For example, suppose each month a researcher collects data from tomato plants. Some months she has 20 plants, other months just 5. The data for one month consist of one variable for each plant. First she creates the following Exec, called PLANTS.MTB:

```
HISTOGRAM C1-CK50
DESCRIBE C1-CK50
ADD K50 50 K51
COPY C1-CK50 C51-CK51
   (etc.)
```

Then, if she has data on 12 plants, she types

```
READ C1-C12
   (data)
END
LET K50 = 12
EXECUTE "PLANTS"
```

Making Execs Interactive

Pausing for input

It is possible to write an Exec which will execute, pause for user input, and then continue executing. This is accomplished by using the special file name TERMINAL with the READ, SET, and INSERT commands.

Here is an example. We have two Execs. The first, PLANTS.MTB, is the same as before. The second, TOMATO.MTB, contains

```
NOTE How many tomato plants do you have this month?
SET C50;
   FILE "TERMINAL";
   NOBS = 1.
COPY C50 K50
EXEC "PLANTS"
```

When you type EXECUTE "TOMATO", the note "How many tomato plants do you have this month?" is printed. The terminal then waits for you to respond. You type a number and press [Enter]. The subcommand NOBS = 1 tells SET to expect just one number. This means the user of the macro does not have to type the word END to signal the end of typing data to SET. The macro TOMATO is then executed with the correct number of plants. (The YESNO command, described on page 33-9, also takes input from the keyboard.)

Note | If you use READ, SET, or INSERT with the subcommand FILE "TERMINAL" while command language is turned off in the Session window (with the menu command **Editor ➤ Disable Command Language**), an error message will be displayed and the Exec will stop.

The command NOECHO suppresses the echo printing of commands, and ECHO turns it back on. These are also described later in this chapter.

Getting yes or no answers from a user

> **YESNO K**

Prompts the user for a decision to execute or skip a block of commands.

YESNO reads a YES or NO response from the terminal and changes the value of its argument, K, accordingly. YESNO sets K = 1 when the user responds YES, and K = 0 when the user responds NO. YESNO takes only one argument and it must be a stored constant.

Any response beginning with an upper or lower case Y is interpreted as a YES; any beginning with an upper or lower case N is interpreted as NO. All other responses are invalid. The user receives the message "Please answer Yes or No" and is given another opportunity to enter an acceptable answer. If a valid response is not obtained after five tries, a NO answer is assumed.

YESNO does not issue a prompt; it only reads a response. The Exec writer must use the NOTE command to prompt the user for a response.

Note | If you use YESNO while command language is turned off in the Session window (with the menu command **Editor ➤ Disable Command Language**), an error message will be displayed and the Exec will stop.

The SET command also accepts a response from the user of an Exec. This is described under *Making Execs Interactive* on page 33-8.

▷ Example of YESNO

This example involves one main Exec, TREE, and four Execs that are called by the main one. SubExec1 contains just one line, DOTPLOT 'Diameter'. SubExec2 contains just one line, DOTPLOT 'Height'. And SubExec3 contains just one line, DOTPLOT 'Volume'. This example shows an example of running TREE.

```
# Reads in tree data and prompts the user for dotplots
RETRIEVE "TREES"
#
NOTE We will look at data on 31 black cherry trees.
NOTE There are three variables: diameter, height, and volume.
NOTE
NOTE Here are descriptive statistics on the three variables.
DESCRIBE C1-C3
NOTE Would you like to see a dotplot of diameter?
YESNO K1
EXECUTE "SubExec1" K1
NOTE
NOTE Would you like to see a dotplot of height?
YESNO K2
EXECUTE "SubExec2" K2
NOTE
NOTE Would you like to see a dotplot of volume?
YESNO K3
EXECUTE "SubExec3" K3
```

The example shows output that would result if the user invoked the Exec, then answered "No" to the first two requests and "Yes" to the last request.

1 Choose **File ➤ Other Files ➤ Run an Exec**.

2 Click **Select File**.

3 Type *TREE* in **File Name**. Click **OK**.

Session window output

```
We will look at data on 31 black cherry trees.
There are three variables: diameter, height, and volume.

Here are descriptive statistics on the three variables.
```

Descriptive Statistics

Variable	N	Mean	Median	TrMean	StDev	SEMean
Diameter	31	13.248	12.900	13.156	3.138	0.564
Height	31	76.00	76.00	76.15	6.37	1.14
Volume	31	30.17	24.20	28.87	16.44	2.95

Variable	Min	Max	Q1	Q3
Diameter	8.300	20.600	11.000	16.000
Height	63.00	87.00	72.00	80.00
Volume	10.20	77.00	19.10	38.30

```
Would you like to see a dotplot of diameter?
NO
Would you like to see a dotplot of height?
NO
Would you like to see a dotplot of volume?
YES
Executing from file: SUBEXEC3.MTB
```

Character Dotplot

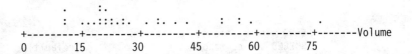

```
               .      :.
            :  ...:::.:.  . :. . .      :  :.           .
          +---------+---------+---------+---------+---------+-------Volume
          0        15        30        45        60        75
```

Using STARTUP Macros and Execs

STARTUP.MAC and STARTUP.MTB are special macro files you can create, either of which is automatically executed every time you start or restart MINITAB. They are handy tools for users who wish to avoid typing the same commands every time they start a MINITAB session.

Users of earlier versions of MINITAB may have an Exec file named STARTUP.MTB. If you are going to write a new startup macro, we suggest writing it as STARTUP.MAC. STARTUP.MAC can be a global or local macro. See chapters 28–32 for information on global and local macros.

When you start or restart MINITAB, MINITAB looks for macro files in the order shown below, and executes the first one it finds, if one exists.

In your current directory	STARTUP.MAC STARTUP.MTB
In the \MACROS subdirectory of the main MINITAB directory	STARTUP.MAC STARTUP.MTB

Create a STARTUP.MAC or STARTUP.MTB file as you would any other macro or Exec, with a text editor or word processor. The file must be called STARTUP.MAC or STARTUP.MTB.

Possible applications of the startup file include:

- setting up an OUTFILE or JOURNAL
- setting switches (BRIEF, OH, OW)
- setting up graphics options (GPRO, GSTD)
- automatically RETRIEVE a saved worksheet
- sending users messages via the NOTE command

Displaying Commands in the Session Window

```
ECHO    the commands that follow
NOECHO  the commands that follow           (default)
```

Controls whether or not commands in an Exec are displayed in the Session window. By default, NOECHO is in effect.

When you EXECUTE a file, the commands are not printed (echoed) on the output. Only output and the comments on NOTE commands (see NOTE in Chapter 31) will be printed. Comments after the # symbol will not be printed. When you want to turn on echo printing of commands use ECHO.

You can type ECHO and NOECHO in the session window before you invoke a macro or place them anywhere within the body of a macro. You can use ECHO and NOECHO several times in a macro to turn echo display on and off.

INDEX

Symbols

Numerics

A

CALL macro command 30-8

calling macros from other macros 30-8

canceling
    a command 27-7
    Execs 33-5
    macros 32-3

case sensitivity in session commands 27-7

Cauchy distribution to generate random data 9-6

CD command in macros 30-11

cdf (cumulative distribution function) 9-8

ceiling 7-7

cells
    active 1-7
    clearing 2-15
    cutting 2-15
    deleting 2-15
    editing 2-6
    erasing 2-15
    inserting 2-17
    restoring 2-6

centering data 7-15

change directory (CD command) 30-11

changing
    column display 2-20
    data types 6-42
    DDE links 10-5
    scales in graphs 18-26

character graphs 13-2, 13-6

characteristic values 8-8

charts 14-18
    accumulate y across x 14-26
    clustering bars 14-24
    creating 14-18, 14-20
    cumulative frequency scale 14-26
    data 14-18, 14-19
    functions for y-axis variables 14-22
    grouping within categories by clustering and stacking 14-24
    of means 14-23
    options 14-20

    ordering category groups by y-values 14-25
    setting y-axis at zero 14-20
    totalling y to 100% within each x category 14-27
    transposing x and y 14-28

Chisquare distribution to generate random data 9-5

circle/ellipse tool 24-4

circles, resizing 24-11

circular DDE links 10-16

CK capability 33-6, 33-8

clearing cells 2-15

client DDE links, creating 10-3

client, DDE 10-2

Clipboard replication 5-7

Clipboard settings 2-11

clipping
    objects 24-13
    outside the data region 19-19
    outside the figure region 19-13
    outside the legend region 19-24

closing
    Graph windows 13-9, 26-2
    projects 3-5
    worksheets 3-9

clustering bars in charts 14-24

coding data 6-38

cold link, in DDE 10-11

color Attribute tool 24-5

color(s)
    3D graphs 20-13
    changing via graph editing 24-5
    defining custom for graphs 24-19
    for annotation elements 17-18
    for data display elements 23-12, 23-17
    for graph frame elements 18-32
    Session window prompt 11-8
    setting for brushing 25-5

column display 2-20

column functions 7-8

column statistics 7-11
    example 7-14
    how to calculate 7-13

columns 1-4
    automatic widening 2-21
    changing display 2-20
    changing format 2-20
    changing type 6-4, 6-42
    changing widths 2-18, 2-20
    checking value order 6-21
    combining text 6-3, 6-37
    compressing display of 2-22
    concatenating 6-37
    copying 2-13
    copying using Manip command 2-13
    date/time 1-7
    deleting 2-15, 2-16
    descriptions of 2-19
    displaying and hiding empty 2-22
    fixed number of decimals 2-24
    fixed width 2-21
    hiding 2-22
    inserting 2-17
    moving 2-18
    name row of 1-7
    naming 2-18
    number row of 1-7
    ranking within 6-3
    sorting 6-3
    stacking 6-3, 6-28
    stacking blocks 6-30
    switching to rows 6-24
    text 1-7
    transposing 6-24
    unstacking 6-3, 6-33
    value ordering text 6-3, 6-19

Columns folder 1-5

combination plots 14-8

command files 33-5

Command Line Editor, using 27-8

commands
    see session commands

Comment font in Session window 11-6

comment symbol (#) with session commands 27-8

comments
    in column descriptions 2-19
    in project descriptions 3-4
    in worksheet descriptions 3-11
comments in macros
    adding 28-8
    comment symbol (#) 28-8
    that display in the Session
      window 28-8
communicating with the user of a
  macro 31-2
comparison operations 7-2
compressing column display 2-22
conditional execution of Execs
  33-7, 33-9
conditions, setting in ODBC 4-6
connection lines 13-3
    creating stepped 15-22
    editing 15-8
    setting connection order 15-23
CONSTANT command in macros
  32-3, 32-7
constants 1-4, 7-12
    deleting 2-16
    displaying 3-21
    KKCAT 29-16
    KKNAME 29-16
    KKSET 29-16
    naming 1-4
    text 29-15
Constants folder 1-5
continuation symbol (&)
    in macros 28-5
    with session commands 27-8
contour plots 14-42, 14-49
    attribute codes 14-53
    changing attributes of
      connection lines and areas
      14-55
    changing mesh 14-52
    colors 14-54
    controlling number and
      position of contour levels
      14-50
    creating 14-50
    data 14-49
    fill types 14-54
    graphics options 14-55

    line types 14-54
    options 14-50
    transposing x and y 14-51
    using connection lines and
      areas with 14-53
    with colored areas 14-55
control statements in macros 30-1
    variables 29-3
controlling other applications with
  DDE 10-14
conversion tables 6-40
converting database data 4-3
coordinate systems for graphs 19-2,
  19-3
coordinates
    data units 19-4
    figure units 19-4
    page units 19-3
copying
    blocks of Session window text
      11-3
    DDE links 10-3
    Graph windows to the
      Clipboard 13-9
    graphs 26-3
    matrices 8-6
    output from the Session
      window into your worksheet
      11-3
    with Graph windows 24-9
copying and pasting
    data 2-9
    graphs 12-7
    session commands 27-8
    Session window output 12-7
core graphs 13-3, 14-1
    annotating 14-4, 17-1
    controlling regions 19-1
    customizing the graph frame
      18-1
    data display elements 14-3
    displaying data 15-1
    editing area attributes 15-12
    editing bar attributes 15-14
    editing connection lines 15-8
    editing projection lines 15-10
    groups 16-1

    groups and multiple graphs
      14-4
    multi-graph 13-3
    multiple graphs 16-1
    overview 14-2
    scatter plot 13-3
    shared graphics options 14-2
    symbol types 15-6
correcting data 2-6
correlation coefficient
    Pearson 23-18
cosine 7-12
count function for chart y-axis
  14-22
creating
    a matrix 8-2
    a simple macro 28-6, 28-9
      see global macros
    DDE links 10-3
    Execs 33-4
    global macros 28-6, 28-9
    macros from a MINITAB session
      28-6
    macros with subcommands
      29-6
critical values, looking up 9-11
cumulative frequency in histograms
  14-31
cumulative frequency scale for a
  chart 14-26
cumulative probability 9-7
current time 7-9
current worksheet 1-3
custom lists 5-6
customer support xvi
customizing the graph frame 18-1
cutting
    cells 2-15
    missing values 2-11

D

data
    converting database 4-3
    copying 2-9
    date/time 1-4, 1-10

H

M

minimum function for chart y-axis 14-23

MINITAB Graphics Format (MGF) files 26-3

minor ticks 18-21

missing value code (*)
constant 7-3, 7-12
with session commands 27-8

missing values 1-12
and graphs 13-10
cutting and pasting 2-11

MLABEL macro command 30-6

MMATRIX macro command 29-13

mouse sensitivity, adjusting 24-8

moving
around the Data window 2-3
columns 2-18
objects and text using the mouse 24-10

MRESET macro command 32-3, 32-7

MTB file 33-4, 33-5

MTITLE macro command 31-10

MTJ file 33-4

MTYPE macro command 29-14, 29-20

multi-graph layouts 16-20

multiple graphs 16-1
overview 16-2

multiple scatter plot
see matrix plots

multiple time series plots, overlaying 14-17

N

N missing 7-11

N nonmissing 7-11

N total 7-11

NAME in macros 31-8

naming
arguments in macros 31-8
columns 2-18

constants 1-4
Graph windows 13-9
matrices 1-4

natural log 7-10
of the gamma function 7-7

navigating the Data window 2-3

nesting Execs 33-7

new
projects 3-3
worksheets 2-3, 3-5

next and previous command 11-10

NEXT macro command 30-5

nmissing function for chart y-axis 14-22

NOCONSTANT command in macros 32-3, 32-7

NODEBUG macro command 32-5

NOECHO command
in Execs 33-12
in macros 32-4

NOPLUG macro command 32-2

Normal distribution to generate random data 9-5

normal scores 7-11

NOSWAP macro command 32-6

NOTE macro command 28-8, 31-2

NOTITLE macro command 31-10

now 7-9

numbers, very large 1-8

numeric data 1-4
converting to date/time 6-43
in MINITAB 1-8

O

object linking and embedding
see OLE

object space (3D graphs) 21-4

object units (3D graphs) 21-4

objects
aligning 24-17
disappearing 24-13
drawing 24-5

flipping and rotating 24-15
moving using the mouse 24-10
resizing and reshaping 24-11
selecting 24-6
selecting multiple 24-7
unlocking data display 24-13

ODBC 4-2
drivers 4-2
managers 4-2
overview 4-2
querying databases 4-4
syntax rules 4-7
troubleshooting 4-8

OH in macros 32-3, 32-7

OLE 26-2, 26-6

one-time data transfer in DDE 10-11

Open Database Connectivity (ODBC)
see ODBC

opening graphs 13-9, 26-3

opening projects 3-3
existing projects 3-3
new projects 3-3
options 3-3

opening worksheets 2-3, 3-5
file types 3-5
from earlier versions of MINITAB 3-19
from later versions of MINITAB 3-19
from other applications 3-12
limitations with text files 3-16
merging worksheets 3-7
new worksheet 3-6
non-MINITAB files 3-12
non-MINITAB files containing date/time data 3-17
options 3-7
space-delimited text file 3-15
worksheets in a MINITAB project 3-6

optional text in syntax boxes 27-11

Oracle, querying data from 4-2

organizing data
in graphs 16-4
stacked 16-5
unstacked 16-5

P